THE
Thirty-First Yearbook

OF THE

NATIONAL SOCIETY FOR THE STUDY OF EDUCATION

PART I

A Program for Teaching Science

Prepared by the Society's Committee on the Teaching of Science

GERALD S. CRAIG, ELLIOT R. DOWNING, CHARLES J. PIEPER, RALPH K. WATKINS, FRANCIS D. CURTIS (*Vice-Chairman*), and S. RALPH POWERS (*Chairman*)

Assisted by the Following Active Members of the Society

FLORENCE G. BILLIG, LILLIAN HETHERSHAW, MORRIS MEISTER, and VICTOR H. NOLL

With Critical Comments by

FRANK N. FREEMAN, J. CAYCE MORRISON, and E. LAURENCE PALMER

———

Edited by
GUY MONTROSE WHIPPLE

———

THIS PART OF THE YEARBOOK WILL BE DISCUSSED AT THE WASHINGTON MEETING OF THE NATIONAL SOCIETY, SATURDAY, FEBRUARY 20, 1932, 8:00 P.M.

———

PUBLIC SCHOOL PUBLISHING COMPANY
BLOOMINGTON, ILLINOIS
1932

AGENTS
PUBLIC SCHOOL PUBLISHING COMPANY
BLOOMINGTON, ILLINOIS
PUBLISHERS OF ALL THE YEARBOOKS OF THE SOCIETY

Published February, 1932
First Printing, 6,000 copies
Second Printing, September, 1933, 2,000 copies

46154

Printed by the
PUBLIC SCHOOL PUBLISHING COMPANY
Bloomington, Illinois

OFFICERS OF THE SOCIETY
for 1931-32

Board of Directors
(Term of office expires March 1st of the year indicated)
WILLIAM C. BAGLEY (1934)
Teachers College, Columbia University, New York City

WERRETT W. CHARTERS, *Chairman* (1935)*
Ohio State University, Columbus, Ohio

M. E. HAGGERTY (1934)
University of Minnesota, Minneapolis, Minnesota

FRANK N. FREEMAN (1932)
University of Chicago, Chicago, Illinois

ERNEST HORN (1933)
State University of Iowa, Iowa City, Iowa

LEONARD V. KOOS (1933)
University of Chicago, Chicago, Illinois

WILLIS L. UHL (1935)†
University of Washington, Seattle, Washington

GUY MONTROSE WHIPPLE (*Ex-officio*)
Danvers, Massachusetts

Secretary-Treasurer
GUY MONTROSE WHIPPLE (1932)
Danvers, Massachusetts

* Reëlected for three years beginning March, 1932.
† Elected for three years beginning March, 1932.

iii

TABLE OF CONTENTS

For Minutes of the Annual Meeting, Proceedings of the Board of Directors,
Report of the Treasurer, List of Active Members, see Part II of this
Yearbook.

v

EDITOR'S PREFACE

The idea of producing a yearbook in the field of the teaching of science was first placed before the Board of Directors of the Society at a meeting of the Board held at Dallas in February, 1927, when Director Whipple reported upon his participation as a representative of the Society in the meetings of the Council of the American Association for the Advancement of Science. At that time an attempt had been made to interest the Council in a movement for bringing high-school and college students to a better appreciation of the spirit of science and of its methods. In view of the failure of that attempt to secure any action, the Board of Directors concluded that this Society might well undertake to develop a yearbook within its own membership.

This conclusion was fortified a year later at the Boston meeting of the Board when a request was received for a yearbook dealing with science in the elementary school, but at this meeting and at the subsequent meeting in November, 1928, the Board felt that at that time too many commitments had already been made to justify the launching of another yearbook committee.

At the Chicago meeting of the Board, in May, 1929, however, the Secretary was instructed to canvass the possibilities for a yearbook on science teaching. Correspondence and conferences were then held with seven or eight persons prominent in this field, with the result that at the Atlantic City meeting of the Board, in February, 1930, the Secretary's report recommended that the Society undertake a yearbook on the teaching of science, that a preliminary report of some two hundred fifty pages be planned for publication in February, 1932, to deal primarily with the course of study in science in the public schools, with some attention to methods of instruction and to the training of teachers, and that Professors S. R. Powers and F. D. Curtis be given general responsibility for the development of the report. This recommendation was adopted after the Board had conferred with Professors Powers and Curtis at some length concerning the program of the proposed yearbook and particularly concerning the possibility of securing a committee personnel that would insure adequate representation of all the important aspects of the situation. After this conference the Board formally appointed the Committee on the Teaching of Science (Messrs.

Craig, Curtis, Downing, Powers, Pieper, and Watkins), with Professor Powers as chairman and Professor Curtis as vice-chairman.

For the expenses of the Science Committee the Board appropriated five hundred dollars in 1930 and an additional seven hundred dollars in 1931. Approximately one thousand dollars has been expended by the Committee in the work of preparing its report.

The Board of Directors, at its Detroit meeting, November, 1931, sought to carry out the policy, which has been developed in certain recent yearbooks, of having the report of the yearbook committee reviewed by a group of persons not members of the yearbook committee, and of having these critical reviews included in the printed volume. To this end the Board invited Professors Ross A. Baker, of the College of the City of New York; E. Laurence Palmer, of Cornell University; F. N. Freeman, of the University of Chicago; E. G. Conklin, of Princeton University; and Dr. J. Cayce Morrison, of the New York State Education Department, to read the galley proof of the Science Yearbook and submit critical comments upon it. We regret that Professors Baker and Conklin have been obliged to decline to assist us in this way.

Members of the Society will realize, we trust, the obvious difficulty that confronts these reviewers, because, despite the efforts and the hopes of our yearbook committees and of the editor, and the excellent coöperation of the publishers, it is seemingly impossible ever to get the yearbook into type at a date that will afford a reviewing committee reasonable time to read and digest the presentation and to prepare a seasoned and judicial critique of it.

The Editor can vouch for the serious and systematic way in which the Committee undertook the preparation of this report. It unquestionably represents the matured thought and labor of six men who are nationally known for their familiarity with the teaching of science in the public schools. The Chairman of the Committee need not apologize for saying, as he does, that the Committee presents its report with a feeling of "pride in accomplishment." It is a good yearbook and will inevitably alter the complexion of science teaching in the public schools of this country.

G. M. W.

INTRODUCTION

The Committee that has prepared this report was appointed at the time of the meeting of the Society in Atlantic City in February of 1930.

The Committee assumed that its task was to assemble and interpret material showing the trends in the teaching of science and to formulate recommendations for further work. The material assembled for the interpretation of trends includes current practices, the results of research in the teaching of science, and the best thought in the fields of philosophy and psychology.

In the preparation of this report, attention has been directed primarily to problems associated with the planning of a program for the teaching of science. There are evident discrepancies between the best thought in education and current practices in the teaching of science. A principle that seems to have full acceptance among educators is that education should be seen as a continuous process that begins with the learning experiences of early childhood and continues throughout the period of life. The aim of the school is to furnish elements of enrichment to this program of continuous education, but in the selection of materials for the teaching of science this guiding principle has not had full recognition. Uncoördinated and often opposing agencies have contributed instructional material. Thus, science for the elementary school has been organized as Nature Study, while science for the senior high school has consisted of organized bodies of knowledge selected from the special fields of science. There have been courses in botany that have been developed by the botanist, courses in zoölogy by the zoölogist, courses in physics by the physicist, courses in chemistry by the chemist. Workers in secondary education have witnessed a good deal of rivalry between specialists in these fields as each group of specialists has sought to strengthen the position held by their subject. As a result, much of the activity in science education has been in support of subjects, and the question of educational values for children in the elementary and secondary schools has not been given the prominence it deserves. Again, there has been evident a lack of integration between the work of the elementary and of the secondary schools, and within the secondary school there has been a lack of integration between the work in the special sciences.

Under the influence of these uncoördinated and often conflicting agencies, science has not attained the recognition in the schools that it deserves. This lack of recognition is particularly noticeable in the elementary schools. In a period that has been repeatedly characterized as an age of science, the elementary school has contributed but few 'elements of enrichment' from science to the 'continuous process of education.' It follows from this that the great mass of our adult population must have made most of their adjustments to this age of science through experiences they have had outside the school.

In this volume, the Committee has focused its attention upon the essential elements in the program of education; namely, the gradually maturing children on the one hand and the materials of education on the other. The maturing children are organisms endowed with capacity to learn from experience; the materials of education are the products of race experience. The search for specific materials of education is a search for those products of race experience that will most satisfactorily and effectively orient the children in the life of to-day. The influence on the life of to-day that is being exerted by developments in the field of science gives to this field a place of prominence in the program of education.

The volume presents: first, a general plan for an integrated program of science teaching; second, an adaptation of this general plan to the successive grades of each of the administrative units of the public school; and third, a suggested program for the education of teachers of science.

The general features of the report are set forth in the first ten chapters. Chapters I to V give in order: (1) the Committee's interpretation of what seem to be best practices in planning the work of elementary and secondary schools, together with the more general features of its own recommendations for science teaching; (2) criticisms of some current practices that must be modified in order to accomplish the program outline; (3) an analysis, with illustrations, that shows some of the contributions to life enrichment that may be expected from the field of science; (4) a definition of the field of science that is at least fairly comprehensive, given in terms of major principles and generalizations that may be used for guidance in selecting the specific objectives of science teaching; and (5) a brief interpretation of the principles of psychology that have guided the Committee in constructing its program.

In Chapters VI to IX, inclusive, there is an analysis of the contributions from educational research that relate to the field of science teaching. In these chapters are presented, in order, interpretations of research relating: (1) to problems of classroom teaching; (2) to problems of laboratory teaching; (3) to the content of science courses; and (4) to curricular developments in school centers.

Chapters X to XV, inclusive, carry recommendations for each of the administrative units of the public school. These are followed by a chapter (XVI) on rooms and equipment for science teaching, with recommendations for each of the administrative units.

In Chapter XVII, on science teaching on the college level, attention is given to problems associated with the integration of high-school and college courses.

In Chapter XVIII, on the education of teachers of science, it is assumed that the requisites for success in such teaching are: first, that the teacher shall be a liberally educated person; second, that he shall be a specialist in science; and third, that he shall be professionally educated, in the sense that he will be familiar with the problems associated with teaching and in command of the techniques that are necessary for successful work in the classroom. The program for the education of teachers is, therefore, a program of liberal education, including a good measure of specialization, and at the same time a program of professional education.

The reader of this report will find no recommendations for drastic or revolutionary changes. The Committee's effort has been to aid teachers and curriculum specialists to work constructively from present practices toward the attainment of more worthy outcomes. It may be expected in any program of education that many educational experiences will be selected from the field of science. In order that educational values may be realized, it is necessary that the teacher be guided in thinking by a consistent educational philosophy; that he have some understanding of how children learn; and that he have such a comprehensive understanding of the field of science that he will be able to explore deeply into it. It is the hope of the Committee that its report will point the way to the progressive attainment of the standards suggested in these considerations.

In the discussion of the psychology of learning, no attention has been given to controversial theories. The underlying assumption of this discussion is that children learn from experience and that the process of learning involves the association of related experiences into increasingly enlarged understandings. An educational program is acceptable to all psychologists if it provides learning experiences that are rich because of their relations to human affairs, and if it provides, by one means or another, an association of these experiences such that, as the child progresses through the schools, he gets an increasingly enlarged understanding of the world in which he lives and of the problems associated with living. In a program of science education it is necessary that the learners acquire a stock of ideas that have been tested for truthfulness, and it is very desirable that the learner acquire some understanding of procedures that have been developed for testing ideas. Thinking is done with ideas. Ideas that have been tested for truthfulness and that relate to the problems about which people think are fundamental elements in the work of education.

In the course of its work the Committee held five meetings. Individual members were assigned the task of making preliminary drafts of the several chapters outlined by the Committee to comprise the body of the Yearbook. These drafts formed the basis of extended discussion by the entire Committee, during which the Committee found itself in complete agreement upon all the major issues and during which differences of opinion with respect to details were adjusted or statements that, after debate, any member was unwilling to support were deleted. The Committee wishes to make clear to the readers of the Yearbook that the footnotes appended to the several chapter titles in order to designate the member of the Committee to which the original drafting of each chapter was assigned do not mean that the member in question is alone responsible for the views expressed; on the contrary, each chapter represents the unanimous views of the entire Committee.

In order to make the work widely representative, specialists outside the Committee have been asked to contribute. We acknowledge with gratitude the contributions from Dr. Florence G. Billig, Professor Lillian Hethershaw, Dr. Morris Meister, and Dr. Victor H. Noll. Similarly we gratefully acknowledge the work of the reviewers. It is with no small amount of effort that these men have read the galleys of this manuscript and prepared the comments that are included in this volume.

It is with a feeling of pride in accomplishment that the Committee submits to the Society its unanimous report.

For the Committee,

S. RALPH POWERS, Chairman.

CHAPTER I

THE PLAN OF THE PUBLIC SCHOOLS AND THE PROGRAM OF SCIENCE TEACHING[1]

The public-school administrator and the teachers must consider the problems of the program of studies in relation to the general purposes of the public-school system and more particularly in relation to the aims and purposes of the various units of the system.

THE GENERAL PLAN OF PUBLIC EDUCATION

The program as a whole and each of its units have been planned for the accomplishment of rather well-defined purposes, and the attainment of these purposes is justified by their contributions to the aim of education. Ideally, the subjects of study and other elements of the curriculum are introduced into the administrative units because they contribute to the attainment of objectives which in turn are justified by their contribution to the aim of education.

Attention is here directed primarily to one portion of the program of studies: to the problems of science teaching and to the contribution of science teaching to the attainment of the purposes of the elementary and secondary schools. These are considered from the standpoint of their educational values for children of these levels, and in relation to the contribution of science teaching on these levels to the preparation for the more intensive and more specialized study in the college and university. Consideration is also given to the training of science teachers.

The divisions of the public-school system are elementary, secondary, collegiate, and university, but it is the exigencies of administration that in the main support these divisions. The education of the child is conceived as a gradual building-up process. While it is true that the specific educational objectives of the later years of secondary education are quite in contrast with those of the early years of the elementary schools, yet the dividing line between these two divisions of the system should not be clearly evident. As the child progresses

---

[1] For the Committee, by S. Ralph Powers. This chapter, like the others in this Yearbook that were drafted by one member of the Committee, has been read and criticized by all the other members, so that it is to be understood by the reader as representing the views of the entire Committee.

1

from elementary to secondary education and from secondary to collegiate and university work, he should experience changes in content and in methods of instruction as gradual transitions paralleling the changes in mental maturity which accompany his physical growth and maturation.

Provision has been made in the elementary school for training all the nation's children, and legal compulsion practically guarantees the attendance through the period of elementary education of all who are mentally and physically fit. The grades of this level should provide the background of cultural and practical training which shall in largest measure prepare children for those responsibilities which are theirs and for those which they must face as they attain greater maturity. The program of studies will present problems that are real to children of this level; it will reveal to them elements for life enrichment which ordinarily lie outside routine experience; and it will recognize the need for training that will prepare the child for the experience of living and for further study in the grades on more mature levels. Mere recognition of the fact that this is an age of science suggests something of the purpose of this field in the program of the elementary school.

Increasingly large proportions of American children are entering upon and continuing through the period of secondary education. On this level, opportunity is afforded for increasingly intensified and enlarged study of the educational materials that are deemed fundamental to the welfare of the individual and of the race. In an effective program of public education, the work of the secondary and later levels will have its beginning in the elementary school on the lowest levels of maturity at which it may profitably be placed. The work of successive grade levels, elementary, secondary, and collegiate, will take departure from the earliest offering and be consciously and intelligently correlated with it. There seems to be no defensible exception to this principle, whether in language, mathematics, the practical arts, or science. The junior high school has been designed to effect a more satisfactory articulation and correlation between the elementary and the secondary school. The work on this level should be consciously modeled so as to provide the continuous enlargement and enrichment of the work which has its beginning in the curriculum of the elementary school. Mental growth is gradual. For insuring growth in any field, the enlargement of the curriculum should be gradual, paralleling the mental growth of the children. The principles guiding practices in the organization of our public-school system are based on the assumption that the progress of children through the successive grades should be from grade levels of general training toward grade levels in which the pupils have opportunity to explore the work of special fields. The general program of the lower grades of the elementary school and the program of elective subjects in the senior high school are quite in contrast, but an effective curriculum is one in which the learning progresses gradually and uninterruptedly from the lower to the upper levels.

FITTING THE PROGRAM OF SCIENCE TEACHING INTO THIS PLAN

The general plan of public education just presented is the one into which the program of science education must be fitted. This plan seems consistent with the accepted principle of educational psychology, that learning is a continuous and gradual process which begins in infancy and continues throughout the period of life. Learning begins with the acquisition of the simplest learning elements. These impinge upon the nervous system in the form of simple sense perceptions. These simplest perceptions are the bases of conceptions and these in turn of generalizations. Conceptions and generalizations are, therefore, related hierarchies of simple learning elements. When these are formulated, they may function in thought as simple elements. More mature learning involves association of these relatively simple hierarchies into more and more complex ones, and so the process of learning goes on. It is the aim of the school to provide the experiences which will make possible the most efficient growth in learning. Effective accomplishment of this aim is conditioned upon the ability of the curriculum-worker to make available to the children of succeeding grade levels the learning experiences which are appropriate for continuous mental growth.

The general plan of public education set forth above may be considered a product of the past twenty years. It has been attained as a result of rather far-reaching reorganization. The principles upon which the present organization rest are quite in contrast with those which guided in the earlier period of American education. The recency of this reorganization is ample explanation of the fact that the organization of the subjects of study is at many places out of harmony with the principles that are now guiding elementary and secondary education.

Full understanding of the problems of science teaching in elementary and secondary schools requires an analysis which will show in some particulars the conflict that exists between principles guiding practices in elementary and secondary education and those guiding practices in the teaching of science in these school units. This conflict, which is not peculiar to science, exists because of the difficulties in keeping pace in the curriculum with the best thought in education.

The Serial and the Saltatory Theories

The present plan for public education is, in the main, consistent with the teachings of modern philosophy and psychology; but the plans of the several subjects of study are still too much under the influence of psychological theories the truth of which is now in large part denied. Two of these, the serial and the saltatory theories, relate to fundamental considerations concerning the mental growth of children, and have such a direct bearing on problems of science teaching that they are here briefly reviewed:

The serial theory postulates that mental abilities appear in serial order, and develop one after another as the child matures. The saltatory theory states that the development of mental abilities is relatively rapid and is characterized by sudden and relatively abrupt (saltatory) changes. It has been assumed that these saltatory changes are most striking at the period of the onset of adolescence. These two theories, ardently supported by G. Stanley Hall and his followers, have usually been associated with one another. Taken together, they maintain that certain mental processes, such as memory and observation, begin their development early in life, develop rapidly, and approach a maximum before other mental traits appear. Reasoning, a more complex ability, develops later. The implications of these older theories furnished support for a stratified program with a definite break between elementary and secondary education. They required materials and methods of instruction adapted to abilities that were thought to be most in evidence during the successive stages of the child's development. "Strike while the iron is hot" was a phrase familiar in this connection. Hence, in order that abilities might be exercised when they were most in evidence, it was maintained that sense perception and sensory discrimination should be emphasized in the education of very young children; that subjects of study depending for mastery upon more or less mechanical processes, especially motor ability and memory, should be assigned to education before the age of twelve; and that those subjects which demand reasoning ability should be reserved for emphasis at and after adolescence, in the secondary school.

THE TRADITIONAL SCIENCE PROGRAM

The traditional program of science teaching was formulated during the period in the history of American education when these older theories had general acceptance. Nature study, with emphasis on observation, collection, and memorization of names, was given a place in the program of elementary education which came prior to the onset of adolescence. The special sciences, with emphasis on systems of organization of knowledge, were given a place in the secondary school and taught during and following the period of puberty. The continued influence of these obsolete theories may still be found in some of the programs of nature study in the elementary school and in the special science programs of the senior high school. The extent to which the characteristics of the old theories are still in evidence in the subjects of study included in the curriculum of today is a measure of the extent to which the curriculum is out of harmony with the plan of public education currently accepted.

THE NEWER SCIENCE PROGRAM

Probably no educational or psychological theories have had a greater influence on practices in the schools than these old theories of serial and saltatory development of mental traits. But almost from the time of their origin, these theories have had their opponents. They were never accepted by James; they have been openly opposed by Dewey, Thorndike, and many others; and, as originally stated, they are now entirely discredited. The burden of evidence from studies in the psychology of learning and in individual differences is overwhelmingly in support of the theory of gradual and concomitant development of mental traits. There is now a demand for a continuous and correlated program of study. The new theory requires a curriculum in which learning experiences shall be arrayed in such a manner that, as the child progresses through successive grades, he will have opportunity for continuous enlargement of his knowledge of the problems, principles, and generalizations that scholarly men find worthy of study. This new interpretation of the process of mental growth has now such general acceptance that it has determined the character of our institutions for elementary and secondary education, but it has not yet had full recognition in determining the objectives, content, and method of the subjects of study. Efforts to clear the field are in process.

In order to meet the demands of public education, the Committee has formulated a plan for a continuous and correlated program of science. It is one that recognizes the principles of psychology and of philosophy that have guided in planning our public-school system. It is arranged so as to facilitate the study of those large truths of science that have within them the greatest potentialities for influencing human thought and actions.

Simple experiences will result in an evolving reification of these, among other, understandings: (1) the manner in which organisms are adapted for life in the physical environment; (2) the interdependence of certain organisms; (3) the manner in which natural forces are continually changing the surface of the earth; (4) the relation of certain meteorological phenomena to underlying causes; (5) many simple energy transformations; (6) the relationship of the earth and other astronomical bodies; and (7) a conception of the cause-and-effect relation.

1. In the Elementary Grades

New courses of study for the elementary grades illustrating this plan have been prepared for use in a number of school systems. The work of the lowest grades is arranged in small and simple teaching units. The units of succeeding grades are more comprehensive.

2. In the Junior High School

Guided by the implications of modern psychological theory, the work of the junior high school will differ from the work of the elementary school only in that it will be adapted to pupils of a more mature level by making provision for more intensive study of units.

For common practices let us assume a program of three periods each week for the study of science through the seventh and eighth grades and of five periods each week through the ninth grade of the junior high school. With this time allowance for study, the pupils will gain rapidly in ability to do intensive work. The number of units outlined for study in the seventh grade should not be large, and the number for the ninth grade should be even smaller. As in the elementary school, these units will be integrated through dynamic experiences, resulting in a functional comprehension of principles, major generalizations, and associated scientific attitudes that function in human thought and behavior. A further objective of junior-high-school instruction is to reveal the fields in which there is opportunity for more intensive and specialized study of science.

The tendency is increasingly in evidence in progressive schools organized on the 8-4 plan to provide for pupils of the seventh and eighth grades a program similar in content to that offered in schools organized as junior high schools. This trend is in harmony with the recommendation of this Committee. Courses in science developed for use in the seventh and eighth grades of the junior high school are seen as proper content for courses in seventh and eighth grades of the 8-4 plan. Similarly, this Committee recommends the ninth-grade course of the junior high school as appropriate for the ninth grade of the four-year high school. In other words, the sequence recommended for the seventh, eighth, and ninth grades may for practical purposes be considered the same, whatever the form of organization.

The Committee considers it unwise to attempt to crystallize the offering for these three grades. The solution of the problems associated with determination of what these courses, particularly those offered for the ninth grade, shall be, must be left for further experimentation. The Committee's recommendation is for a continuous and correlated program. Definite suggestions for the accomplishment of this program are given in Chapter XIII.

3. In the Senior High School

In the senior high school there is opportunity for exploration within the special fields. For the pupil it is an exploration and possibly a beginning of specialization. Biology is the field for special study of living things, while the physical sciences offer a field for the study of energy and its manifestations through inorganic matter. It seems entirely practical to suggest for the three years of the senior high school an elective offering of at least four one-year units. Ideally, these should probably be organized as two two-year sequences, one in the field of biology and the other in the field of physical science. The two courses of biology will be, the first more general and less specialized, and the second less general and more specialized. The same criterion will guide in the case of the physical sciences. The first unit will be more general and less specialized and the second will be less general and more specialized. Practically, the first unit of physical science will probably be most heavily weighted from what is now physics, while the second will be most heavily weighted from what is now chemistry. In general the course in biological science should precede the course in physical science, and students should not take a second-level course until they have taken the first-level course in both these fields. This suggestion is offered as a practical procedure for accomplishing an integration of the work in biology and in the fields of physics and chemistry. It is in the field of the physical sciences that this integration is most sorely needed. For the larger schools this plan seems entirely practical. For smaller schools with an enrollment that does not justify an offering of four one-year courses, it is suggested that there be a constant offering of the first course in each division and that the second course of each division be offered on alternate years.

The recommendation of the Committee on the Reorganization of Science in Secondary Schools[1] was as follows:

A. The Junior-Senior High School

Seventh or eighth year—Five periods a week, or both years with three periods a week in each year—General Science, including hygiene.

Ninth year—Biological science, including hygiene; courses may consist of general biology, botany, or zoölogy.

Tenth year, eleventh year, twelfth year—Differentiated elective courses in sufficient number to meet special needs and interests, as follows:

(a) Chemistry—General chemistry, and chemistry specialized for various curriculum needs, such as household chemistry, industrial chemistry, etc.

(b) Physics—General physics; and physics specialized for various curriculum needs, such as physics of the home, industrial physics, etc.

(c) General geography, or physiography.

(d) Advanced biological sciences.

B. The Large Comprehensive Four-Year High School

The conditions usually prevailing in these schools make possible a wide differentiation of science courses, since there are likely to be enough pupils with special interests to constitute adequate classes in differentiated science courses. In such four-year high schools the following plan is recommended:

First year—General science, including hygiene.

Second year—Biological science, including hygiene; courses may consist of general biology, botany, or zoology.

---

[1] *Bureau of Education Bulletin*, No. 26, 1920, p. 23.

Third and fourth years—Differentiated elective courses to meet special needs and interests as follows:

(a) Chemistry—General chemistry, and chemistry specialized for various curriculum needs, such as household chemistry, industrial chemistry, etc.
(b) Physics—General physics, and physics specialized for various curriculum needs, such as household chemistry, industrial physics, etc.
(c) General geography or physiography.
(d) Advanced biological sciences.

In order to accomplish a closer integration of the work of successive grades, this Committee recommends the following sequences, which are similar in time allotments to the proposals just quoted. It is recommended that the work of the seventh, eighth, and ninth grades be required and that the work of the senior high school be elective. The sequence and the requirements should be the same, irrespective of whether or not the school system has accepted the junior-high-school organization for grades seven, eight, and nine.

A. Grades Seven to Twelve

Seventh and eighth years—Science, three periods per week in each year.

Ninth year—Science, five periods per week.

Tenth year—Biological science or physical science (physics).

Eleventh year—First-year physical science (physics) or first-year biological science; second-year biological science or second-year physical science (chemistry).

Twelfth year—Elective selected from those listed under the offerings for tenth and eleventh grades and such other electives as the school may choose to offer.

B. The Four-Year High School

Same as above for grades nine to twelve.

A practical approach to the ideal suggested in the plans of organization recommended by this Committee will have been made when curriculum-workers in each of the fields of science come together to compare their problems.

The program here briefly set forth is practical in the sense that it is definable and attainable and in the sense that it is consistent with the point of view of American education. It suggests a method for accomplishing a continuous and correlated program for the study of science from the first grade through the twelfth. The same principles may be applied in effecting a closer correlation of the work of the high school and the college. Furthermore, the acceptance of this program does not require any drastic, certainly no cataclysmic, changes in our present practices.

This program is one that shows how those major generalizations of science which ramify most deeply into human affairs may be broken up into learning experiences that may be used in grades on different levels of maturity. There is enough in these major generalizations, with their associated scientific attitudes, to furnish materials for study on all levels ranging from the grades to the university. Study will be sufficiently intensive to enable the learner to acquire, not only an understanding of the phenomena of science, but also some real appreciation of the methods of scientific study and investigation and some appreciation of scientific attitudes. Attainment of scientific attitudes without understanding of science is, in the opinion of this Committee, an absurdity.

The major generalizations of science and the associated scientific attitudes are so important and so extensive in scope that the student may live with them throughout his life. Definable educational values from science teaching will have been attained if students acquire (1) an ability to utilize the findings of science that have application in their own experiences; (2) an ability to interpret the natural phenomena of their environment; and (3) an appreciation of scientific attitudes through an understanding of, and ability to use, some of the methods of study that have been used by creative workers in the field of science. As the pupil progresses through the grades, his study becomes increasingly intensive and increasingly specialized. The special sciences of the upper years of the high school and of college are offered as electives in which the pupil or the student has opportunity for intensive and specialized study.

This pattern is one for a curricular organization which gradually unfolds increasingly enlarged interpretations in sequential order, paralleling the growth in maturity of the learner and his increasing ability to envisage them. It is a program for a continuous and integrated sequence of science study and its acceptance defines the field for teacher training. Accepted principles of educational psychology, as well as of principles that guide practices in elementary, secondary, and collegiate education, are offered in support of this pattern.

SUMMARY

1. For practical purposes mental growth is considered to be gradual and continuous and not saltatory and serial.

2. The plan of the public school requires a curriculum that is planned to recognize the principle that mental growth is gradual and continuous, and it requires a program that shall demand increasingly intensive and increasingly specialized study as the child progresses toward the upper grades. Definite provisions for the beginnings of specialization shall be made in the senior high school.

3. In recognition of the principles that are guiding the practices in the public schools, the Committee proposes the following program:

   Grades I-VI: A program of elementary science. Objectives selected for their contribution to enlargement of understanding of phenomena that are important for their relation to experiences that are common to everybody.

   Grades VII-IX: A program of science, the objectives of which are selected for their contribution to enlarged interpretations and exploration and guidance. The recommendation for grades seven to nine is the same whether the work be organized on the 8-4 or 6-6 plan.

   Grades X-XII: A program of senior-high-school science. Objectives selected so as to provide for the beginnings of specialization. Courses are elective and will be taken by students who elect to do intensive study of related objectives. At least two fields for special study will be open—the biological and the physical. Larger schools may extend the offering of other special sciences to include such courses as the demand may justify.

CHAPTER II

SOME CRITICISMS OF CURRENT PRACTICES IN THE TEACHING OF SCIENCE IN ELEMENTARY AND SECONDARY SCHOOLS[1]

I. SCIENCE IN THE ELEMENTARY SCHOOL

Current statements of aims and objectives of science for the elementary school show the influence of the points of view that have been formulated during the past half century by workers in the field of nature study. Guided as they were by the philosophy of education formulated under the influence of psychological postulates no longer tenable, many of these statements are inconsistent with the principles of education accepted for guidance today. Many features in the traditional program may be seen, for example, to exemplify, directly or indirectly, Hall's theories of the serial and the saltatory development of mental traits. This acceptance has shown itself in an emphasis upon one kind of science for the elementary grades and another kind of science for the secondary school. One sees also a much fuller acceptance of theories of transfer of training than finds support in current psychology. And there are evident unjustifiable and, in fact, extravagant claims for emotional, esthetic, and disciplinary outcomes which are suggestive of conduct assumed to be worthy. In some of the more enthusiastic claims it would appear that practically all the desirable attributes of human behavior are assured as outcomes to individuals privileged to study in the field of science. It appears to have been assumed that the study of science exercises these attributes and that, when once exercised, there is complete transfer of the abilities developed to all situations which the learner may later face. Many of these claims find no support in sound educational psychology or in acceptable educational philosophy. It seems certain that such claims are of negative, not positive, value to curriculum-workers. Many of them are intangible and in large measure indefinable. They muddle thought where there is need for clarification. A necessary preliminary to a program of constructive action is, therefore, that one give some attention to clearing the field.

---

[1] For the Committee, by S. Ralph Powers.

A Typical Example of Extravagant Claims

A typical extravagant statement of emotional, esthetic, and disciplinary outcomes from science teaching may be found in the *Fourth Yearbook, Department of Superintendence, National Education Association* (1926). Since this report has had wide circulation and since it serves well to illustrate the points of the preceding paragraph, it is here briefly reviewed. There is presented a detailed list of "Aims and Objectives for the Teaching of Nature Study and Elementary Science." There are, in fact, listed seventy statements numbered in serial order. These statements are grouped under the general headings Ethical, Spiritual, Esthetic, Intellectual, Social, Civic, Economic, Vital, Avocational, Vocational, and Practical. It seems almost as if no adjective that is descriptive of desirable human relationships has been omitted. Following this listing of aims and objectives, there is a listing of pupil activities and experiences recommended for each grade level from kindergarten through grade six, from the performance of which the children may be expected to attain the seventy aims of the report. Following each "activity" or "experience" is a series of key numbers which refer to the aims and objectives to which the activity may contribute. Questionable features of the report are brought into evidence if one examines the "Activities and Experiences" on the one hand and the "Aims and Objectives" on the other. One finds, for example, in the outline for the kindergarten that the activity, "Feeding Squirrels," contributes to no fewer than eighteen of the seventy aims and objectives! Statements numbered one to five from this list are quoted as illustrations:

1. Ability to perceive the truth.
2. Belief in the value of truth.
3. Desire to follow the truth—moral uprightness.
4. Realization of one's relationship to all other living things and to the universe as a whole, and one's dependence upon his fellows, upon other forms of life, and upon the forces of nature.
5. Realization of the wisdom of nature's laws and of one's dependence for successful living upon obedience to them.

Another illustration from the same *Fourth Yearbook* is that of an activity for the sixth grade which is one of "collecting, pressing, and mounting sprays showing alternate and opposite arrangement of leaves." This activity is considered in relation to "solving the problem: what are some of the special adaptations which help plants to live?" This activity contributes to the accomplishment of four of the five aims and objectives stated in the preceding paragraph and to some nineteen additional ones, including the following (numbers correspond to those used in the report):

8. Ability to catch glimpses of the cosmic forces as revealed in natural manifestations, in living creatures, in mankind, in man's highest examples, in the record of man's thoughts and actions and aspirations as presented in nature, in literature, music, and art dealing with nature, and in science.

10. An attitude and desire of obedience to the law of love. Confidence in, and habitual practice of, sympathy, humaneness, kindness, regularity, patience, persistence, diligence, care, steadfastness, self-control, industry, thrift, and intellectual honesty. Desire to create happiness.

It is the conviction of this Committee that these claims for the educational values derived by a kindergarten child from feeding squirrels and by a sixth-grade child from collecting, pressing, and mounting leaves are manifestly extravagant. There are some hundreds of activities suggested with similarly extravagant claims. Furthermore, the *Fourth Yearbook* is convincing evidence that the committee that prepared it cherished an apparently indefensible faith in the attainment of transfer and disciplinary values. In the illustrations given, the relationship between the activity and the objective is far from evident, and it seems probable that, so far as the children of these grades are concerned, no such relationship exists.

This *Fourth Yearbook*, although an extreme illustration, is not unfairly representative of much that has been written about the educational value of nature study. It is compiled from many sources and carries the endorsement of well-known workers in this field. In the opinion of the present Committee nature study and elementary science as outlined in the *Fourth Yearbook* cannot be successful. The fact that nature study has had its support in such tenets as those just mentioned is sufficient to explain its failure. For many years it has been out of step with principles and practices of elementary education, and it has sought support in psychological postulates long since obsolete.

Attempts to Teach Science by Correlation with Other Subjects

In still another particular of elementary science is there need for a clarification of the field. Those who have supported a program of instruction in nature study or elementary science have found it difficult to secure recognition in the elementary school because the instructional time is already assigned to the traditional subjects. Efforts to gain recognition have therefore taken the form of efforts to correlate science with these established subjects, and in such instances, science has been incidental to them. It has been said that there are many opportunities for natural correlation of science with art, literature, and language. "Much of the material used in the science lessons may be reproduced by the child by means of freehand drawings with colored crayons for younger children, and outline drawings and paintings in water colors for older children."[2] Science may be correlated with literature, for "Our poets write often of birds, flowers, and trees; and whenever these forms are studied in the science lesson, the study of some appropriate poem will add greatly to the child's appreciation of the object studied."[3] The author continues with a reference to opportunities for correlation with manual training in the making of bird-houses and fly-traps. Illustrations could be extended that show the opportunities for the correlation of science and nature study with arithmetic, language, and other studies.

This discussion should not be interpreted as hostile to proposals for breaking down the boundaries between subjects in the elementary school. The tendency now in evidence to accomplish a closer integration of the work of the elementary school seems to be founded upon sound support. But it is recommended that when the integration is attempted, it shall be of problems and not of the traditional subjects of study. In practice the integration of subjects of study has tended to shift attention away from the question of educational value of science to the question of what is suggested by the field of science for a lesson in art, literature, or manual training. It is seen as an appendage to English, art, or other subjects and not in relation to solving problems and meeting the situations of common experience. Under this condition, science is incidental to the other subject; and, when the teacher has been trained in the other subject and not in science, it becomes accidental, with the chances favoring little or no recognition.

Efforts to determine what science may contribute to art (or other subjects) have failed, and must fail, to develop a program of science

---

[2] Trafton, G. H. *The Teaching of Science in the Elementary School.* Houghton Mifflin: Boston, 1918, p. 23.
[3] *Ibid.,* p. 23.

teaching that will reveal the field of science to children. Emphasis has been in the wrong place. Efforts to determine what science has contributed and may contribute to the enrichment of life are certain to be more fruitful of educational values.

Commonly Accepted Principles of Nature Study

There are three principles which have had general acceptance as representing the best thought in the field of nature study:

1. Child psychology is distinct from the psychology of adults; this distinction justifies and requires a difference between nature study for elementary schools and science for high schools.
2. Nature study should be primarily observation of common natural objects and processes; the grouping of the facts learned in nature study to form principles and generalizations should be reserved for high school and college study.
3. A major value of nature study lies in the discipline which it gives in habits of thoughtful observation.

There is in these 'accepted principles' an emphasis on facts, with an exclusion of principles; an emphasis on nature study for discipline, with no clarification of the meaning of discipline; and an effort to draw a distinction between child and adult psychology. There is in these 'principles' a fairly clear definition of the point of view that has functioned in shaping the work in nature study and a fairly clear definition of the support for such current practices as those that have been illustrated earlier in this chapter. In the opinion of this Committee most of these postulations are directly in conflict with the teaching of modern psychology and educational theory. This Committee assumes (1) that the process of mental growth is gradual and that children differ from adults in a relative and not in an absolute way; and (2) that the values from the study of science are the contributions that it makes to the student's ability to interpret the phenomena of common experience and the contribution that it makes to the development of his ability to think by somewhat more refined methods.

This Committee sees a more adequate recognition of its point of view in some of the newly organized courses, which are commonly designated as "Science for the Elementary School." It, therefore, endorses this designation, and, on account of the traditions associated with the name, has dropped the term 'nature study' in its references to courses in science for the elementary schools. These courses in question are described in a later chapter.

II. Science in the Secondary School

The trend in the reorganization of secondary education was in many of its aspects rather definitely crystallized by the well-known report of the Commission on the Reorganization of Secondary Education on "Cardinal Principles of Secondary Education," which was published as United States Bureau of Education Bulletin Number 35, 1918.

The Commission recognized the changes that had taken place and the changes that were in process, and it called attention to fundamental considerations which showed the manner in which the needs of society and the plan of the institutions (the schools) that were purporting to meet these needs were out of harmony.

It recommended particularly (1) the plan for a continuous and progressive program from the kindergarten to the university, in which the learner may gradually progress from the grades of unspecialized training, through grades offering opportunity for exploration, into the upper levels (the university) in which the primary purpose is specialization; (2) that greater attention be given to individual differences in intellectual ability and in interest; (3) that educational objectives be formulated with recognition of the needs of individuals and the needs of society; (4) that current conceptions of 'general discipline' be thoroughly revised.

Having defined the changes in educational theory particularly as these changes apply to the four foregoing points, the Commission stated as the main objectives of education: (1) health, (2) command of fundamental processes, (3) worthy home membership, (4) vocation, (5) citizenship, (6) worthy use of leisure, (7) ethical character.

This report focused attention upon the contributions from the scientific study of educational problems, and it placed emphasis on education for direct functional values. It may be pointed to as an important landmark in the progress toward the development of our present philosophies of education.

Report of 1920 on the Reorganization of Science

In addition to the "Cardinal Principles" the same Commission issued a series of reports on reorganization of the various high-school subjects. The committee dealing with science considered the aims and purposes of science teaching[4] with reference to the main objectives of education as outlined by the Commission. They stated that science instruction was especially valuable in the realization of six of these objectives; namely, health, worthy home membership, vocation, citizenship, worthy use of leisure, and ethical character. In matters of health, science was emphasized for its contribution to personal and community problems. In worthy home membership, its importance depends upon the fact that it "touches the efficiency of the home, and life within the home at every angle." Specifically, the bulletin mentions care of children and of the home-heating and ventilating system, electrical devices, and the "many conveniences that make the modern home comfortable and attractive." The contribution of science to vocational guidance is "a more intelligent understanding of the world's work" and it "should impress students selecting certain vocations with the importance of making thorough and adequate preparation for their life work." It was stated that courses in applied science will be of value to many pupils for vocational preparation if properly adapted to their needs and that these should contribute to the worker's enjoyment by enabling him to understand the underlying principles that have application in his work. The contribution to citizenship is in "the increased respect which the citizen should obtain for the expert," and in the development of ability to select experts for personal and community service and to evaluate and appreciate the importance of the service which is rendered. The contribution to worthy use of leisure time comes from the fact that "science opens the door to many useful and pleasurable avocations." Specifically the report mentions photography, observations of the out-of-doors, and appreciation of literature regarding science. In relation to ethical character, the committee says that the study of science establishes a "more adequate conception of truth and a confidence in the laws of cause and effect" and that it "should help develop sane and sound methods of thinking upon the problems of life."

The recognized achievement of the Commission on Reorganization has been to shift emphasis in thinking concerning educational problems from values assumed to be associated with mastery of subjects to values which are more directly associated with human relations.

[4] *Reorganization of Science in Secondary Schools.* U. S. Bureau Educ. Bull., 1920. No. 26.

Throughout the report of the Committee on Reorganization of Science there is emphasis on the importance of science for its direct applications to everyday affairs. The committee's contribution to method lies in its endorsement of the spirit of the problem and the project methods and its recognition of the interests of children and adults in the choice of curriculum materials. Viewed from the standpoint of the problems of today, certain inadequacies in these reports are evident enough. There is emphasis throughout these reports on immediate and applied values, with but little suggestion of the important influence that the enlargement of knowledge which has come during the past century and the present one has had in determining the character and in setting the problems of our present civilization. Nor is there any direct reference to the influence which this development has had on the thinking and on the mental and social adjustments of the individuals of our society.

Studies of Interests and Needs in the Field of Science

Applied to the field of science, the point of view supported by these two reports has stimulated efforts to determine the materials to be used for instruction through analyses of the interests of laymen in the phenomena of science and of their needs for instruction in this field. These analyses have taken the form of (1) studies of interests of children and adults as revealed in the questions they ask in response to questionnaires, and (2) studies of scientific principles that have recognition in newspapers, magazines, and other printed matter.

Children's interests have been investigated by Curtis,[5] Pollock,[6] Downing,[7] and others. These studies were made presumably in an effort to find the scientific concepts that are already functioning in the minds of children, with the thought that these concepts may suggest points of departure for further exploration into the fields of science in which children display spontaneous interest. At the same time it has been presumed that the findings from these studies will furnish some guidance in the selection, from one of the vast areas of human knowledge, of subject matter that has a measure of objective support.

If any conclusion may be drawn from these studies, it is that the interests are enormously varied. It may be presumed that environ-

---

[5] Curtis, Francis D. *A Digest of Investigations in the Teaching of Science.* Blakiston: Philadelphia, 1926, pp. 330-331.
[6] Curtis, Francis D. *Op. cit.,* p. 265.
[7] Curtis, Francis D. *Op. cit.,* p. 129.

mental factors of most recent experience exert some influence on the questions that are asked. It is quite clear, moreover, that neither the children nor many of the adults had explored into the field of science far enough to find all the concepts and generalizations that may serve as the bases of abiding interests. It is undoubtedly a truism that one cannot ask a question about a phenomenon that has not been revealed to him and it is in equal measure a truism that not all important phenomena have been revealed to laymen. The foregoing analyses show the inadequacies of questionnaire studies of children's interests as a basis for course-of-study work in science. There is obvious need for curriculum studies that will explore more deeply into the field.

The purpose of the studies of the allusions to science found in newspapers and magazines is approximately the same as the purpose underlying the studies of children's questions. These, too, have been made in an effort to determine the facts and principles that are used in unspecialized treatises. Finley and Caldwell[8] analyzed newspaper articles, while Searles and Ruch[9] dealt with popular magazines.

These studies of children's interests and of newspaper science have exerted some wholesome influences toward modifying existing courses, and they have served an important function in keeping alive the feeling that courses do need revision and that the sources of these revisions must be sought through research. Further investigations will build upon these earlier ones.

The publication of the "Cardinal Principles," as we have said, was an important factor in shifting emphasis in the high school away from the development of subjects and toward the development of individuals. The report is, however, inadequate for complete guidance in planning courses of study, for it has been interpreted as emphasizing in too large measure the immediate and therefore superficial values.

Junior-High-School Science in the *Fifth Yearbook,* *Department of Superintendence*

The influence of the "Cardinal Principles" may be clearly seen in the report of the *Fifth Yearbook, Department of Superintendence, National Education Association* (1927), in which are listed the aims

---

[8] Finley, Charles W., and Caldwell, Otis W. *Biology in the Public Press.* Lincoln School of Teachers College: New York, 1923.
[9] Searles, A. H., and Ruch, G. M. "A study of science articles in magazines." *School Science and Mathematics,* 26:1926, 389-396.

of science teaching for the junior high school. The list of 23 statements has been compiled from 169 sources and is given as a summary of claims by educational writers who have attempted to define values for this field. The tabular arrangement shows the frequency of mention of each aim in the sources. The statement having highest frequency is "Choice of, and Efficiency in, a Vocation"; the second in order of frequency is "Health"; the third is "To Understand One's Environment." Included within the list are statements of aims, the wording of which is the same, or nearly the same, as that used in the statements of the seven "ultimate aims" given in the "Cardinal Principles of Secondary Education." There are others which suggest general transfer values as primary purposes of science teaching.

One recommendation that is given in the *Fifth Yearbook* (p. 150) is wholly unacceptable to this Committee. It is quoted in full.

> In planning a course of study in junior-high-school science as a part of a program continuous throughout the years of the pupil's public-school life, the dominating idea for the seventh year may well be the study of plant and animal life, going somewhat beyond mere observational nature study, as is appropriate in view of the increased maturity of the pupils. For the eighth year, the determining theme might well be health, comprising in the subject matter of instruction the manifold topics relating directly or indirectly to the maintenance and upbuilding of individual and community health. For the ninth year, the dominating theme might be man's control of his environment, including in the subject matter of instruction studies of the sources of material and energy, and the transformation and uses of both.

The Committee feels bound to make clear that it does not find itself in agreement with these recommendations. We say "bound to make clear" because three members of this Committee were also members of the Fifth Yearbook Committee. They wish to state that this section of the *Fifth Yearbook*, entitled "The Science Program in the Schools," was in no sense an expression of the combined views of that committee, since these three members were not consulted with respect to this section of the report or, in fact, given any opportunity to examine it prior to its publication.

This brief reference to the field of junior-high-school science is made in order to show something of the trend that has been followed and in order to call attention to the major factors that have directed this trend. It is in this field particularly that efforts have been made to bring science into human affairs, and there can be no doubt that significant progress has been made. Some very good courses of study have been written, and excellent texts are available. The fact remains, however, that there is still an enormous variation in practices. The Committee recognizes that it is unwise to attempt at this time a complete standardization of practices, yet it also recognizes that criteria are available for evaluating certain of them. It conceives its task as that of applying these criteria, in so far as they can be used for refining practices, and also of integrating and interpreting the experiences of the past twenty years with general-science courses. A more complete committment, with illustrations, is given in later chapters.

Senior-High-School Science

Of the senior-high-school subjects—biology, physics, and chemistry —that receive attention in this report, biology has been most influenced by the efforts in reorganization. The first courses in biology that received serious recognition in the secondary schools were courses in botany and in zoölogy. The support for these courses was sought, in large part, in their contributions to religious thinking. In 1848 Louis Agassiz wrote in the preface of a textbook as follows: "Should our aim be attained, this work will produce more enlarged ideas of man's relations to Nature, and more exalted conceptions of the Plan of Creation and its great Creator."[10] Similar support for instruction in zoölogy was found in the prefaces of many of the books written in the interval between 1840 and a comparatively recent time. Similar support was offered for instruction in botany. Asa Gray's work of 1858 is a well-known illustration in this field.

The biological subjects were also supported in terms of the then current theories of formal discipline. In the efforts to develop rigid courses, the tendency to emphasize taxonomy and morphology were much in evidence. Support for such study was sought for its training in systematizing and for its training in accuracy in detailed observation. With the reaction that has come against the former theories of mental discipline, this support for taxonomic and morphological study has been lost. The past twenty years have, therefore, seen an increased emphasis on other phases of the work, particularly physiology and ecology, and during the last few years a greatly increased emphasis on behavior. With this change to the study of functions and relations has

---

[10] Finley, Charles William. *Biology in Secondary Schools and the Training of Biology Teachers.* Bureau of Publications, Teachers College, Columbia University; New York City, 1926, p. 8.

come a clearer recognition of the importance of study which is organized about those principles of biology that have application in the study of all living things. This recognition has supported courses in general biology. The Committee on the Reorganization of Science[11] recommended for the tenth grade a course in general biology. Some fairly successful efforts directed toward the organization of such a course had been made previous to the time of this report. The past decade has seen fairly general acceptance of the point of view of general biology.

This Committee endorses the recommendation of the Committee on the Reorganization of Science. Our program of subjects in science provides a place for general biology in the tenth grade of the senior high school and recommends that this course be organized about the laws and principles that constitute the important generalizations of this field. It must be made perfectly clear that the tripartite organization of biology into units of botany, zoölogy, and human physiology is in no sense the type of general biology program recommended by us. Further details respecting content and organization of this course are given in later chapters.

The traditional support for physics and chemistry has been stated in terms of (1) formal discipline, (2) knowledge, and (3) college preparation; and the offerings in these fields have been least affected by the movement initiated by educators for reorganization. These courses in science secured a place in the program of studies in competition with traditional college-preparatory subjects at a time in the history of education when the major support for all subjects was given in terms of formal discipline. This support had such general recognition and gained such complete acceptance that it has held a place in the minds of teachers of these subjects, even though the philosophical and psychological tenets which were the basis of the support have now been greatly modified and, in large part, denied. In the questionnaire studies that have been made in an effort to discover the objectives of chemistry and physics that have recognition by teachers, objectives that express the disciplinary claims have invariably had largest recognition.

A second objective, which has occupied a place of prominence, especially in biology, physics, and chemistry, is 'to impart to the pupils a broad knowledge of the field.' For its accomplishment the texts in use have become encyclopedias of information. In the field of chemistry, for example, the texts have had an interesting evolution. When chemistry was first given a place among the subjects of instruction in

[11] Bureau of Education Bulletin, No. 26, 1920.

colleges, the bulk of the chemical information that was known and organized as science was included within a small text. But with the development of the subject has come an enormous enlargement of knowledge. Many new fields have been opened. Much of this new knowledge has been added to the texts and most of what was in the older books has been retained, until the material now sets for high-school pupils a task that is practically insurmountable. A recent report shows that, by actual count, one of the two textbooks in chemistry that are most widely used employs 386 terms which are names of elements and their compounds, and the other 435 such terms.[12] Each book contains equations for a multitude of chemical changes and descriptions of many chemical processes. With such texts in the hands of teachers, the work of instruction has been directed toward acquiring the ability to use the names of these compounds and elements and to write the equations for the many chemical changes that are given.

Recent studies in measurement show that this knowledge objective is not effectively attained. At the end of one year of instruction, pupils have far from an adequate mastery of this material, while after even a short interval of time, much of the 'knowledge' they did have has been forgotten. These results furnish convincing evidence that the attempts to attain the knowledge objective do not yield effective functional outcomes from the study of the specialized science.

The third objective of senior-high-school science is 'college preparation.' Available data suggest at once that much of the support for this objective is of doubtful validity. A large proportion of pupils who study high-school science do not enter college, and, of those who do, a relatively small proportion will specialize in a field of science. For most students, then, this objective can hardly be supported and its validity is questioned even for those who do enter classes in college chemistry. A recent study by Noll[13] shows that the effects of instruction in the high school on students who subsequently take college chemistry cannot be detected by the ordinary measures of attainment after nine months of instruction on the college level. Other studies by Mabee[14] and by Cornog and Colbert[15] have shown that attainment in

[12] Powers, S. R. "The vocabularies of high-school science textbooks," Teachers College Record, 26:1925, 368-382.

[13] Noll, Victor H. Laboratory Instruction in the Field of Inorganic Chemistry. University of Minnesota Press, 1930.

[14] Mabee, F. C. "A test of achievement in college classes and results obtained by its use in both high school and college classes." Jour. of Chemical Education, January, 3: 1926, 70-76.

many high-school classes at the end of one year of instruction is superior to attainment in many college classes after a corresponding interval. Results from studies such as these furnish convincing evidence that emphasis upon the preparatory objective as a major support for instruction in high-school science has, in current practice, resulted in a large amount of wasted effort.

These objectives—the disciplinary, the knowledge, and the preparatory—are the ones which, more than anything else, have guided and are guiding the instructional efforts of chemistry teachers. None of these is being effectively attained, and, as commonly conceived, none is worthy of the potentialities of the subject. The common interpretation of the disciplinary, or training, objective is one which has developed from the faculty psychology. The knowledge, or informational, objective implies the acquisition of an organized and extensive knowledge of systematic chemistry. The preparatory objective cannot be functional for a large proportion of high-school pupils, and it appears not to be functional for those pupils for whom it might seem to be a valid objective.

Teachers and curriculum-workers in the field of senior-high-school science may well raise the question, "What knowledge is of most worth?" We shall attempt in vain to teach all the factual material that has been outlined under the special divisions commonly recognized. Furthermore, much of what is taught is unrelated to the life activities of any but the specialist and is soon forgotten by others and apparently with no appreciable loss to them.

The question of functional values for the special subjects has not been seriously studied and this level defines a field for fruitful curriculum research. Specialists in science have contributed enormously to determining the character of our present civilization, and they have contributed enormously to a fuller interpretation of the phenomena of everyday experiences that challenge the interests of liberally educated people. These considerations suggest the turn that curriculum research on this level must take. Studies of the interests of children and the interests of 'educated laymen' have served as a proper approach in the determination of functional content, but they are inadequate in that they do not go deeply enough. The services of those who have explored more thoroughly into the fields must be enlisted.

---

[15] Cornog and Colbert. "A quantitative analysis of aims in teaching high-school chemistry." *Sch. Sci. and Math.*, 24: 1924, 168-173.

CHAPTER III

WHAT ARE SOME OF THE CONTRIBUTIONS OF SCIENCE TO LIBERAL EDUCATION?[1]

This analysis of the educational values is given in an effort to call to mind some of the situations and some of the problems of everyday life and to show something of the background out of which they have come. Its aim is to illustrate how tested ideas have contributed to building up the things that are secure in our institutions and in our behavior. It illustrates some of the accomplishments in building security and some of the methods that have been the basis of attitudes that are functioning in human behavior.

The attitudes of science are those of respect for tested truth and the methods by which it is revealed. Enriched living is the goal toward which science is striving, and it is the hope of science that, through tested truth, it may help to neutralize prejudice and animosity, and reduce the friction between individuals who are the entities of our human social order.

This is an age of science. What does it mean to say that "this is an age of science"? In what particulars has science affected our institutions, set our problems, and modified our manner of thinking? What is there in our accomplishments that is secure and what potentialities are in them for further progress toward alleviating maladjustments and promoting human satisfactions and thus building greater security? The achievements of science are the products of the recent period and yet its tested truths have influenced and are influencing in enormous measure the present social order. Tested truths should be the units with which we think. In a program of general (or liberal) education those truths which are the foundation of our social order and those methods which may be effectively used to reveal truth must be given prominence in the curriculum.

In this analysis, values are considered under two general headings: (1) those values which arise from the direct use of the facts, principles, and generalizations of science in everyday life, and (2) those values which are secured concomitantly from the study of natural sciences through forming generalizations respecting methods and through form-

[1] For the Committee, by S. Ralph Powers.

27

ing generalizations from which scientific attitudes may reasonably be expected to develop. Attention is now directed to the first of these two values.

SCIENCE AND THE PRESENT SOCIAL ORDER

The individual cannot adapt himself to the conditions under which he lives without giving attention to the factors out of which these conditions have developed. This is an age of science, first in the sense that present modes of living are possible only because of contributions that have come from this field, and second, in the sense that the principles that guide our thinking have been enormously influenced by contributions from the work of scientists. The direct values from the study of science will be considered in relation to its contributions to the development of the present industrial civilization and in relation to its contributions to modern thought.

Control of Energy Has Transformed Our Manner of Living

On the physical side, science has, in a short period of time, transformed our manner of living. This mechanical age has come as a result of man's increased control of energy transformations. The release and control of energy from natural resources has made available a great wealth of energy. With the manufacture of machinery, this energy is available to do the work of the world. Rate of production has increased and the world's store of available wealth has been made enormously greater. This development has fostered a centralization of wealth in great industries, and it has, as a result of using energy from natural resources in place of energy from human beings, reduced the demand for labor. Men have been freed from toil. We have changed rapidly from an age of human labor to an age of machine labor. Adjustment to this changed condition must be based upon an understanding of the conditions and forces that have produced it.

Learning to control energy has, in still other ways, affected our manner of living. Energy from natural resources has made us mobile. Movement is accomplished with ease, speed, and comfort. The great majority of those who graduate from the high school will own and drive automobiles, and many, if not most, of them will fly. Machines transform energy of natural resources into mechanical energy which is used to transport goods and people. The wide ramifications of problems associated with transportation are evidence of the importance in liberal education of experiences selected to give an understanding of the developments from science that have made our present accomplishments in mobility possible.

It is a highly refined control of energy transformations that has made modern communication possible. Electrical energy, under control, reproduces in a telephone receiver the words spoken into the transmitter. A small amount of energy transmitted through space from the radio transmitting station is controlled with such a degree of precision that sounds at the microphone are most accurately reproduced by the loud speaker.

This is an electrical age, and, on account of the ease with which electrical energy may be transformed and controlled, the great mass of our population has become, during one generation, users of electrical energy. The electric light bulb is a very recent invention. At the present time about one third of American homes are supplied with current for light and power, and industrialists are pointing to the remaining two thirds as a most attractive field for immediate business development. A large percentage of factories, in fact nearly all, are dependent more or less upon electrical energy. The industrial demands for release of energy from our natural resources are so great that the problems of production and efficient utilization of energy challenge the entire mass of our population. They have become a leading issue of political campaigns. Problems of power development, with their influence on industry, including transportation, communication, and comforts in the home, touch the lives of all and find generous justification for recognition in a program of liberal education.

It must be clear, too, that problems associated with the control of energy are by no means static. The continuous refinement of methods of control is in the direction of control with greater efficiency. Industrial plants are, therefore, in a continuous process of reorganization. Cases are common in which expensive machinery in good condition is removed and sold as junk in order to make place for new machinery that will accomplish energy transformations more efficiently. As a result of new discoveries, new industries take the place of old ones. A recently developed process for the manufacture of wood alcohol from coal has already nearly displaced the one based upon the destructive distillation of wood. It seems likely that processes for the synthetic preparation of gasoline may soon be perfected that will eventually transform this industry. Every large concern maintains a staff of highly trained scientists who are working continually to reduce waste and to increase efficiency through more efficient utilization of materials and energy.

In these foregoing considerations are suggestions of the nature of this industrial age and of the contributions from science that have made it what it is. The liberally educated person knows something of the character of the age in which he lives and something of the conditions that have produced it. A program of education which is a program of preparation for life must carry responsibility for developing a consciousness of the nature of the life into which school children are emerging. It seems certain that man's control of energy transformations has contributed more than any other single factor to the development of our industrial life. The educational program must, therefore, provide types of experiences from which children may learn something about sources of energy and about how it may be transformed, to the end that they may acquire some understanding of the industrial age in which they live and a fuller appreciation of the problems associated with life in it.

Science Has Contributed Enormously to Health and Sanitation

The field of health offers another illustration of the manner in which applied science has contributed to the development of modern standards of living. The importance of sanitary measures and the penalties of ignorance, in the form of illnesses, with attendant losses to the community, are well known. The science of sanitation has shown us how to protect crowded cities and rural communities from contagious diseases which, if uncontrolled, would be terribly destructive. Typhoid fever, diphtheria, smallpox, hydrophobia, scarlet fever, leprosy, malaria, yellow fever, and bubonic plague are among the diseases which are so well understood that they are definitely controllable. If a single case of any of these illnesses were to develop in an American city, the board of health could probably trace it to the cause that produced it, and it is entirely likely that the board would be able to place personal responsibility for the negligence that allowed the case to develop. The maintenance of proper standards of health through control of causes of ill health is a responsibility of the individual and of the community. An aim of the schools is to impart to children such instruction as will enable them to maintain bodily vigor. In meeting this responsibility, attention should be focused upon three objectives: (1) the formation of health habits, (2) the imparting of health information, and (3) the development of a health consciousness. Each of these are now briefly considered.

According to the first objective, the school must assist in the formation of *health habits*. There are forms of behavior so generally recognized as correct that they should be brought to the level of the habitual. Illustrations of these that relate directly to the health of individuals are habits affecting posture, exercise, elimination, work, and sleep. Illustrations relating to the welfare of the group are matters of ventilation, cleanliness, and care of equipment. Realization of this purpose may be seen as an essential part, but by no means a complete discharge, of the responsibilities for health instruction. Health habits prepare only for response to those matters of health that are of expected and frequent recurrence. They cannot be expected to form a background for the varieties of behavior that are essential for adaptation to a changing environment.

A second objective relating to health education is to impart *health information*. Information raises health habits to the level of consciousness and makes them meaningful, and information provides a background which is a basis for intelligent action. No number of habitual acts are sufficient to protect an individual and his community from typhoid fever. It is not sufficient to know that scientists have acquired control of typhoid fever. If the individual is to protect himself and to help protect his community from this illness, he must know the manner in which it is controlled. Specifically, he must know that polluted water is one source of the organism that causes the disease, and he must know how water is polluted and how it may be made sanitary. As regards those habits that do function directly as an aid to the maintenance of bodily vigor, it is well established that these are much more readily reduced to the level of habitual behavior if instruction pertaining to them is built upon a scientific foundation.

For the third objective there is responsibility for developing a *health consciousness*. The citizen needs an appreciation of what health means to him and to the community. A health consciousness may be developed from recognition of the comforts to the race that have come as a result of continuous progress in the control of the causes of ill health. A health consciousness, on a proper foundation of understanding, induces an obligation to carry forward programs of activity designed to protect the welfare of the group.

Health habits (insofar as they are secure), health understandings, and health consciousness have their foundation for support in the work of specialists. When attention is directed to the practical attainments during the present generation in the elevation of health standards, the record seems most impressive. But those who have no more than a general education in matters of health are conscious of possibilities for further achievement. Principles of science, the understanding of which are essential to the maintenance of present standards of health, and principles that suggest the way to attain still higher standards have abundant justification as curriculum content in our elementary and secondary schools.

Science Has Increased Our Control of the Food Supply

In his struggle for existence in this complex civilization, man is continually in conflict with the forces of nature. Among primitive people the natural balance of life places limitations upon man's development as an organism in this balance. A prime factor in the struggle for existence is the struggle for food. Natural processes tend to limit the food supply and to keep it far below what is demanded for a congested human population. Measures have been taken to increase the land area under cultivation, and continued cultivation demands knowledge of artificial procedures for maintaining soil fertility. Through scientific agriculture man has acquired control of the factors of nature that are needed for the production of food for a congested population.

In his study of living things, man has learned that, by modification, he may in considerable measure control the character of oncoming generations of plants and animals. Cattle have been modified, some in the direction of producing more beef, others in the direction of producing more and richer milk. Chickens are bred for laying; horses are bred for speed; sheep are bred for wool. These products of breeding are 'good stock' only in the sense that they are more productive of food or of other materials and qualities desired by man. In a natural struggle for existence these fine stocks, without the aid of man, might soon become extinct. An important contribution to the understanding of the artificiality of the conditions in which we live comes through knowledge of the manner in which man has modified the natural balance of life.

Science Sheds Light on the Genesis of Human Traits

In this connection it should be noted that the same biological laws that govern the growth and development of plant and lower animal organisms also govern the growth and development of the human organism. Individuals should know that the characteristics of their children, such as stature, obesity, and intelligence, are, within rather well-defined limits, determined by their own characteristics and those of the man or woman chosen for husband or wife. We are in possession of knowledge with which we may modify the character of the human race itself. This is one of the responsibilities with which the world's citizenry must learn to live. The abuse of this responsibility will certainly bring its own punishment and the proper exercise of it will bring its rewards.

Significance for Education

Illustrations of the applications of science could be extended to greater length. Those just given are enough to suggest (1) something of the extent to which man has acquired control of his physical and biological environment, (2) something of the extent to which he has used these controls to modify the character of his environment, and (3) something of the complexity of the life into which oncoming generations are entering. Our civilization is a highly artificial thing, in the sense that it is a product of man's own ingenuity. The qualities that will determine the civilization of tomorrow are being developed by the activities of the children in the schools to-day. The activities of these children are, in turn, largely determined by the learning experiences that the schools provide for them.

In a program of general education which is for the most part the program of the public schools, the work of instruction will be directed toward increasing the understanding of those principles and generalizations of science that have had largest application in molding the character of our society and of those which have within them potentialities for influence in the future. Attainments of such understandings are important, if not in large measure essential, for an understanding of our social life and for effective participation in it. Understanding of principles underlying such problems as are suggested by the following are samples of desirable outcomes: (1) the sources of energy and its efficient utilization, (2) the discovery of the causes of ill health and the means of control of these causes to the end that health standards may be raised, (3) the maintenance of soil fertility, (4) the applications of the laws of heredity, and (5) the control of plant and animal pests.

SCIENCE AND HUMAN ADJUSTMENTS

There can be no adequate adaptation to this life in which we find ourselves and which we call civilization, the nature of which is so largely determined by man's ingenuity, without some understanding of the human achievements that have made it possible. These achievements have been in the nature of continuously enlarged control over natural forces. It is equally true that there can be no adequate understanding of modern thought without some comprehensive understanding of the major generalizations that have been formulated from study of the nature of things. These tested truths, together with the evidence on which they stand, are the basis of the knowledge by means of which the individual interprets the phenomena of experience. Educational values that come from ability to interpret natural phenomena may be even more far-reaching in importance in general training than the values that come from the understanding of applications like those already illustrated. The intellectual attainment of a people may be to a large extent measured by the ability of its individuals to interpret the phenomena of their common experiences. In this discussion it cannot be presumed that the development and use of such concepts are the prerogative of the philosopher or highly trained scientist. It is undoubtedly true that the thinking of the whole mass of the people has been influenced by partial or comprehensive understanding of the major generalizations of science. The progress already made in the direction of attaining freedom from the bondage of superstitition and from the shackles of necromancy, alchemy, witchcraft, astrology, and other errors of understanding, furnishes abundant evidence of the importance of instruction directed toward assisting the learner to understand the phenomena of his common observation. Some attempt to rationalize observation is made by all thinking people. The most satisfactory rationalization is that which is based upon most carefully tested truth. Some illustrations of contributions from science that have influenced and are influencing thought will be given.

How Science Influences Thinking

Such common phenomena as lightning, earthquakes, and storms are no longer looked upon as mysterious afflictions visited upon the people by an irate deity. These are now seen as effects which result from natural causes, many of which are well understood. Eclipses and comets are no longer looked upon as good or bad omens, for their causes are satisfactorily explained. General understanding of causes such as these is of distinct educational value. It gives to the learner a feeling of security in the presence of natural forces, for he is freed from the mental terror that attends ignorance.

Through the results of scientific study the world has progressed from the status which prevailed when the common belief was that the earth was flat, the center of the universe, and the dominating influence among the heavenly bodies, to the present time when the movements of the heavenly bodies are more clearly comprehended and the earth is seen as but one of the planets that revolves about the sun and the sun as but one of an undetermined number of stars that make up our galaxy. This galaxy is, in turn, one of an undetermined number of galaxies distributed through space, the dimensions of which seem incomprehensible. Accompanying this enlargement of knowledge has come a changed conception of man's place in the scheme of things. Attendant upon the discoveries that have revealed the true relations between the earth and other bodies has come an enlarged conception of the age of the earth and of the duration of time.

This generation has seen an enormous expansion in knowledge of the nature of matter. The relationship of matter and energy has been suggested by recognition of the electron as a discrete particle of electricity. Moseley's work on atomic numbers has served to refine the classification of the chemical elements, and this, together with other work, furnishes a presumptive basis for the conclusion that all elements on earth and in the universe are made up of groupings of electrons and protons.

In the study of living things, equally great strides have been made. Interrelationships of organisms with each other and their interactions with the physical environment have been more clearly envisaged. Organisms are continually struggling, each group against the other, for survival; but all are held in check by the limitations of the physical environment. The trend of this struggle is toward a balance in nature. Wind, rain, fire, and other factors of nature are continually disturbing the natural balance; now one organism and then another is in the ascendency. Then, in obedience to the urge to reproduce their kind, the dominant organisms overpopulate the area to such an extent that they are checked by starvation. In this struggle for existence, man is seen as an organism guided by a conscious intent to control the factors of nature that tend to limit his development.

Studies in other directions have revealed facts that are the basis of acceptable generalizations concerning the history of life on earth. This work makes available a body of tested truth from which to draw more secure interpretations concerning man as a biological organism and his place in the 'plan of nature.' The processes of growth have been extensively studied. In considerable measure, heredity is under control and the knowledge of heredity applied in artificial selection has contributed to the security of man as the dominating organism of his environment. Studies in behavior are of recent origin, but we have already learned much about why we behave as we do and why other organisms behave as they do, and we have learned something about measures to be taken to control behavior. Results from studies in this field will undoubtedly occupy a place of increasing prominence in human thinking.

The Values for Humanity from Understanding Scientific Conceptions

The values that come from the understanding of conceptions such as are suggested by the foregoing are probably second to none in their potential influence on the happiness of individuals. These are the considerations that have application in private and personal thought. In some manner, either for good or for evil, they affect the thoughts of all rational beings, whatever their level of intellect or schooling.

During the past decade there has been a great deal of discussion of controversial issues in religion. The controversy is between the Fundamentalist, on the one hand, who in substance accepts and supports the literal interpretations of the Old Testament, and the Modernist, on the other hand, who calls for such modification of religious thought as seems to him necessary to make it consistent with his interpretation of the findings of science and his interpretation of the method of science that are the products of the modern age. The issues of this discussion cannot be considered without reference to conceptions and generalizations like those illustrated. Neither Fundamentalist nor Modernist can intelligently weigh the issues of his belief without extensive and accurate knowledge of them.

Evidence of the importance of the connotations of scientific conceptions and generalizations is supplied, further, by observations of the extent to which they are challenging to the interests of children and adults. There is an abiding interest in study that interprets the nature of things. Many of the stimuli to which we respond have their origin in phenomena of the environment. There is satisfaction from instruction that develops tested knowledge which will function in making responses that must be made. There is satisfaction from the understanding of reasons for happenings, for such understanding makes it possible to respond to a greater variety of stimuli, and this in turn makes for a more flexible adaptation to the conditions of life. As respects natural phenomena, the reasons for happenings are found in the contributions that have come from the work of scientists. The general question of interest in instructional material is resolved into the more specific question whether the instructional material has been so selected as to supply learning which is helpful in making responses to situations (stimuli) that come within the learner's experience. The situations with which science is concerned abound in stimuli. There will be no lack of interest in instruction which results in satisfactory adjustment to these stimuli.

Much of the interest in natural phenomena is, no doubt, seated deeply in ingrained fears, and these fears have undoubtedly developed out of ignorance. Fear arises from the inability to make a satisfactory adjustment to a stimulus. The savage has been afraid of comets, the aurora, eclipses, and other natural phenomena that are strange and unusual. His fear is for his personal safety. For protection he has rested his faith in an appeal to spirits or to other mysterious agencies that are, as products of his own mind, stronger forces. Ordinary phenomena are now explained as effects that result from natural causes and many of these effects are clearly traced to the causes that produce them. There is, then, a natural interest in instruction that develops such an explanation of these phenomena that the learner is able to develop scientific attitudes which insure a satisfactory mental adjustment in the presence of these phenomena.

There are probably no educational experiences that contribute so immediately to the happiness of an individual as those which liberate his mind from fears and in other ways guide his thinking.

CONCOMITANTS AND INDIRECT VALUES IN THE STUDY OF SCIENCE

Our purpose to this point has been to call attention, with illustrations, to the manner in which the findings of science have had direct application as factors in modifying our social institutions and systems of thought. Emphasis has been on *direct* informational value, with the thought that functional information furnishes the ideas that are essential to thought processes. Security in thinking is more likely to result when the ideas with which thinking is done have been scientifically tested for truthfulness. Attention is now directed to those values which arise *indirectly* from the study of science.

Scientific Attitudes

In addition to informational outcomes there are necessarily many concomitants to any form of functional learning. Attention may now be focused upon the methods that have been employed in problem-solving and that should be further applied in the solution of new problems. Science teachers may consciously take steps to clarify the methods of scientific study and may provide exercises in the use of the methods for solving challenging problems.

Attitudes are also necessarily concomitant with the understanding of ideas and the understanding of methods. In their origins, attitudes are based upon understanding (or the lack of it), and they are the reaction of a personality to learning experiences. Desirable attitudes, that is, attitudes that are consistent with truth, are the ones that are formed as a result of satisfactory experiences in learning.

The method of science emphasizes careful and accurate observation of controlled and uncontrolled phenomena as a means for determining truth, and it also requires the formulation of hypotheses to explain the relationship of observed phenomena. Hypotheses are statements of most reasonable explanations and these are subjected to further tests for truth and adequacy by further observation. The scientific attitudes are characterized by respect for truth and by freedom from prejudice and personal bias. An educational program for an age of science will recognize both the content and the method of science.

A word of caution seems in place lest efforts to define scientific attitudes result in setting them apart, in thinking, from the tested truth with which they are necessarily associated. What the educator must recognize is that intrinsically there is no method apart from a method of doing something, and that, in their development at least, attitudes are necessarily attitudes toward an object, a situation, or phenomena. A rich experience with scientific method is one which makes positive demands upon the use of the method for the solution of real problems. Hence, a major responsibility in planning a program of instruction is that subject matter be so selected and so arranged that real problems arise out of it. Attention is focused upon the scientific method as it is used in study. Scientific attitudes result from the impingement of implications respecting the generalizations and methods of science on the personality of an individual. Neither the method nor the attitude can exist *in vacuo*.

There is abundant evidence that the conceptions, generalizations, attitudes, and methods of this field of expanding knowledge are of fundamental importance in the program of general education and that they are genuinely challenging to the interests of children and of educated adults. Interest is challenged by recognition of the part that developments in science have played in forming the present social order and of the contribution of science to understanding of causes of natural phenomena. There is interest in understanding how vast sources of energy are tapped and transformed to useful purposes and in the manner in which man has modified the biological environment of which he is a part. Children and adults are attracted by the generalizations relating to the age of the earth; the extent of space; the movements of the heavenly bodies; the nature of matter and energy; and the development of organisms, the nature of their adaptations, and the functioning of their parts. The interest is found in the satisfaction that comes from attending to evidence that leads to a satisfactory conclusion and in the connotations of these conclusions.

The contributions of science are a product of the recent period. The body of tested knowledge has increased through the past one hundred years at an accelerated pace. Only small samplings of this have found place in the general program of liberal education, though enormous applications of it have been made in developing the present social order. The extent to which this new body of content has within it the potentialities for thus influencing mental and social adjustments, that is, for liberalizing the learner, may be measured by the extent to which this information makes it possible for the learner to respond to situations which come within his experience and without which response would be thwarted. Another measure of educational value of experiences that is suggested by the foregoing is found in the extent to which such experiences assist an individual to adapt himself to the human society of which he is a part. These considerations suggest the real tests of the educative value of science, whether the content be selected for so-called 'practical' values or for cultural or liberalizing values. In general education, no sharp division can be drawn between subject matter of these two kinds.

SUMMARY

This brief overview of the field of science and these references to the relations of science to human affairs suggest the sources to which we may turn to find curricular materials. The search for objectives will be one that seeks to determine the major generalizations and the associated scientific attitudes that have come from the field. The curriculum-worker will test these ideas for relative importance by a study of the extent to which they ramify into human affairs and by an evaluation of the potentialities which they possess for influencing the physical and mental adjustments of human beings. The teacher will capitalize the experiences of children and make them meaningful by associating them in such a manner that they contribute to the continued enlargement of the child's understanding of fundamental truths. The program of science teaching will be one which seeks to interpret the contributions of science to health, to safety, and to the development of the economic order; and it will be one which seeks to interpret the principles and generalizations that have largest application in effecting mental and emotional adjustment of the individual to the cosmos of which he is a part.

This Committee stresses the importance of subject matter and recognizes the responsibility for selection of subject matter which shall be functional for guidance toward a more satisfactory adjustment of the individual to the society of which he must be a part. In this society man must meet and solve problems. The schools will prepare children for their responsibilities by providing experiences with a body of subject matter (1) that has been tested for truthfulness, (2) that exercises methods that have been used in solving problems, and (3) that furnishes practice in the use of these methods—in short, with subject matter that contributes to the ultimate comprehension of major generalizations and to the development of associated scientific attitudes. A body of subject matter tested for truthfulness and found secure is a primary consideration in a program of education designed to train in scientific methods of study and designed to inculcate attitudes of open-mindedness and of respect for truth. The extent to which such a program is valid for general education is measured by the extent to which the subject matter, methods, and attitudes are functional in the thinking of educated laymen.

CHAPTER IV

THE OBJECTIVES OF SCIENCE TEACHING IN RELATION TO THE AIM OF EDUCATION*

In Chapter I an effort has been made to portray the nature of the school system that, in the light of present educational theory, seems acceptable in our democratic social order. This has been presented as the plan of education into which the program of science teaching must be fitted.

In Chapter II has been considered the contrast that prevails between the acceptable plan of public education and the provision in the curriculum for fulfilling this plan.

In Chapter III there has been given a brief overview of the fields of science, with a suggestion of the extensive influence which contribution from this field has had and is having in determining our institutions, our philosophies of life, and our methods of thinking.

From these presentations it is clear, we trust, that practices are not abreast of the best thought in curriculum work. Indeed, many prevailing practices in the schools find their only support in philosophical and psychological postulations that are recognized not only as obsolete but even as directly opposed to the postulations on which the organization of our school system is based. A problem of first rank importance to the educational worker, especially in the field of curriculum, is to define the aim of education in such a way that the definition will function as a guiding thought, will direct the teacher in choosing what to do in order to attain the aim. The Committee, after analysis of philosophical works, accepts what seems to be a sound definition of the aim and assumes responsibility for defining objectives toward which efforts in instruction and learning may be directed. The attainment of these objectives will carry the learner progressively forward toward a fuller realization of the aim.[1]

---

* For the Committee, by S. Ralph Powers.

[1] In this discussion, the objectives which are attained as a result of activities are seen as contributory to the aim. This discussion of the curriculum attempts to associate aims, objectives, and activities.

In this discussion the attainment of an objective means the attainment of understanding, together with the development of mental attitudes that may be associated with understanding, and it means the development of ability to use techniques and methods of working and thinking. The definitions of the understandings, techniques, methods, and mental attitudes are stated as declarative sentences. Strictly speaking, these declarative sentences define the objectives of science teaching. In order to simplify the discussion these sentences are called the objectives of science teaching.

A Statement of the Aim of Education

An aim of education that seems consistent with the postulations of modern philosophy is, *Life Enrichment through Participation in a Democratic Social Order.* Education is an effect which comes from experiences operating as causes. The education of an individual is the effect on his whole behavior that has come from the experiences in which he has participated. A planned program of education (the ambition of educational workers) is one that provides experiences that will contribute as fully as may be to the attainment of life enrichment.

Learning may be seen as a progressive and continuous process of forming connections between situations and responses. In the school, special care is taken to establish connections between life situations and responses which are recognized as truth. The process of connection-forming is most effectively accomplished if the program of education is so planned that situations and responses which belong together are actually brought together. The best knowledge of other individuals, or groups of individuals, working as learners, furnishes the only guidance that is known for bringing together those situations and responses that should be connected in learning.

The abstractions formed from the connections of related situations and responses are principles and generalizations. The point of view taken here is that life enrichment is in part, and in large part, developed from the understanding of principles and generalizations that ramify into human experience. These principles and generalizations are functional in that they furnish a background for intelligent response to stimuli that recur in common, unspecialized experience. The understanding of principles and generalizations comes from the association of ideas that are developed from experiences. These understandings are products of the activities of the school if the ideas from which they come are products of classroom activities. It is clear, then, that the school will contribute to life enrichment if its activities are of the kind from which ideas may be developed and if the ideas may in turn be associated into principles and generalizations that are interwoven into human experience. This point of view is important because it suggests a definable procedure for accomplishing an integration of school activities and life activities. Functional learning is conditioned upon attainment of some such integration.

A functional understanding of a principle has been attained if the learner has acquired ability to associate with the principle the ideas from his immediate and from his subsequent experiences that are related to it and if he is able to apply the principle in practical situations. The principles and generalizations that ramify most widely into human affairs may be stated as objectives of science education. The objective may be seen then as differing from the aim of education chiefly in its scope. The aim of education is life enrichment. The enriched life is one that enables the individual to participate intelligently and with satisfaction in the experiences of living. The objectives may be stated as the principles and generalizations that are functional for the individual, in that they enable him to interpret the experiences of living. The objectives may be formulated (1) as statements that function directly in thinking, (2) as statements that describe methods of thinking, and (3) as statements that describe attitudes toward products of thought and toward methods of thinking. These three types of objectives, although distinguishable, cannot be regarded as mutually exclusive. From the point of view of their origins in the educative process, these objectives are closely similar. The findings from science have contributed enormously to thinking, to methods of study, and to the development of scientific attitudes that affect behavior. The principles and generalizations of science must, therefore, occupy considerable place in a program of general education, the aim of which is life enrichment.

Steps in Laying Out the Science Curriculum

The first steps in the program of curriculum work in science for the public schools may be directed toward the determination of those major generalizations and associated scientific attitudes which together define the field. The curriculum-worker will test these for usefulness by study of the extent to which they touch the interests and relate to the welfare of human beings. Some progress in this has already been made. For a tentative definition of these major generalizations, educational workers have turned to the writings of men of science, with particular attention to the material which they have written for general (that is, for unspecialized) readers. This has seemed a most fruitful field for study, for this material is the product of careful thought concerning the needs and interests of the general reader, and it represents the effort to meet these needs by men who have sufficient breadth and thoroughness of training to overview the fields of which they write.

The major generalizations and associated scientific attitudes are seen as of such importance that understandings of them are made the objectives of science teaching. These statements are so far-reaching in their implications that they may be said to encompass the fields of science. They touch life in so many ways that their attainment as educational objectives constitutes a large part of the program of life enrichment. The program for their attainment must be considered in relation to the whole program of education. Principles and generalizations of science are objectives. Learning experiences result from activities selected for their contribution to the enlargement of the meaning of these objectives.

It has already been stated (in Chapter I) that the plan of public education is one that provides learning experiences for the successive grades that are appropriate for continual mental growth. Our plan of science education is offered as one that is in agreement with, in fact, is a necessary part of, the plan of public education.

On the practical side, it should be said that in any subject a program of education which is inconsistent with the plan of general education can hardly be successful. Furthermore, a program which is inconsistent with the abilities of teachers in service to develop is also doomed to failure.

Organization about Large Objectives

In the light of the foregoing, it is proposed that the curriculum in science for a program of general education be organized about large objectives, that understanding and enlargement of these objectives shall constitute the contribution of science teaching to the ultimate aim of education, and that the course of study be so organized that each succeeding grade level shall present an increasingly enlarged and increasingly mature development of the objectives.

Analysis of a Typical Generalization

The method by means of which a generalization of science may function as an educational objective may be illustrated by the analysis of one of them into learning experiences which are appropriate for use on different grade levels. Take, for example, the scientist's conception of the age of the earth. This conception has been developed by study of the changes that have taken place on the earth and by study of the rate at which these changes go on.

Children of the lower grades may see that a small stream in the neighborhood of the school is slowly carrying away the earth which lines its banks. Following each heavy rainfall the change is sufficient to be noticeable. The bed in which the stream flows is made deeper and wider as the muddy water flows away toward the sea. The experiences associated with these observations are the foundation for the simple generalization: many years have been required for the stream bed to form. On more mature grade levels it may be shown that the hills on each side of the stream have been formed by the continuous action of the flowing water. The valley between the hills may or may not be wide. Suppose it is one hundred feet wide and suppose the hills are fifty feet high: that may show that the sum total of the effects of the several small streams of the community has been to carry away cubic miles of earth. After this elementary treatment of the work of streams has been given, the children may be told that the geologists' estimate of the average rate at which the North American continent is being worn away by water is approximately one foot in 9,000 years.

On more mature grade levels additionally enlarged notions of the geologic history of the earth's surface may be presented. Evidence is at hand to show that the erosive action of running water and of other agencies has continued in some regions until the stream has cut its bed down to the ocean level. In this manner the Colorado River has formed the deep canyon in which it now flows, for at one time its bed was high above its present level. Furthermore, in the walls of the canyon there are extensive limestone deposits which contain fossils of marine animals. Geologists accept this fact as evidence that this region was at one time beneath the sea and that as a result of wrinkling and folding of the earth's surface this ancient sea bottom has been elevated until it is now many hundreds of feet above the level of the ocean. Since this elevation the river has cut its way down through the elevated rock for hundreds of feet. Geologists find records of changes in this region which could hardly have occurred in less than 700,000,000 years. These records identify changes that took place through a long era which preceded the period of planation.

The history of the Hudson River and of the formations which constitute its valley takes the mind through a period of time so vast that it is difficult to comprehend. At the present time the Hudson is an arm of the Atlantic, a 'drowned' river, the flow of which is interrupted by the rise and fall of the tides. Its rock bed is very deep, in fact, extends down for more than 700 feet below sea level. Its channel extends out to the edge of the Atlantic continental shelf as a veritable canyon beneath the sea. Yet this channel must have been cut by the erosive action of running water. There is evidence in these observations that the land of the New York City region was once much more elevated than at present and that the deep bed of the Hudson was once a gorge, similar to that of the Yellowstone River but on a smaller scale.

The rock on either side of the Hudson River tells a story of events still more ancient than those we have just mentioned. On the west stands the towering cliff known as the Palisades—the eroded edge of a huge sheet of once molten rock which has been pushed in between layers of sedimentary rock, shale, and sandstone. These sediments, forming a deposit many thousands of feet in thickness, were laid down in a sinking continental basin during the Age of Reptiles. The skeleton of a dinosaur has been found embedded in the cemented sediments at the edge of the river.

Of the enormous period of time between the earliest of the geologic eras and the Age of Reptiles, during which time animal life developed from the simplest forms to the highly complex reptile type, there is no record in this region. The geologist tells us that deposits may have been laid down, but if so, they have been subsequently eroded, for nothing remains. On the eastern bank, however, he points to the gnarled and contorted schists, marbles, and gneisses which form the Island of Manhattan. They were made in the first of the five geological eras, the Archaeozoic. They were crumpled into mountains comparable to the Rocky Mountains in height and were the scene of great igneous activity. To-day nothing but their bases remains; they have been worn down almost to sea level. We question the geologist concerning the origin of these ancient rocks, and we are told that they are but metamorphosed sediments made from the erosion of still more ancient rocks.

On both sides of the Hudson we find the deposits of clay and boulders left by the last great glacier, and we see the grooves that it gouged in the rocks. If the whole of geologic time be represented by 24 hours, this glacier receded less than 4 seconds ago. Yet this took place long before the dawn of human history. Such, in brief, is the record of the Hudson and of the rocks which form its banks.

In addition to the informative value of such material as the foregoing, effective accomplishment of learning in this field contributes to the development of other important objectives that may be seen as concomitants. The development of the primary objective illustrates clearly some of the attributes of the scientific methods which have been used by geologists. Observation and awareness of natural phenomena stimulate an attitude of inquiry concerning the reasons for happenings. How did the rolling country on each side of streams and rivers come to be as it is? Why is it that marine fossils are found embedded in rock high up in mountains? Observation of a relationship between time and change furnishes the urge to determine how long these changes have been going on. Solution of these inquiries is attempted by correlation of observations, formulation of hypotheses as possible explanation, and testing of these hypotheses by assembling and correlating additional observations. Hypotheses are tested by examining them to determine their consistency with all observations. For example, the observation of marine fossils in the rocks of the western mountains suggests at once the hypothesis that these fossiliferous rocks were once part of the bed of the ocean. Observation and study of the contour of these rocks and of their relationship to neighboring rock deposits reveal only data which support this hypothesis. Diastrophism is an established phenomenon, so the geologist is led safely to the conclusion that, owing to upheavals and folding of the earth's crust, a region which was once part of the bed of the ocean is now a high mountain.

This analysis illustrates some of the methods of scientific study. It illustrates (1) the scientist's dependence upon factual information, (2) the factual bases of hypotheses, and (3) the testing of hypotheses through securing more factual information. It shows how hypotheses may be tested by the criterion of cause and effect and by the criterion of internal consistency; that is, agreement of fact with fact. It reveals that science may contribute and has contributed a factual background for beliefs and interpretations which become crystallized into scientific attitudes and that these in turn may be substituted for the background supported only by tradition, mysticism, and superstition.

The study of such content as has just been outlined makes for an awareness of nature. Through such study the learner comes to a clearer comprehension of his place in the scheme of nature, and he may come to a clearer comprehension of his limitations and of his strengths in the face of natural forces.

The learner is practiced in intelligent observation and interpretation, and by this means acquires an understanding of the natural phenomena of his environment. He gains an appreciation of the scientific method by going vicariously with the geologist through experiences encountered in real investigations. He must understand the geologist's problems, know some of his data, and understand how he has applied the data to the solution of the problems. 'Subject matter,' as used here, includes both problems and data for solution of these problems, together with such activities as are necessary to clarify and visualize the problems and the data. The pupil is vicariously a discoverer. He is taken through the experiences of a discoverer, and these experiences are clarified so that he may come, in as large measure as possible, to an appreciation of the methods of thought and action used by a scientific worker. The objective is rich enough to suggest situations that will provide direct as well as vicarious experience with the scientific method and rich enough to furnish a background for scientific attitudes toward the findings and the methods of scientific workers.

There is evidence in these histories—of the small stream that flows, by chance, past the school, of the Colorado River, of the Hudson River, of the formation and destruction of mountains, of the formation of sedimentary rock, and of diastrophism—that the earth during inconceivable eons of time has passed through tremendous but orderly physical changes. This enlarged conception of the age of the earth and of the succession of changes that have taken place and are taking place on its surface, properly considered, is a potential source of the profound inspiration that furnishes the drive for further intellectual effort. A dominant purpose of science instruction is to guide the learner so that he may reach an intelligent understanding of his environment and of the methods of study which have led to acceptable explanations of natural phenomena. The satisfaction arising from such understandings furnishes the most secure foundation for desirable attitudes.

There are two related generalizations developed in the foregoing illustration. These are:

(1) The earth seems very old when its age is measured in ordinary units of time.

(2) The surface of the earth has not always had its present appearance and is constantly changing.

The criteria for testing the validity of these generalizations are suggested by the questions:

(1) Do the experiences by means of which the objective (or the sub-objectives of different grade levels) is attained challenge the interests of children?

(2) Are the statements sufficiently specific to suggest to the teacher and to the curriculum-worker the activities appropriate to the attainment of the objective?

(3) Does the attainment of the objective enlarge the learner's horizon and contribute to his ultimate attainment of scientific attitudes so that he may make more satisfactory adjustments to the problems and to the challenging stimuli that will enter his life as an educated layman? Does the attainment of the objective modify his behavior in ways that will be satisfying to him and in such ways that his behavior will not run in conflict with the welfare of other members of the social order?

In a real sense the criteria suggested by the foregoing questions may be summarized by the one question: Does the attainment of the objective contribute to life enrichment for the child of the grade level for which the learning activities are arrayed and for the individual after he has emerged from childhood to the status of an educated layman? In the application of these criteria, attention will be directed to consideration of values for knowledge, values for methods, and values for attitudes.

This analysis has been given to show how a major generalization of science may be broken up so that it suggests learning experiences which may be used in grades on different levels of maturity. This one provides experiences which may be used on all levels ranging from the lower grades to the university. The work of running water, rock formations, the erosive action of growing plants, the formation of coal beds, glaciers, and related topics are commonly included in courses of study for the elementary and junior high school. These should be so presented as to amplify for the learner the meaning of the scientific generalizations concerning the age of the earth and the changes that are taking place on its surface. These changes may be presented in relation to rate of change so that, as the child progresses from grade to grade, he gets an increasingly enlarged conception of the length of time these forces have been at work. It is suggested that we may expect to accomplish a grade placement of material relating to this objective by analyzing the major generalization into the smaller generalizations, principles, and concepts from which it has been synthesized and by subsequent subdivision of these until they are reduced to elements which are appropriate for the different grades. This point of view is in harmony with the point of view of elementary and secondary education. The learning process should be a building-up process. Elementary concepts and generalizations will be developed on lower grade levels, and successive levels will provide for assembling and associating the elementary learning into increasingly enlarged interpretations. Some one has well said: "Introduce children to big ideas and do it early." The Committee accepts this as a guiding principle for curriculum work in science and offers this analysis as illustrative of ways and means for its application.

Another Illustrative Analysis

A brief analysis of the statement: Energy for vital and physical processes comes from the sun, will show that this is another of the major generalizations of science.

The fact that the sun is a source of light and heat may be taught in the elementary grades. Subsequently it may be shown that energy from the sun may be transformed into energy of falling water and into energy of wood, coal, and petroleum. Energy from falling water and from coal may be transformed into mechanical energy and used in industry or it may be further transformed into electricity. It is through increasing control of these energy changes that man has made himself more secure in the struggle for existence and has developed the present mechanical age. Mechanical devices—steam and gas engines, dynamos, motors, electromagnets—are energy transformers, and functional knowledge of these mechanical devices will result from an understanding of the manner in which they operate to accomplish a transformation.

This analysis reveals subject matter and problems that are appropriate for study on all levels of mental maturity, ranging from that of the elementary school upward through the university. The analysis may be set forth in the curriculum in such a manner that it gives to the learner, as he progresses from grade to grade, a continuous enlargement of the energy concept, and in such a manner that he may secure some appreciation of, and practice in the use of, the methods of study used by scientific workers in developing this body of knowledge. It leads to the fields of physics and chemistry and reveals these as opportunities for the fruitful exercise of intellect of the highest rank. It reveals the physical sciences as the fields out of which the present mechanical age has developed and as fields which must be further developed if the human race is to continue in health and prosperity.

A Suggested Pattern for Curricular Organization

Other illustrations might be given, but the foregoing seem sufficient to illustrate how the major generalizations may be used to guide in the selection of content and activities. These major generalizations are of such importance and so extensive in scope that the individual may live with them throughout his training period and throughout his life. Definable educational values from science teaching will have been attained if individuals acquire (1) an ability to utilize the findings of science that have application in their own experiences, (2) an ability to interpret the natural phenomena of their environment, and (3) an understanding of, and ability to use, some of the methods of study that have been used by creative workers in the fields of science. As the child progresses through the grades, his study becomes increasingly intensive and increasingly specialized. The units for study in the junior high school are sufficiently intensive to reveal something of the scope of the special sciences. These special subjects are offered in the upper years of the high school and in the college as electives in which the student has opportunity for intensive and specialized study of one of the major generalizations or of a few related ones. The suggested pattern for curricular organization is one which gradually unfolds increasingly enlarged interpretations in sequential order, paralleling the growth in maturity of the learner and his increasing ability to envisage them. This program sets forth a definition of science for the elementary, secondary, and collegiate schools, and it shows how the work on different grade levels may be integrated about common themes. Furthermore, this procedure sets forth the possible educative outcomes of science in such definite form that curricular techniques may be developed for evaluating them. Accepted principles of educational psychology and principles that guide practices in elementary, secondary, and collegiate education are offered in support of this pattern.

Some Suggestions from Curricular Research

This point of view has already received recognition in curricular research. In his course of study project, Craig[2] postulated the three following criteria for the selection of objectives:

1. Certain objectives that are selected for elementary school science should conform to those scientific conceptions (1) which, when understood, greatly influence the thought reaction of the individual; (2) which have modified thinking in many fields.

2. Certain objectives that are selected for elementary-school science should conform to those goals (information, skills, and habits) in science that are important because of their function in establishing health, economy, and safety in private and public life.

3. Certain objectives that are selected for elementary-school science should conform to those facts, principles, generalizations, and hypotheses of science which are essential to the interpretation of the natural phenomena which commonly challenge children.

In the pursuit of this study, Craig compiled for subsequent evaluation a tentative list of statements to be used for guidance in selecting objectives of science for the elementary school. These were taken from four sources: (1) the volumes of *Nature Study Review*, (2) courses of study in elementary science and nature study, (3) professional literature on science teaching, and (4) authoritative treatises on astronomy, biology, chemistry, geology, and physics.

---

[2] Craig, G. S. *Certain Techniques Used in Developing a Course of Study in Science for the Horace Mann Elementary School.* Teachers College, Columbia University, Contributions to Education, No. 276, 1927, pp. 12 and 13.

The tentative list compiled from these sources contained 82 statements. These were submitted for evaluation to 188 educated laymen. The purpose of this evaluation was to determine which statements were considered by the laymen to be of largest functional value. In the instructions to the educated laymen they were asked to rate the tentative objectives on a scale of five points, ranging from those which are of so much importance in their experience as conceptions or as useful information that they "would be loath to be ignorant of them" to those that were unimportant. From these ratings a rank order of the objectives was made. Six objectives that related to the field of health education each received high rank. Among the objectives were some generalizations concerning the methods used in scientific investigation and some concerning attitudes toward the findings of science and toward scientific methods. These statements were generally rated high in the list. The other ranking objectives had to do with interpretations concerning energy, animals, plants, astronomical bodies, and rocks.

Craig made a further evaluation of these objectives by studying them in relation to the questions asked by children. Using what seems to be an acceptable technique, he gathered nearly 7,000 questions from children of grades one to eight, inclusive. More extensive studies have been made, but from the standpoint of this Committee the value of Craig's list lies in the analysis and interpretations of his findings. The objectives were rated by determining the number of children's questions that could be answered by learning what lay within the scope of each of the objectives.

Downing[3] has reported a list of principles of science found in twenty textbooks on general science that were published between 1915 and 1927. In another of Downing's reports[4] he gives a list of principles of physics that appear in two or more of four independent studies done under his direction. These studies were: one by Watson and one by Widner of the principles of physics appearing in farm journals; one by Harris of the principles of physics found in trade journals; and one by Coon, a "job-analysis of the activities of the house-wife to find what principles of science she needs and to what problematic situations these apply."

---

[3] Curtis, F. D. *Second Digest of Investigations in the Teaching of Science.* Blakiston: Philadelpnia, 1931, p. 75.

[4] Curtis, *op. cit.,* p. 211.

A study by Sites[5] reports the "chemical principles used in science magazines, which are probably needed to enable the individual to read such magazines intelligently."

The following statements,[6] modified somewhat from the original lists, are deemed by the Committee to be of importance sufficient to justify their use for guidance in the selection of specific objectives for science in the elementary school, in the junior high school, and for the special sciences of the senior high school.

Principles and Generalizations Suggested by the Committee as Valuable for Guidance in the Selection of Specific Objectives of Science Teaching

1. The sun is the chief source of energy for the earth.
2. Through interdependence of species and the struggle for existence a balance tends to be maintained among the many forms of life.
3. The earth's position in relation to the sun and moon is a determining factor of life on earth.
4. All life comes from life and produces its own kind of living organism.
5. Matter and energy cannot be created or destroyed, but may be changed from one form to another.
6. Species have survived because of adaptations and adjustments which have fitted them to the conditions under which they live.
7. The energy of solar radiation is continually working changes in the surface of the earth.
8. There have been profound changes in the climate, not only of certain regions, but also of the earth as a whole.
9. The evolution of the earth has come as a result of natural forces.
10. Units of time are defined by the earth's movements in relation to the sun.
11. All life has evolved from simple forms.
12. The earth seems very old when its age is measured in the ordinary units of time.
13. Distances in space seem extremely vast when compared with distances on earth.
14. The physical environment has great influence on the structural forms of life and on plant and animal habitats.

---

[5] Curtis, *op. cit.*, p. 269.
[6] The Committee recognizes that this list is incomplete and that the statements are in need of further refinement.

15. Man can modify the nature of plant and animal forms through application of his knowledge of the laws of heredity.
16. There is a great variety in the size, structure, and habits of living things.
17. There are processes that go on within an organism that are vital to its continued existence.
18. Chemical and physical changes are manifestations of energy changes.
19. There are fewer than one hundred chemical elements.
20. Every substance is one of the following: (a) a chemical element, (b) a chemical compound, (c) a mechanical mixture.
21. Certain material substances and certain physical conditions are limiting factors to life.
22. Light is a limiting factor to life.
23. Sound is caused by waves which are produced by a vibrating body and which can affect the auditory nerves of the ear.
24. Gravitation is the attractive force that influences or governs the movements of astronomical bodies.
25. Machines are devices for accomplishing useful transformations of energy.
26. Any machine, no matter how complicated, may be analyzed into a few simple types.
27. The properties of the different elements depend on the number and arrangement of the electrons and protons contained in their atoms.
28. All matter is probably electrical in structure.
29. The applications of electricity and magnetism in the home and in industry have revolutionized the methods of living of many people.
30. Heredity determines the differences between parents and offspring as well as the resemblances.
31. The kinetic energy of the molecules determines the physical states of matter.
32. The gravitational attraction between the earth and a mass of unconfined gas or liquid causes the pressure of the liquid or gas on the surface of the earth.
33. Liquid or gas pressure is exerted equally in all directions.
34. Chemical changes are accompanied by energy changes.
35. A change in rate or direction of motion of an object requires the application of an external force.
36. Radiant energy travels in straight lines through a uniform medium.

37. Electricity is a form of energy that results from disturbing the position or the regular paths of electrons.
38. In a chemical change a quantitative relationship exists between the amounts of substances reacting and the amounts of the substances that are the products of the reaction.

Studies in Evaluation of Topics for Science Courses

Curtis[7] has approached the problem from a different angle and has contributed a comprehensive synthesis and evaluation of studies that have been made of evaluated topics for use in general-science courses. The studies on which he drew were analyses of syllabi, textbooks, interest studies, newspapers and magazines, and some other sources. This comprehensive list of topics with their relative importance as revealed by the statistical technique employed furnishes a most useful check list for the curriculum-worker in science, since it furnishes guidance in the choice of materials with which to develop understandings of the principles and generalizations in the foregoing list.

An outstanding contribution of these studies is that they have shifted attention from things to meanings. These investigators have accepted the point of view of modern psychology and have assumed that learning activities should be directed toward the acquisition of meanings and understandings. The techniques which they have applied have given some evaluations to show the relative importance of topics, principles, and generalizations of science in which children and adults have interest. Further work in this field of the curriculum will give a further refinement of the definition of major generalizations and a further refinement of evaluations in terms of their educational worth. In the program of education the understanding of major generalizations and the development of associated scientific attitudes become the objectives of science teaching and these objectives are justified in the educational program for their contribution to enriched living.

Studies in Evaluation of Attitudes

Some efforts have been made to define and evaluate objectives of science teaching that relate to methods and attitudes. Curtis[8] has done pioneer work in this field and his definition stands to-day as one

[7] Curtis, F. D. *A Synthesis and Evaluation of Subject Matter Topics in General Science.* Ginn: Boston, 1929.
[8] Curtis, F. D. *Some Values Derived from Extensive Reading in General Science.* Teachers College Contributions to Education, No. 163, 1924, pp. 41-49.

of the most useful and inclusive. His definition of the scientific attitudes is based upon an analysis of literature dealing with philosophical phases of scientific thought, including Karl Pearson's *A Grammar of Science*, John Dewey's *How We Think,* and other books of a similar nature. A preliminary outline was prepared and submitted to high-school and college teachers for evaluation. As a result of his work, Curtis formulated the following outline of scientific attitudes.[9]

The Scientific Attitudes

I. Conviction of universal basic cause and effect relations, rendering untenable
  a. Superstitious beliefs in general, as 'signs' of 'good luck' or 'bad luck,' and charms;
  b. 'Unexplainable mysteries;'
  c. 'Beats all' attitude, commonly revealed by
    1. Too ready credulity;
    2. Tendency to magnify the importance of coincidence.
II. Sensitive curiosity concerning reasons for happenings, coupled with ideals
  a. Of careful and accurate observation or of equally careful and accurate use of pertinent data previously collected by others;
  b. Of patient collecting of data;
  c. Of persistence in the search for adequate explanation.
III. Habit of delayed response, holding views tentatively for suitable reflection (varying with the matter in hand)
  a. To permit adequate consideration of possible options;
  b. To permit a conscious plan of attack, clearly looking forward to a prediction of the probable outcome or solution.

IV. Habit of weighing evidence with respect to its
  a. Pertinence;
  b. Soundness;
  c. Adequacy.
V. Respect for another's point of view, an open-mindedness, and willingness to be convinced by evidence.

Craig[10] included in his investigation a list of some five statements which are descriptive of or related to the qualities defined in Curtis' outline of scientific attitudes. In his investigation each of these statements received high rating by the "educated laymen." This list is as follows:

---

[9] *Ibid.*, p. 48.
[10] Craig, Gerald S. *Certain Techniques Used in Developing a Course of Study in Science for the Horace Mann Elementary School.* Teachers College Contributions to Education, No. 276, p. 21.

1. Man's conception of truth changes.
2. Orderliness prevails in nature. Effects result from causes.
3. The formulation of hypotheses and testing them by experimental study are essential steps in the scientific method.
4. Attainments in science have bred confidence in the scientific methods.
5. Much knowledge remains to be revealed.

Provision of Learning Experiences

Only a little progress has been made toward objective determination of the learning experiences that should be provided for such attainment of these objectives as is most functional in general education.

This Committee recommends that science for the elementary school be organized in such a way that the learning experiences of elementary-school children may be so integrated as to give them some understanding of such major generalizations. In the junior high school related objectives may be seen as defining the successive units of instruction and as offering opportunity for protracted and more intensive study. In the senior high school provision will be made for special subjects in which there is opportunity for still more thorough study, thorough to the extent that the special subject will offer opportunity for intensive exploration of the field and for the beginnings of specialization.

A fundamental principle of learning is: things that belong together should be brought together. This plan is offered as one that will assist the curriculum-worker in bringing together the learning experiences that belong together, and that will assist the teacher to capitalize and make meaningful the spontaneous experiences of children. The things that belong together are the learning experiences from which come ideas that may be associated into principles and generalizations that function in the experiences of living.

This Committee, then, recognizes the aim of science teaching to be contributory to the aim of education; viz., life enrichment. It recognizes the objectives of science teaching to be the functional understanding of the major generalizations of science and the development of associated scientific attitudes.

CHAPTER V

THE PSYCHOLOGY OF SCIENCE TEACHING*

In a discussion of the psychology of learning the question of what to teach—of what knowledge is of most worth—rises to a place of prominence. Current practices in science teaching and in other fields have been severely and justly criticized for overemphasis on memory work for the purpose of enabling the pupil to reproduce unrelated facts. Moreover, there has been so much looseness in claims for various impracticable and vaguely defined outcomes of science teaching that it would seem as if the real materials of education—problems in which methods may be used and situations and conditions toward which attitudes may be developed—have too small a place. Knowledge that has been, and that may be, tested for truthfulness is essential in education as a basis for problem solving and for understanding.

The enriched life has been defined as one that is able to make self-satisfying responses to the stimuli of experience and to avoid responses that are in conflict with the best welfare of ourselves and others. The processes of education should aim to provide direct learning experiences which will develop ability to interpret and to become adjusted to these stimuli. Such an adjustment reflects ability to use knowledge effectively, and exercise of this ability results in further learning. Functional knowledge, as illustrated in the preceding chapter, is a dynamic driving force carrying the learner ever forward in the process of acquiring new functional knowledge and consequently carrying him ever forward in the development of ability to make adjustments that are increasingly more satisfying. The aim of education in the schools is to start and to assist children on the road to rich living.

This Committee accepts the thesis that functional methods of work are gained in the acquisition of knowledge that is useful as a basis for rational behavior, and that functional knowledge and useful methods are the foundations of scientific attitudes. In this scheme primary learning is the acquisition of functional knowledge. Among the concomitants of primary learning is the development of ideals in the form of scientific attitudes. These ideals will serve as a dynamic driving force, carrying the learner forward in the acquisition of more

---

* For the Committee, by S. Ralph Powers.

59

functional knowledge, and they will function in thinking about the knowledge after it is acquired.

Accomplishment of the program suggested by the foregoing is conditioned upon the ability of the curriculum-worker to sense the trends in human thought and to make an array of learning experiences that will give to the novice an orientation with respect to these trends. The stimuli of experience are the determiners of human thought. Problem situations that are real in the experiences of children must constitute the core of the curriculum. Learning takes place as a process of integration of the ideas that are products of real experience. The method of science tests these ideas for truthfulness. The process of learning involves the integration of facts and experiences; it results in the association of related ideas and the definition of the relationship between related ideas. The process of learning is one of building up bigger and bigger, that is more comprehensive, ideas. This Committee postulates the definition of a major generalization as one that is built up from growing understandings of principles that in turn are developed from the smaller ideas that are the products of necessary and desirable experiences in living. The purpose of education in science is to orient learners, on whatever grade level, in the fields of these major generalizations. This is an age of science and scientists have formulated generalizations that associate related ideas. The curriculum-worker will accept as objectives of science teaching such generalizations as associate ideas that are products of learning experiences which people are meeting in life situations. Such a curriculum must provide orientation with respect to the trends of human thought. Such a curriculum will be the basis of knowledge that will function as a dynamic driving force, carrying the learner ever forward toward more comprehensive understanding of the generalizations that ramify most widely into the affairs of humankind.

In considering the processes of learning, we recognize the learner as an individual with inherent tendencies toward activity, with ability to respond to the effects of his own activity in terms of satisfaction and annoyance, and with ability to reflect, to generalize, and to arrive at attitudes which the learner may characterize in himself as feelings of proper adjustment or of mental disturbance. A proper adjustment is one that enables the individual to react most satisfactorily to the stimuli that cause annoyance. The facts of the environment furnish the stimuli for activity and they condition the response. The experiences of the learner may be such that activities are attended by a minimum of satisfaction and a maximum of annoyance, or they may be attended by a maximum of satisfaction and a minimum of annoyance. Satisfactions result from activities that develop abilities to meet new situations. A proper mental adjustment is characterized by an eagerness for increase in ability to live richly according to some standard which the individual has generalized and set up as one that is consistent with his own best welfare and the welfare of the social order of which he is a part. A feeling of proper adjustment *is not* disturbed if the activities that have produced it and the activities that are induced by it are satisfying, in that the exercise of those activities gives to the learner a feeling of security in the struggle for existence; and if the exercise of the activities wins the approval of others of the social order. A feeling of proper adjustment *is* disturbed if the activities associated with it are in conflict with activities that make for proper adjustment to others. In an age of science the individuals of our society are stimulated to activities by the factors that characterize the age. The program of education must therefore include objectives, the attainment of which will result in a feeling of proper adjustment to an age of science.

In Chapter IV there are listed principles and generalizations (complex ideas) which furnish at least a partial definition of the fields of science that are challenging to the interests of children and adults. This list is illustrative and, at the same time, fairly comprehensive. A characteristic of this age is the challenge that it carries to think clearly about such facts as are associated with control of energy, control of the causes of ill health, meteorological phenomena, heredity, natural and artificial selection, cosmic and biological evolution, time, space, life processes, chemical changes, gravitation, machinery, and the nature of matter. These are the considerations that influence in large part the intellectual activities of to-day, and the task of the school is to give to the learner some orientation with respect to these influences.

In a program of curriculum work the statements that define the trends of human thought are used for guidance in planning the program of learning activities in which learners will participate. Those statements most widely applicable in life and most generally challenging to the interests of children should receive most consideration in the curriculum of the elementary school, and those that represent more specialized interests should be reserved for the later years of the school program. The program of inducting children into the trends of human thought respecting the phenomena of science is hindered by the limited knowledge of the psychology of learning in this field. However, some progress has been made, and recent studies offer sufficient guidance to furnish a foundation that seems secure for further work.

The aim of science teaching, according to this Committee, is to contribute to life enrichment through the development of (1) ability to become adjusted to the stimuli of immediate experience, and of (2) ability to make additional and increasingly more satisfying and more complete adjustments. In our increasingly complicated civilization, ability to make effective adjustment is dependent upon knowledge that is functional, in that it may be associated with the phenomena of experience. Growth in ability to make adjustment is dependent upon knowledge of the methods of work and study and upon the development of motives and attitudes that will determine how these methods will be exercised. Stimuli furnish a continuous experience with problem situations. These problems are solved by making associations of the knowledge that we possess, in such a way that we are able to form an interpretation consistent with the problem situation. In order to arrive at this solution the problem must be clearly recognized and the interpretation must be clearly formulated.

Examples of Problem-Solving

An example of problem-solving may be seen in the solution of the problem defined by the question, Why does a hydrogen-filled balloon rise when it is released? The knowledge necessary for the solution of this problem is about as follows:

1. A body in air is pushed upward by a force equal to the weight of the air that it displaces.

2. The density of the gas in the balloon is less than the density of air, consequently the volume of the gas in the balloon weighs less than an equal volume of air.

Solution: The weight of the balloon plus the weight of the gas in it is less than the weight of the air that it displaces. Consequently, the balloon is forced upward by air pressure.

The items of knowledge in this illustration are, in terms of their origin in the learning process, extremely complex hierarchies of lesser ideas. In order that these hierarchies may function in problem-solving, it is necessary that the ideas of which they are a composite be understandingly associated with each other and that the composites themselves be associated with the problem stimulated by the rising balloon. The statement of the solution is a hierarchy that may be thought of as a composite of the ideas that are associated in arriving at the solution. This most complex hierarchy may now function in the solution of new problems.

A new problem may be suggested by the question: Why does an airplane rise? Items of knowledge that function in the solution of this problem are:

1. An object that rises in air is forced up by air pressure or by some other force that is sufficient to overcome the gravitational attraction between the earth and the object.

2. An airplane is so constructed that, as it moves rapidly, the air pressure on its upper surface is reduced and the air pressure on its under surface is increased.

3. An airplane propeller is so constructed that as it rotates it develops an increase in air pressure behind it and a decrease in air pressure in front of it. The resultant force from this unbalanced pressure drives the airplane forward.

Solution: In the case of a rapidly moving airplane driven forward by the thrust of the propeller, the increase in air pressure on the under surface of the plane and the decrease in pressure on the upper surface develop a resultant force in an upward direction that is greater than the downward force due to the earth's gravitational attraction for the plane.

Each of these items of knowledge is again an extremely complex hierarchy. Understanding of them requires that the learner have an enormous number of ideas and that he be able to make a proper association of the ideas. The problem is difficult (1) because it is difficult for a learner to encounter the experiences from which this vast array of ideas may be developed, and (2) because it is difficult to associate such a vast array of ideas. However, the process of learning is one of acquiring ideas from experience and of associating the ideas into increasingly complex hierarchies. The ideas are the formulations of results from learning and they may be extremely complex.

How are ideas acquired? The answer to this question may be given in such a way as to furnish guidance (1) for the curriculum-worker—the individual who assumes responsibility for planning the experiences from which ideas come, and (2) for the teacher—the individual who assumes responsibility for assisting children to profit from experiences. In a school situation the curriculum-worker and the teacher may be the same person.

Some Generalizations about Learning

The generalizations of the psychologist that have most direct application for the curriculum-worker may be stated as follows:

1. We learn best the responses we actually make, and others in proportion to their resemblance to these.
2. Specific objectives are selected for their value to the pupils, both in the present and in the future, and responses are taught which these objectives indicate as desirable for the pupils to learn to make.
3. Experiences that belong together, in that they are the ones that may be associated in forming an idea, should be brought together.

Transfer of Training

The first two of these generalizations will call to mind at once the old controversy concerning the transfer of training. There can be no denial that one meets and interprets new situations in the light of his old situations. The extent of transfer may, therefore, be measured in terms of the degree to which new problems are solved with the ideas about content and methods and the attitudes developed from previous experience. The responsibility of the curriculum-worker is to provide stimuli to which responses will be made and so to select stimuli that the experiences in responding will be the experiences that relate to the business of living. The experiences of living are necessarily related, for the whole process of living is one of responding to a variety of stimuli related to the process of living. In general, the learning that is most directly functional in meeting a real situation is most likely to be functional—that is, an 'identical element'—in other situations. Conversely, the learning that is least directly functional in meeting a real situation is least likely to be functional; that is, an 'identical element' in any real situation. From these considerations the curriculum-worker should be led to select specific objectives for their direct and immediate value to the learner. Attainment of direct values is at the same time an attainment of understandings that are most likely to function for transfer.

A measure of the values for transfer of science or of any other subject is found in the extent to which the ideas, skills, and attitudes acquired from experiences in this field are the same as the ones that are required to solve the problems that arise in life situations. The fact that this is an age of science is, therefore, evidence of the importance in learning of scientific ideas, skills, and attitudes.

It is clear that current conceptions of the psychology of learning place emphasis on learning procedures that will result in direct and definable values. Practically, it may be said that learning outcomes that are of most importance for their direct values are at the same time of most importance for transfer values. A functional curriculum is one which provides experiences from which the individual learns to make the responses that it is necessary or desirable to make. A practical procedure in the selection of experiences is that of first selecting objectives (stated as principles and generalizations) which have most direct relationship to the things that people do and think, and then of selecting experiences that contribute to an enlarged understanding of these objectives. The experiences that contribute ideas which are associated with an objective are the experiences that belong together. In a well-ordered curriculum or in a well-ordered class exercise these experiences are brought together.

Consider as an illustration of an objective the principle used in the solution of the problem earlier in this chapter: a body in air is pushed upward by a force equal to the weight of the air that it displaces. Among the ideas that must be associated in attaining this objective are:

1. Air is a substance and as such it occupies space, has weight, and exerts pressure.
2. At any given point, air pressure is equal in all directions.
3. The force of air pressure above an object differs from the force of air pressure below the object by an amount equal to the weight of the air displaced by the object.

These are ideas (complex in themselves) that belong together for the attainment of this objective. A generalization from these complex ideas is the principle stated as the objective. Each of these ideas may be an objective at some levels of maturity. In an effective learning situation the ideas that belong together for attaining any one of these objectives are brought together.

PSYCHOLOGICAL PRINCIPLES THAT MAY GUIDE THE TEACHER

The foregoing discussion considers psychological principles that may be used for guidance in the selection and arrangement of learning experiences. Attention is directed now to those psychological principles that may be used to guide the teacher in capitalizing the results from these experiences. These two sets of principles are not mutually exclusive. They are considered separately only in order to bring to the focus of attention certain applications of them. In one study[1] in the psychology of learning they have been stated as follows:

1. Learning is more efficiently done when interest becomes inherent in the material to be learned. (Principle of interest)
2. A problem to be solved will focus attention on the elements in the situation which appear to be relevant to the solution of the problem. (Principle of mind-set)
3. Consciousness of unanswered questions brings a state of dissatisfaction which is removed by finding the answers to the questions. This satisfaction strengthens the bonds (associations) formed. (Principle of satisfaction)
4. Do not form bonds (associations) which must be broken. Form bonds (associations) of the desired strength with the desired responses. (Principle of use)
5. Attach responses to the situations in which they are used. The greatest amount of transfer is to be expected when situations have as many elements in common as possible and when these elements are brought into consciousness. (Principle of analogy)
6. Make situations and responses to be connected identifiable in the mind of the learner. (Principle of identifiability)
7. Other things being equal, repetition of recently made connections strengthens bonds (associations). (Principle of use and recency)

FACTS, CONCEPTS, AND THINKING

The learning process is concerned first with reactions to stimuli that produce sensations, as of color, odor, sound, etc. Facts are statements of results, or effects, from sensory perception. We may state as a fact, that the apple is red or that air has weight. These facts associate the quality of redness with an apple and the quality of weight with air.

---

[1] Laton, Anita D. *The Psychology of Learning Applied to Health Education through Biology.* Teachers College Contributions to Education, No. 344, 1929.

A concept may be simple or it may be complex. One's concept of air may be that it has weight, that it is colorless and odorless, that it is more dense than hydrogen or helium, that it is less dense than chlorine, and that it is a mixture of chemical elements and compounds. Thinking is a process of dealing with recalled facts and experiences. In the process of thinking, a new association of recalled facts is made. The recalled facts are the ones that are associated (or seem to be associated) with the problem situation that has stimulated thinking. In the process of thinking, facts or ideas come into consciousness and those which are related to the problem are associated in its solution.

The solution of the problem expresses the relationship between the related facts. The solution may be stated as an hypothesis, a conception, a principle, a law, or a generalization. The solution is really a conscious response made to several features of the problem situation that are present in consciousness as recalled ideas. The solution is strikingly like a complex perception, except that at least some of the ideas associated are not actually present to the senses but are only recalled. Whether the result is a concept, an hypothesis, a principle, or a generalizaton matters little so far as the learning process is concerned.

Critical thinking may be thought of as that form of mental activity that tests the adequacy of associations that have been tentatively formed as hypotheses or erroneously formed in an effort to state a truth. An hypothesis is a tentative statement of the relationship between ideas. It is adequate only so long as it is seen to be consistent with all other ideas that are accepted as facts.

Constructive thinking may be thought of as the mental process of building-up; that is, of establishing additional associations in the mind. In their origins in the process of thinking these products of thought are closely similar.

Creative thinking differs from other thinking chiefly in the nature of the outcomes. Creative thinking results in the formation, from ideas that are recalled or directly present to the senses, of new hypotheses, new principles and laws, or new generalizations. From the standpoint of the thinker all thinking is, in a measure, creative.

It is clear from the foregoing that success in thinking depends upon an abundance of ideas in the form of particular and general facts and principles. In the task of teaching, attention is directed to the selection of stimuli in relation to sensations, to the relation of sensations to percepts and to facts, and to the relation of facts to the problem that has stimulated thinking. On the one hand, the material must be arrayed, by the teacher or by the learner, so that the learner may progress uninterruptedly from the experiences to the thinking that is desired. There must be no unbridged gaps between them. On the other hand, the teacher must see to it that the problems about which thinking is supposed to be done are of such a nature that they are challenging to the learner and of such a nature that their solutions are attended with motives and attitudes that furnish the drive for a career of rich living.

The teacher will give attention first to the principle of interest. If interest is established, the interest is in a problem situation. The problem must be stated with sufficient clarity to allow the learner to see that a variety of ideas that he has in mind may be tested for relationship to it. According to the principle of mind-set, clarification of the problem will enable the learner to focus attention upon those of his ideas which appear to be relevant to the problem. All of his pertinent resources will be in a state of readiness. Recognition of the inadequacy of his ideas for the solution of the problem results in a feeling of dissatisfaction that furnishes a drive to seek new experiences that will in turn lead to new ideas. The teacher will assist the learner to clarify and array his ideas so that they may be attached to the problem situation in which they are to be used. The greater the number of ideas that are associated in a problem situation, the more meaningful the situation becomes. In order that the outcome of learning may be made identifiable to the learner, he should formulate, with or without the aid of the teacher, a clear statement that tells the relationship of the ideas that have been associated. This statement, by means of which he identifies his learning, may take the form of hypothesis, concept, principle, law, or generalization. This statement may be one of knowledge or it may be one that is descriptive of mental attitudes toward knowledge or toward the methods by which knowledge is obtained.

STUDIES OF LEARNING IN THE FIELD OF SCIENCE

Careful studies in the psychology of learning in the field of science are not numerous. The foregoing discussion has been obviously for the most part general and applicable to learning in any field. However, some studies are available.

Laton's Study

Laton studied the outcomes of learning in an experiment in which the learning program was purposefully planned so that the principles of learning had clear recognition. She conducted an experiment with paired biology classes in the teaching of some units in health education that are normally a part of the course in high-school biology. The results from her experiment seem to justify the conclusion that "application of the facts and principles which experimental work in the psychology of learning has established can be profitably made to the teaching of such complex subject matter as that of biological science directed toward health education on the secondary-school level."[3]

Black's Study

Black[4] studied the nature of some concepts held by high-school students concerning certain physical phenomena. Specifically, he attempted to find out to what extent these concepts were vague and naïve and to what extent they were scientific.

The concepts explored concerned heat, light, gravity, mass, weight, and ebullition. The students, in Grades VI to XII, had studied neither general science nor physics. Black also explored the concepts held by students in Grade IX who had studied general science and those held by some students in Grades X, XI, and XII who had studied physics. This exploration into the minds of those who had and those who had not studied science enabled the investigator to catalog a large sampling of the correct and of the erroneous notions held by the non-science group, and it enabled him to determine in some measure the effects of instruction in the correction of erroneous concepts.

In the first part of the study the examinations were administered to science and to non-science students in unselected schools. All data in this part of the study were obtained from pupils' written responses to the common form of questioning, for example, "Tell in your own words what you mean by the *weight* of a thing." Another example, "Tell in your own words what you mean by the *mass* of a piece of lead."

The second part of the study involved experimental teaching designed to study the effects of certain procedures on the formation of particular scientific concepts. The same methods of examination were used in both parts of the study, except that in the case of the experimental groups the examinations were supplemented by personal interviews.

The results showed that more than 90 percent of the non-science groups of all grades failed to associate the idea of gravity with the weight of a thing. Nearly 90 percent of those who had studied general science also failed to make this association. Most of those in these groups defined weight as heaviness (or lightness) or number of pounds in a thing. However, nearly 60

[3] Laton, Anita D., *op. cit.*, p. 100.

[4] Black, Oswald F. *The Development of Certain Concepts of Physics in High-School Students.* Die Weste (publishers): Potchefstroom, South Africa. Distributed through S. R. Powers' office, Teachers College, Columbia University.

percent of those who had studied physics in eleventh and twelfth-grade classes did associate *object* and *earth's pull* in defining weight.

Another table shows the responses to the statement, "If a stone is thrown into the air it will always return to the earth. Tell why." Approximately 70 percent of the non-science answered by saying that gravity pulls it down. These results show that even non-science pupils have some understanding of gravity, but that they fail to use it in an attempt to form a scientific definition of weight. Answers to other questions showed that their notions of gravity were quite vague. Most of them were unable to respond at all to a question as to how it would affect the weight of an object if it were taken many miles from the earth's surface, and most of them were unable to give any reason why the weight of an object would be slightly greater at the poles than at the equator.

This analysis illustrates the nature of the difficulties that students have in acquiring a scientific conception of the term *weight,* and it suggests the procedures that may be used in teaching to correct these difficulties.

Black's program of experimental teaching[5] is too detailed to reproduce here. By means of it he was able to eliminate many, but by no means all, of the erroneous concepts.

Along with his study of the conception of weight, Black studied concepts of mass, using similar techniques. He found that pupils did not possess the percepts necessary for forming a scientific definition of mass and that he was unable to develop these percepts for any considerable percentage of the pupils in his program of experimental teaching. The nature of the difficulties that persist after instruction is illustrated by the following interview with a girl of the 12th grade, age 17 years and 4 months, I.Q. 115.[6]

Q. When you talk of the *mass* of a body, what do you mean?
A. The quantity of matter it contains.
Q. What do you mean by "quantity of matter"?
A. The amount of material in it.
Q. How would you know which of two objects contains more material in it?
A. The larger one would.
Q. So, amount of material, or mass, is the 'volume' of the material?
A. No, mass is not volume.
Q. Well, you said the larger one?
A. I mean the heavier one.
Q. So, you mean mass is weight?
A. No, it is not weight.

---

[5] *Ibid.,* pp. 151-168.
[6] *Ibid.,* pp. 165-166.

Q. Well, you said the heavier one.
A. The heavier one will have more mass, but mass is not weight; gravity has nothing to do with mass.
Q. Then what is mass?
A. I never did understand what it was.
Q. Did you like to learn about weight, mass, and gravity?
A. Yes, but it was too difficult.
Q. But I think you understood everything, did you not?
A. No.
Q. But you know what gravity is and what it does?
A. Yes.
Q. And what weight is?
A. Yes.
Q. And mass?
A. No, I never did see that.

From his experiment Black concludes:[7]

1. Scientific concepts of gravity and weight can be formed by both physics students and general-science students.
2. Scientific concepts of mass cannot be formed by students in the ninth grade by either of the methods used in his experiment.
3. The majority of physics students in the experimental classes did not form a scientific notion of mass.

Other parts of Black's report show similarly the nature of the concepts held concerning other topics that were studied and how these concepts were modified by his program of experimental teaching.

This study in the psychology of learning is cited at length because it illustrates the nature of some of the procedures that attend learning and because it illustrates also some of the difficulties that hinder learning. Some of the concepts that the experimenter attempted to develop are so difficult (so many ideas must be associated to develop them and some of the associations are so abstruse) that ordinary methods of teaching in general science and in physics are inadequate for developing them. In the case of the concept, *mass*, experiences for some of the necessary ideas are so remotely related to life that full responsibility for developing them rests upon the teacher's work in the classroom. In such a case it is difficult so to arrange a learning situation that the psychological principles of learning, particularly those of interest, mind-set, satisfaction, and use, may be employed. Undoubtedly less difficulty would attend the development of concepts requiring associations

---

[7] *Ibid.,* pp. 167-168.

that are equally abstruse if the experiences that furnish the ideas to be associated were the experiences encountered by the pupils in ordinary life experience.

Horton's Study

In a program of experimental teaching in the chemistry laboratory, Horton[8] has studied the outcomes of laboratory teaching designed to develop laboratory techniques and the ability to use laboratory techniques and procedures in problem-solving. At the time of this experiment, Horton was Chairman of the Department of Chemistry in one of the large high schools of New York City, and the work was done in this department. All of the teachers of chemistry coöperated with him.

The course of instruction in problem-solving required that the experimental classes discontinue the use of the laboratory manual and that pupils devise their own experiments. Teachers were instructed to demonstrate all the "experiments" required by the Syllabus of the New York State Regents, and pupils were required to write up these demonstrated experiments in a manner regularly followed in the school. A home assignment was given (or developed) one day each week on the day preceding the regular laboratory day. The nature of this assignment may be seen from the following which is quoted from the "Teachers Guide."[9]

This home assignment is to be in the nature of a perplexity arising from the chemistry topic for the week. A list of such suggested problems has been made and may be used if no good problem comes from the class. For class instruction, it seems best now to raise one perplexity for the class, stated as a topic but not definitely worded in the form of a question. Each student should follow the following procedure: (1) make a definite question; (2) make a guess as to the answer (hypothesis); (3) devise an experiment to test the truth or validity of this hypothesis; and (4) make a sketch of the apparatus set-up to do this experiment. This outline of the scientific procedure to be used in arriving at a belief or in solving the difficulty should be written in the notebook according to a form given to each student.

In setting the problematic situations the teachers were guided, at least in part, by the fact that the syllabus recommended the following types:[10]

---

[8] Horton, Ralph E. *Measurable Outcomes of Individual Laboratory Work in High-School Chemistry.* Teachers College Contributions to Education, No. 303, 1928.

[9] *Ibid.,* p. 65.

[10] *Ibid.,* p. 66.

a. Prediction of chemical action, or no chemical action, between stated substances, together with statements of necessary conditions of temperature, and the like.
b. Preparation of substances from prescribed materials, involving simple methods not specifically mentioned in the syllabus or the textbook.
c. Ability to make chemical judgments concerning such things as practicability, economy and convenience, parts played by constituents in reactions, equilibrium reactions, and simple cases of hydrolysis.

Illustrations of the problematic situations that the pupils faced are the following:

Do metals other than zinc liberate hydrogen from hydrochloric acid?
Which of the substances, silk, wool, wood, soft coal, give H_2S by destructive distillation?

In this experiment it may be seen that pupils were given the regular experiences associated with laboratory instruction in chemistry; that is, the ones regularly required in the syllabus by the method of laboratory demonstration. In addition, they were given opportunities to use the ideas that came from these regular experiences in the solution of problems. The problem-solving demanded ability to recall ideas, to select the ideas that are related to the problem, and to associate them in such a way that the association becomes a solution.

In order to test the extent to which this outcome may be attained, classes in problem-solving were paired with classes using the common method of laboratory procedure. The results were measured with a performance test designated as a "Test of Class Performance of Laboratory Projects."[11] In this pupils were required to face problem situations in the laboratory and arrive at solutions. One of the two problems used in this test was stated as follows: "A certain gas is prepared by action of hydrochloric acid on calcium carbonate (marble). The gas is very slightly soluble in water at ordinary temperature and pressure and is heavier than air. You are to prepare and test it." The pupils had had no previous experience with the preparation of carbon dioxide. The procedure was analyzed into seven steps and the students were rated on their ability to do each one of these steps. There was a very significant difference between the control and the experimental group in favor of the experimental group. One may, therefore, conclude from this that, following Horton's techniques, pupils do gain ability to form *new* associations of ideas developed from the study of chemistry.

---

[11] *Ibid.*, p. 73.

Another performance test used by this experimenter to measure the difference between these two groups was called a "Test of Ability to Make Apparatus Set-Ups in Chemistry."[12] The students were given the apparatus necessary to make ten "set-ups." They did not use the apparatus other than to set it up. The directions and one of the "set-ups" are given for illustration.

> Directions: Set up the apparatus as you would in order to prepare and separate each of the following substances having the properties indicated:
> 1. A gas prepared by heating solids that are mixed together. The gas is soluble in water and heavier than air.
> [And so on for nine other set-ups.]

The difference between the abilities of the experimental group (problem method) and the control (usual laboratory method) was again very large. From this it is clear that practice in associating the ideas necessary for the problem-solving that had been done in the class developed ability to make the set-ups required in the examinations.

Horton arranged a third group which he called a "Generalization Group."[13] Pupils in this group were taught by the regular laboratory method during the first ten weeks of the term, but thereafter received training "designed to test the effect of conscious, careful generalization of laboratory methods and techniques." The process of generalization was one of associating each set-up with the properties of the substances with which it was used. For example, the generalization respecting the apparatus used in the preparation of ammonia was that the apparatus was one for preparing from two solids a gas that is lighter than air and soluble in water. Fifteen sets of apparatus were thus identified.

This experimental group was compared with the Problem-Solving Group and with a Control Group that had been taught by the usual laboratory methods. The same examinations were used, namely, "Test of Class Performance of Laboratory Projects" and "Test of Ability to Make Apparatus Set-Ups." In both of these examinations the Generalization Group greatly excelled the Control Group, but in neither case was the success anywhere nearly so great as the excess of the Problem Group over the Control Group.[14] It follows from this, however, that the method which Horton used in his Generalization Group was more effective than the ordinary laboratory method for associating

---

[12] *Ibid.*, p. 75.
[13] *Ibid.*, p. 68.
[14] *Ibid.*, pp. 85-86.

meanings with laboratory apparatus and for developing ability in the kind of problem-solving demanded for his tests.

Horton's experiments show that situations may be set in such a way that the ideas which the pupils get from experiences with chemistry may be used in problem-solving. Problem-solving involves the process of making new associations of ideas. His work shows that practice in forming new associations of ideas (problem-solving) develops an increase in ability to make other new associations. The experiment with "generalization of laboratory methods and techniques" shows that percepts may be built up that characterize certain arrangements (set-ups) of apparatus, and that ideas formed from these percepts may be associated with ideas concerning the properties of the substances in connection with which the arrangement of apparatus is used.

No attention has been given in the foregoing paragraphs to the question of whether learning activities are pupil-directed or teacher-directed. A discussion of this question is not necessary. In any event children learn from experiences, and in any event effectiveness in learning is conditioned by the extent to which learning experiences that belong together (because they may be associated) are brought together. A desirable learning situation will certainly result if the teacher sets a stimulating environment and if the children are allowed and encouraged to respond to challenging stimuli. The stimuli will be challenging if they are seen by the children to be related to the life they must live.

Conclusions Stressed by the Committee

In concluding this chapter on the psychology of science teaching, this Committee emphasizes the following points:

1. Functional learning is that which relates most directly to the life situations that challenge interest.
2. The process of learning is one of forming situation-response connections.
3. A task of the curriculum-worker is one of making arrays of experiences from which functional learning may result.
4. Learning is specific. We learn from the responses we actually make.
5. A task of the teacher is one of making certain that the student profits from learning experiences. The outcome of learning must be made identifiable to the learner.

CHAPTER VI

SOME CONTRIBUTIONS OF EDUCATIONAL RESEARCH TO THE SOLUTION OF TEACHING PROBLEMS IN THE SCIENCE CLASSROOM*

Educational research, in the modern sense of the term, was first applied to problems in the teaching of science a little more than twenty years ago.[1] During the period since the publication of the results of these pioneer efforts there has been a large and rapidly increasing number of investigations of a wide variety of problems touching many phases of science teaching.

It is unlikely that any problem in this field has yet been solved completely and beyond question; nevertheless, the progressive teacher will find in the practical applications of the results of investigations already available, a sure means for professional growth and improvement.

In this chapter an attempt will be made to summarize the results of a number of research investigations which bear upon classroom problems in the field of the teaching of science. It should be understood, of course, that the following list includes by no means all that have been reported. It should be clear, too, that these results of available research are only tentative and that in all cases they await verification or modification in the light of the results of future investigations.

No logical order of problems or discussions is possible because of the varied nature of the investigations the reports of which are available. Moreover, the selection of the studies which are here briefly reviewed is confined largely to the learning phases of science teaching, since aims, trends, and curricular materials appropriate to the various levels are discussed in detail in other chapters.

VOCABULARIES OF SCIENCE TEXTBOOKS

The earliest extensive study of the science vocabulary found in widely used textbooks was that of Pressey.[2] Using an elaborate tech-

---

* For the Committee, by Francis D. Curtis.

[1] Curtis, Francis D. *A Digest of Investigations in the Teaching of Science.* Blakiston: Philadelphia, Vol. I, 1926, pp. 27 and 119.

[2] Pressey, Luella C. "The determination of the technical vocabulary of the school subjects." *School and Society,* 20:1924, 91-96. See also Curtis, *op. cit.,* I, 301-304.

nique employing chiefly teacher judgment, the investigator determined an "essential," an "accessory," and an "auxiliary" vocabulary for each of the various high-school sciences (as well as for other high-school subjects), and a "common science vocabulary" for all of the branches of secondary-school science.[3]

In commenting upon the length and difficulty of these various vocabulary lists obtained from her study, the investigator first quotes the opinion of foreign-language teachers to the effect that a pupil does well in a year's study to acquire from eight hundred to a thousand new words in a new language; then states that "the pupil in any of the sciences . . . has as great, or a greater, vocabulary to master, wholly aside from acquisition of considerable subject matter."

Working coincidentally, but using a more objective, and therefore a more convincing, investigational technique, Powers[4] contributed two extensive studies of the nature and difficulty of the vocabulary found in textbooks on various branches of high-school science. The first of these investigations was devoted to an analysis of "more than one million running words" in textbooks of general science, biology, and chemistry, to determine the number and frequency of appearance of "uncommon" words used in these textbooks.[5] The investigator draws these conclusions from his findings: "It can hardly be denied that the vocabulary burden of all these texts (analyzed in this study) is unnecessarily large." He suggests that vocabulary difficulty in science textbooks be reduced by the substitution of phrases for technical terms, and by the introduction of "only such technical terms . . . as the authors find need for after they are introduced."

Powers' second investigation[6] was devoted to an extension of the previous study to include an analysis of the vocabulary of more text-

---

[3] These lists for the various science subjects and also the "common science vocabulary" may be obtained from the Public School Publishing Co., Bloomington, Illinois.

[4] Powers, S. R. "The vocabularies of high-school science textbooks," and "A vocabulary of scientific terms for high-school students." *Teachers College Record*, 26: 1925, 368-392, and 28: 1926, 220-245. See also Curtis, *op. cit.*, II, 348-350 and 351-352.

[5] In this study a word is defined as "uncommon" if it does not appear in Thorndike's "Ten Thousand Words." See Thorndike, E. L., *The Teacher's Word Book*. New York: Bureau of Publications, Teachers College, Columbia University, 1921.

[6] Powers, S. R. *Important Terms Compiled from Textbooks for General Science, Biology, Physics, and Chemistry, and from Other Reading Materials for Scientific Subjects*. New York: Bureau of Publications, Teachers College, Columbia University, 1926.

books (including two of physics) and of some scientific books and fifty scientific articles from periodicals. The purpose of this study was to determine "a list of 'uncommon' words found to be most important on the basis of range and frequency of usage in science texts and in other reading material about scientific subjects." The investigator concludes from his data that "authors of textbooks are using in their books many words which children will never see again after they have finished the required classroom work," and that intelligence on the part of authors in regard to vocabulary load and difficulty "is of paramount importance in the work of adapting the materials of science textbooks to the ability levels of the pupils for whom they are written." The investigator lists 1828 "uncommon" scientific terms which his analyses have shown to be most important and which lie outside of Thorndike's list.

The need and the potential value of such a list of scientific terms to supplement the Thorndike list is emphasized in an earlier study by Curtis[7] in which he states: "It would seem . . . from this study that the addition to a child's reading vocabulary of each thousand of the most frequently occurring words does not add greatly to his equipment for an intelligent reading of science in the public press, and that the new trend of vocabulary-building based upon *The Teacher's Word Book* does not in itself promise to provide adequately for the needs of pupils in science . . . It is possible, too, for a pupil to have gained, through training and otherwise, a serviceable familiarity with a term in its commoner meanings without having encountered the word in its scientific connotations. A further difficulty is that a considerable portion of scientific terms are made up of more than one word and owe their scientific connotations to the combinations and not at all to the separate meanings of the component words."

Chiefly as an outcome of these vocabulary studies by Powers, the writers of most of the recent textbooks of high-school science have not only used a simpler vocabulary than is found in earlier textbooks in the field, but have also attempted to secure a mastery of essential technical vocabulary through repetition and drill. This trend toward great simplification of the materials of instruction is of paramount importance and should be fully encouraged by administrators and teachers.

---

[7] Curtis, Francis D. *Some Values Derived from Extensive Reading of General Science.* New York: Bureau of Publications, Teachers College, Columbia University, 1924, p. 25.

Values of Extensive Reading

In a controlled investigation of the values derived by pupils from voluntary reading of scientific books or articles, Curtis[8] arrives at these conclusions: (1) that "extensive reading functions in adding to the pupil's achievement in general science, whether this reading be done entirely apart from any course in general science, or as an integral or a supplementary part of the regular course in general science"; (2) that "pupils, given proper encouragement and access to suitable books and magazines, will read a great amount of scientific literature for recreation along with their regular school work"; and (3) that "extensive reading of general science apparently of itself serves to give some training in scientific attitudes, but such gains as may thus be secured are inconsiderable as compared with those made when definite instruction in scientific attitudes is given."

This investigation furnishes evidence that a well-equipped science library in the school functions in increasing the pupils' command of scientific materials.[9]

Effect of Teacher Preparation upon Pupil Achievement

In the report of an extensive investigation by Hughes,[10] the part dealing with the effect of teacher preparation in the subject matter of physics upon pupil achievement in that subject should be of especial significance and interest to administrators. The investigator states: "When the achievement of pupils in schools fairly homogeneous in size, intelligence of pupils, equipment, experience of the teachers, content, and time allotment to different divisions, but not homogeneous with respect to the training of teachers in college physics, was compared on

---

[8] *Ibid.* For digest, see his *A Digest of Investigations in the Teaching of Science,* Vol. I, 106-116.

[9] Expert guidance on the purchase of scientific books for the school library is available in the annotated and evaluated bibliography of current scientific books prepared annually by Professor Hanor A. Webb. The bibliography for the preceding year is published each year in the March issue of the *Peabody Journal of Education,* The George Peabody College for Teachers: Nashville, Tennessee. Each year's bibliography is also issued separately as an off-print.

See also list published serially in *Science Education,* beginning October, 1931.

[10] Hughes, J. M. "A study of intelligence and of the training of teachers as factors conditioning the achievement of pupils." *School Review,* 33: 1925, 217-231. See also Curtis, *Digest,* Vol. II, 253-257.

the basis of the last-named factor, [it was found that] the pupils who were taught by teachers who had majored in college physics excelled in average achievement the pupils who were taught by teachers who had not majored in college physics. The superiority was evident on every test."

This investigation seems to present clear evidence that pupils in physics classes are handicapped in their achievement when their teachers lack a thoroughly adequate background of subject matter. Since this is true in physics, a subject to which a teacher is rarely, if ever, assigned without more or less specific subject-matter training, it seems inevitable that pupils are severely penalized in those classes in biology and general science to which administrators have assigned teachers possessing little or no, or at best certainly inadequate, subject-matter preparation. This Committee, therefore, unqualifiedly condemns the practice, wherever it may exist, of assigning any science course to a teacher who is not adequately prepared in the subject matter of that course.

ADJUSTING INSTRUCTION TO DIFFERENCES IN INTELLIGENCE

Correlating intelligence quotients of pupils in several large groups with the achievement scores of these same pupils, Powers[11] arrives at these significant conclusions: "It is indeed likely that it [intelligence] is not so large a factor in successful attainment of marks as it should be. . . . Pupils of mental ability approximating that of the median are about as likely to score well on the achievement tests as are the pupils of superior mental ability. This suggests that class progress is set to the median ability and that superior pupils are not stimulated to use their talents."

The investigator points out the necessity for adapting instruction to the individual differences of the pupils, for setting higher standards for those of higher ability, and for then demanding the accomplishment of these standards. He states further that "in general, pupils who make high scores on the intelligence tests are able to make most rapid progress in school work," and that "when such a condition prevails as the one just described, it implies that we are failing with our most capable pupils."

---

[11] Powers, S. R. "The correlation between measures of mental ability and measures of achievement in chemistry." *School Science and Mathematics*, 28: 1928, 981-986. Curtis, *Digest*, Vol. II, 322-324.

Pupil Progress and Pupil Classification

Administrators and teachers of science will note with interest certain results of an elaborate study by Beauchamp[12] of pupil progress within a class and of the question whether the mental ability of the pupils, as determined by intelligence tests, furnishes a safe guide for classifying the pupils into slow, medium, and fast groups. Among his general conclusions are these: (1) Skill in silent reading "would . . . seem to be a safer guide for classification than the intelligence test." (2) "There are a great many factors influencing the rate of progress [besides general intelligence and skill in silent reading]." (3) "The relative progress of the pupils in a class is not constant." (4) "When the work is done entirely in the classroom, the amount of shifting [of relative positions of the pupils within the class] is greater than if outside work is done." (5) "The difference between the pupils within a class . . . increases with the length of time."

Variety of Questions in the Science Classroom

Attention should be directed to the conclusion which Cunningham[13] draws from the findings of his very practical analysis of the types of questions found in general-science textbooks and laboratory manuals: "Writers of textbooks and laboratory manuals are absolutely unconscious of the fact that there are so many (twenty-two) different and distinct types of problems. Teachers, as a group, are, of course, much less aware of types of problems." The investigator urges the necessity for teachers of science to know not only what are all the various types of questions appropriate to the work in science, but also how best to train the pupils to solve each type. He urges giving pupils abundant practice in solving each type.

Visual Aids in Teaching Science

The merits of motion pictures as instructional aids in science teaching have been evaluated in several recent investigations. Of these,

---

[12] Beauchamp, Wilbur L. *An Investigation of Pupil Progress in Elementary Physical Science.* (Studies in Secondary Education, II, Supplementary Educational Monographs, No. 26.) Chicago: The University of Chicago, 1925, 14-32. See also Curtis, *Digest,* Vol. II, 108-114.

[13] Cunningham, Harry A. "Types of thought questions in general science textbooks and laboratory manuals." *General Science Quarterly,* 9:1925, 91-95. See also Curtis, *Digest,* Vol. II, 84-86.

the most extensive is that of Wood and Freeman.[14] These investigators divided 3,265 pupils who were studying general science under nearly a hundred teachers in twelve widely distributed cities into two groups approximately equal both in numbers of classes and in numbers of pupils. As nearly as was possible, identical conditions were maintained with both groups of classes, except that motion pictures were used with one group but not with the other. The outcomes of the experiment were evaluated with a battery of tests measuring information, "ability to interpret experiences and to make inferences and judgments," and "ability to recall concrete objects and processes which were included in the study and were also pictured in the films."

In spite of their efforts to make the two groups of classes "equivalent," the investigators discovered eight "handicaps" which the Experiment Group had suffered in comparison with the Control Group during the three months of the investigation. These handicaps included a somewhat lower intelligence and a somewhat lesser initial knowledge of general science. Nevertheless, the Experiment Group, which had used motion pictures, achieved results considerably better on all the tests than the Control Group which had not used motion pictures. Moreover, a questionnaire, directed to practically all of the teachers of the classes in the Experiment Group, revealed the convictions of these teachers that the use of the motion pictures had been highly effective in securing a number of important and desirable outcomes not measurable by the tests employed.

In a less extensive investigation reported a year earlier, Brown[15] attempted to determine which is more effective in imparting factual information, motion pictures or the film slide with which the pictures are presented one after another as 'stills.' The investigator made one experiment with two groups of sixteen high-school freshmen, paired on the basis of intelligence, and followed this later with a check investigation in which he used the same technique with two groups of high-school sophomores paired on the same basis. Although this investigation is open to criticism in certain respects, the data as reported seem to offer some substantiation of the conclusions which the experimenter bases upon them: "In this case, at least, the film slide,

---

[14] Wood, Ben D., and Freeman, Frank N. *Motion Pictures in the Classroom.* Boston: Houghton Mifflin Co., 1929. See also Curtis, *Digest*, Vol. II, 114-119.

[15] Brown, H. E. "Motion picture or film slide?" *School Science and Mathematics*, 28: 1928, 517-526.

with the greater exchange of comment that it allows, proved the better. The differences were so large that I am inclined to believe that they would reappear on a similar investigation. . . . I feel that these two investigations can claim to have proved that for much of learning associated with still mental pictures the strip film is the movie's superior as a learning aid. Beyond that we can make no claims."

With respect to visual aids, it would appear to us that the investigational results thus far secured can in no sense be interpreted as indicating the desirability of allowing the use of motion pictures to supplant other practices and devices which have been found effective in the science classroom. The skillful teacher will use motion pictures and film slides, as supplementary aids to instruction, to vitalize less easily motivated materials and to clarify some of the more difficult processes and concepts. Teachers should, however, be warned against one ever-present danger in the use of motion pictures, and to a lesser extent of film slides in the classroom: unless the lesson plan is made with unusual care to insure a focusing of the teacher's attention upon the specific aims to the end that desirable outcomes may be insured, these visual aids are likely to serve the pupils chiefly as "effortless entertainment," an outcome likely to be obscured by the never-failing enthusiasm of the pupils and the apparent great success of the device.

DIRECTED STUDY

The results of several studies of directed study deserve attention.

In an elaborate investigation of the values of various techniques of directed study employed with classes in general science, Beauchamp[16] arrives at these conclusions, which are of practical significance to every teacher of science: (1) "Specific training in finding the central thought of a paragraph (summarizing), in determining the questions one must be able to answer in order to obtain an adequate understanding of a topic, and in reading an entire block of material through for its general plan results in a more thorough comprehension of the subject matter than undirected study on the same material." (2) "Specific training and practice in answering thought questions based on the application of some scientific principles are more efficient than incidental training

---

[16] Beauchamp, Wilbur L. *A Preliminary Experimental Study of Technique in the Mastery of Subject Matter in Elementary Physical Science.* (Studies in Secondary Education, I, Supplementary Educational Monographs, No. 24) Chicago: The University of Chicago, 1923, 47-87. See also Curtis, *Digest,* Vol. I, 75-85.

in answering thought questions." (3) "Training the pupil to make various types of analyses of the subject matter increases the ability of the pupil to interpret and reproduce what he reads."

In his study to determine the values which pupils derive from training in summarizing materials in chemistry textbooks, Persing[17] arrives at a conclusion which tends to corroborate that of Beauchamp on summarizing: "There is fairly clear evidence that training in summarizing as applied to chemistry means a very decided improvement in learning efficiency." Persing also concludes that improvement in the ability to summarize one type of subject matter carries over to other types.

Chapel,[18] investigating the relative merits of the "unit-supervised study" method and the conventional "lesson assignment-recitation" method, secured results from which he concludes that the former method is superior to the latter.

From the data which he obtained in his investigation of pupils' errors in physics, Clem[19] concludes that substantial values are secured from supervised study, particularly in the mastery of the technical vocabulary in profitable experimenting and in acquiring the technique of problem-solving.

Topical Method versus Problem Method

Hurd[20] contributes an interesting study of the relative values of the topical and the problem method of teaching physics. With the topical method the class periods were devoted to a discussion of topics on the general socialized plan; with the problem method the class periods were devoted to "socialized discussions on problem-solving." The experimenter found a "practically certain" superiority of the topic method over the problem method. He draws this interesting conclusion: "The results of this experiment apparently support the

---

[17] Persing, Kimber M. "A practice study in paragraph summarizing in chemistry." *School Science and Mathematics*, 24: 1924, 598-604. See also Curtis, *Digest*, Vol. I, 104-106.

[18] Chapel, J. C. *The Unit Technique versus the Recitation Technique in the Teaching of High-School Chemistry*. (Master's Thesis. Unpublished, University of Chicago, 1930.)

[19] Clem, A. M. *Pupil Errors in Physics as a Basis for Modifying Technique in Teaching*. (Master's Thesis. Unpublished, University of Chicago, 1930.)

[20] Hurd, A. W. *A Study of the Relative Value of the Topical versus the Problem Method in the Acquisition of Information on the Subject of Heat in High-School Physics, with Its Implications*. (Bulletin of the University of Minnesota, College of Education, 38: 1925, 3-9.) See also Curtis, *Digest*, Vol. II, 224-227.

claim that direct methods of attack result in most accomplishment. It would seem that the best way to secure a desired result is to *teach for that result.*"

PROJECT TEACHING

Watkins[21] reports an elaborate investigation of the relative values of the project method and the conventional recitation-study method of teaching general science. With the project method the pupil selected his project, planned his work, and kept a complete account of his progress toward completing his project. The progress of the pupil was carefully guided by the teacher according to a carefully worked-out technique of six steps: (1) management of class routine, (2) selection of new projects, (3) management of project work, (4) management of pupils, (5) handling of equipment, and (6) management of field trips. The results secured with seventh-, eighth-, and ninth-grade classes in general science in ten schools led the investigator to conclude that the project method, as carried out in this investigation, insures the attainment of more aims, gives a greater possibility for learning in general and for growth, and in many other respects not readily measurable objectively proves superior to the conventional method.

Hurd[22] contributes additional data upon the merits of project teaching in his carefully controlled investigation of the relative effectiveness of two methods of teaching the subject matter of heat in physics, "the individual project work as opposed to work as a group." Hurd says: "From the data it is reasonable to conclude that an individual project method . . . is almost equal to the more conventional textbook-recitation plan in achievement on conventional test material. Might it reasonably be assumed that the training received in industry, initiative, self-reliance, and constructive ability makes it a more desirable method on the whole? Its advantage in allowing pupils to work on problems connected with daily-life applications is also worthy of consideration."

---

[21] Watkins, Ralph K. "The technique and value of project teaching in general science." *General Science Quarterly,* 7: 1923, 235-256, and 8: 1924, 311-341, 387-422. See also Curtis, *Digest,* Vol. 1, 95-100.

[22] Hurd, A. W. "Suggestions on the evaluation of teaching procedures in high-school physics." *School Science and Mathematics,* 27: 1927, 220-226. See also Curtis, *Digest,* Vol. II, 232-234.

Garber,[23] in an experimental study, concludes that the project method is superior. Her chemistry pupils achieved higher scores by it than by a "non-project" method.

In summary the investigations here noted clearly indicate measurable values to be derived by the pupil from 'project teaching,' using the term as it is used in these reports. A study of the data secured and of the pupil reactions and growth during the investigations, moreover, lead the experimenters to conclude that project teaching insures valuable outcomes, not measurable objectively, which may constitute a major contribution to teaching practice. It is likely, however, that only the very gifted teacher possessing unusual training could successfully use the elaborate project technique contributed by Watkins. For the average teacher of science, therefore, the chief value of these two investigations consists in the convincing experimental justification they furnish for the introduction of much project work into every science course.

THE UNIT PLAN

Corbally[24] reports a limited investigation of effectiveness of the unit, or Morrison, plan and the conventional assignment-recitation plan when used in teaching the topic, *steam engine*, to classes in general science. The results on the tests measuring immediate recall and retention of subject matter were slightly in favor of the unit plan, but a study of range in number of errors revealed slight advantages in favor of the conventional plan. From these results the experimenter concludes: "Neither method of teaching studied is distinctly superior to the other. The determining factor is the teacher, not the method or device."

"RESIDUAL TEACHING"

Shriner[25] investigated the relative merits of two teaching techniques, "residual teaching" and "socialized report," when used in teaching general science. The former method consisted of seven steps: (1) exploration, (2) presentation, (3) setting up the problems that need to be taught, (4) reference work, (5) organization of problems,

---

[23] Garber, Ellinor. "The project method in teaching chemistry." *Sch. Sci. and Math.*, 22: 65-73. See also Curtis, *Digest*, Vol. I, 63-65.

[24] Corbally, John E. "A comparison of two methods of teaching one problem in general science." *School Review*, 38: 1930, 61-66. See also Curtis, *Digest*, Vol. II, 105-108.

[25] Shriner, J. T. *A Technique for Residual Teaching in the Secondary Schools.* State College, Pennsylvania: School of Education, The Pennsylvania State College, 1930. See also Curtis, *Digest*, Vol. II, 103-105.

(6) test, and (7) check test. The investigator terms this technique "residual teaching" because its essential feature involves the determination of "residual" materials not mastered by the pupils in the earlier steps of the technique and a careful reteaching of this material in the later steps to increase substantially the degree of mastery. The "socialized report" method consisted of these steps: (1) exploration, (2) socialized report-recitation consisting of reports given out to pupils, question-and-answer method on the topics or reports, (3) an oral quiz, and (4) the test and check test.

As one would expect from a consideration of the relative elaborateness of the two teaching techniques, the investigator secured results with respect to recall and retention of subject matter which he interprets statistically as indicating substantial values in favor of the former method. The chief contribution of this investigation, however, probably consists in the careful exposition of the special composite teaching technique which the investigator terms "residual teaching."

STUDY GUIDES AND CONTRACT TEACHING

Some progress has been made toward determining learning values derived from the use of study guides. Several earlier investigations of this problem failed to produce convincing evidence because of grave errors in the experimental and statistical technique employed. In a recent controlled experiment in the teaching of physics, however, Irene Blank[26] secured statistical results which indicated that pupils who had used study guides made higher scores on achievement tests than similar groups which did not use study guides.

Robertson,[27] however, working with paired groups under carefully controlled conditions in the elementary fields, compared the relative effectiveness of a method using study guides, combined with highly individualized instruction, with a method employing a highly socialized form of "developmental-discussion." The investigator found slight, though not statistically significant, advantages in favor of the latter method. He concludes that the results secured from the "study-guide method" at the fifth-grade level do not justify the great amount of work required of the teacher in constructing the study guides. He

---

[26] Blank, Irene R. "An experiment in directed thinking in physics." *University of Pittsburgh School of Education Journal*, 5: 1930, 90-96.
[27] Robertson, Martin L. "A study of the relative effectiveness of two methods of teaching elementary science." (Unpublished study, University of Michigan, 1930.) See Curtis, *Digest*, Vol. II, 58-61.

points out, however, that this "study-guide method," in contrast with the "developmental-discussion method," gives the children valuable training in study habits and in organizing materials; but yet, on the other hand, "this 'developmental-discussion method' gives training in oral discussion and in various phases of socialized training which the other does not afford."

IMPLICATIONS FROM THE FOREGOING INVESTIGATIONS OF TEACHING METHODS

From the standpoint of the administrator and the classroom teacher it would seem that the practical contribution of these investigations into the relative values of various teaching methods and practices consists largely in their presentation of cumulative evidence of real values to be derived from teaching science in ways other than the conventional textbook-recitation plan. It is clear, however, considering the somewhat limited experimental evidence thus far available, that the use of any 'new method' exclusively would find little more justification than the retention of any conventional procedure for exclusive classroom use. The teacher of science ambitious to increase the effectiveness of his instruction will welcome the invention of each new method, device, or plan, or each improvement of an older technique as a potential means of increasing his classroom efficiency; he will master many and varied teaching techniques to the end that he may more effectively adapt his methods and the instructional materials to the individual differences of the pupils in his charge.

CORRECTING EXAMINATION PAPERS

Curtis and Woods[28] report an extended study of the use of examination papers for teaching purposes in the science classroom. With four sets of new-type examinations, as nearly alike in type and equal in difficulty as possible, and all administered during the same period, the investigators used the following correction techniques: with the first set during a subsequent class period, the pupils checked the incorrect responses on their own papers as the teacher gave the correct responses; with the second set, the teacher merely checked the incorrect items on each paper, but wrote no corrections on the papers; with the third

---

[28] Curtis, Francis D., and Woods, Gerald G. "A study of the relative teaching values of four common practices in correcting examination papers." *School Review*, 37: 1929, 615-623. See also Curtis, *Digest*, Vol. II, 114-119.

and fourth sets, the teacher wrote all the corrections on the papers. Like the first set, the second and third sets were discussed item by item with the pupils in class during a subsequent period. The fourth set, however, was similarly discussed by the pupils in part only; the pupils were allowed to look over their corrected papers, but the discussion was limited to the items about which the pupils inquired.

The investigators summarized their findings thus: "Insofar as the results of the investigation here reported may be indicative, it seems reasonable to conclude that when new-type examinations are made a teaching device, as in this investigation, the method of correction which requires the least of the teacher's time and energy; namely, that under which the pupils check the incorrect items on their own papers during a discussion of the test items is the most profitable for the pupils of the four methods studied. Pupils from the seventh grade through the eleventh grade, moreover, are able to correct their own papers with a degree of accuracy which is probably sufficiently high. The method which does not provide for systematic discussion of the test items apparently results in considerably less value to pupils than does any of the three methods which provide such discussion. The laborious method by which the teacher corrects all errors on each paper seems not only wasteful of the teacher's time and energy, but also entirely unjustified in the light of subsequent benefit to the pupil."

CHAPTER VII

SOME CONTRIBUTIONS OF EDUCATIONAL RESEARCH TO THE SOLUTION OF TEACHING PROBLEMS IN THE SCIENCE LABORATORY*

In the best modern schools, laboratory work and the various other activities of the science classroom are frequently carried on in the same room, and together they constitute a carefully integrated whole. The materials briefly presented in this chapter should therefore be considered as a continuation of those in Chapter VI. They have been grouped separately here for the sake of securing perhaps a clearer and more unified treatment of related groups of problems. The discussions, nevertheless, cover so wide a variety of problems, so diverse in nature as to make impossible a logical order of sequence.

Resourcefulness

Webb, and later, Webb and Beauchamp, have made two unique studies[1] of "resourcefulness"; that is, the ability to solve manipulatory problems and to meet emergencies of various sorts within the laboratory. These investigators administered to several groups of high-school pupils and college students a battery of tests, which included an ingenious "Test of Resourcefulness" of their own invention, certain intelligence tests, and certain achievement tests in physics and chemistry. From various correlations and other comparisons of data, they arrive at these, among other, general conclusions: (1) "Students with absolutely no laboratory experience showed no laboratory resourcefulness whatever; they refused to touch the apparatus." (2) "If resourcefulness is really one of the qualities upon which success in life is founded, then we should present more problems involving resourceful activity in our classroom teaching, our quizzes, examinations, and tests. Some of the emphasis placed upon memoriter methods and achievements may well be redirected toward the development of practical resourcefulness

---

* For the Committee, by Francis D. Curtis.
[1] (1) Webb, Hanor A. "Testing laboratory resourcefulness." *School Science and Mathematics*, 22:1922, 259-267; (2) Beauchamp, Robert O., and Webb, Hanor A. "Resourcefulness, an unmeasured ability." *Ibid.*, 27:1927, 457-465. See also Curtis, Francis D. *Digest of Investigations in the Teaching of Science in the Elementary and Secondary Schools.* Philadelphia: Blakiston, Vol. I, 65-67, and Vol. II, 356-362.

in meeting daily problems." (3) "If experience is one of the foundations of resourcefulness, then good training in the schools should include many experiences with actual objects, in varied fields of activity,
related as frequently as possible to actual situations of practical living.
The solution of simple perplexities gives training for more complex
dilemmas."

REPORTING LABORATORY EXERCISES

Several investigations have been made of the merits of reporting
laboratory exercises. In the earliest of these, Phillips,[2] working with
a high-school group in physics, reached the conclusion that "notebook-
recording is valuable in securing definiteness of information."

Stubbs[3] made a careful investigation to determine which of two
methods of recording laboratory exercises in chemistry secures the better results—the complete, or essay, method, by which the pupil records
the title, the materials used, the object, the procedure, the results, and
the conclusions, formulating these as answers to the direct questions in
the laboratory manual, or the completion method, by which the pupil
merely fills in the blanks and answers the questions in spaces provided
in the manual.

The experimenter also made a second investigation of the relative
values of two types of report—the completion type of report and one
in which the pupil records his notes under three heads: what he did,
what he observed, and what conclusions he drew, formulating these
conclusions as direct answers. The investigator concludes (1) that
"the writing of the procedure or method followed does not appreciably
aid the memory in retaining the main facts of the experiment"; (2)
that "a mere copying of methods, which are given in print, or even
recording these in the pupil's own words, does not appreciably aid
[the pupil in] grasping the main points of the exercise" and is therefore "largely a waste of time"; and (3) that "the many extra hours
needed by the pupils to write separate detailed notes and by the instructor to correct them are not justified by the results obtained."

---

[2] Phillips, Thomas D. "A study of notebook and laboratory work as an
effective aid in science teaching." *School Review*, 28:1920, 451-453. See also
Curtis, *op. cit.*, Vol. I, 46-48.

[3] Stubbs, Morris F. "An experimental study of methods for recording laboratory notes in high-school chemistry." *School Science and Mathematics*, 26:1926,
233-239. Also Curtis, *op. cit.*, Vol. II, 317-320.

Another study of techniques for reporting laboratory exercises is that of Moore, Dykhouse, and Curtis,[4] of the "conventional" method and the diagram, or "motion-picture," method with respect both to effectiveness in teaching subject matter and to the amount of time consumed in teaching the same materials by the two methods. With the conventional method the pupil recorded his laboratory notes under four headings: (1) the statement of the problem; (2) the methods; that is, a complete verbal description of the manipulations and the observations; (3) a statement of the conclusions; and (4) a labeled diagram of the apparatus used. With the so-called "motion-picture" method the pupil recorded his laboratory notes in three steps: (1) a statement of the problem; (2) a series of labeled diagrams showing the various states of manipulation, and indicating the observations in the progress of the exercise; and (3) a statement of the conclusions.

The investigators found slight, though not statistically significant, advantages in favor of the diagram (motion-picture) method in both schools in which the investigation was conducted. Recording the manipulations and observations by the diagram method, however, was found to require about 10 percent less time than recording the same steps in essay form. The investigators summarize their interpretations of their findings thus: "It seems reasonable to conclude that the diagram method has a marked advantage over the conventional method, since it effects at least as good learning of subject matter in considerably less time. It seems reasonable to infer, moreover, that if the time thus saved were spent in performing more laboratory exercises or in drill upon essentials, the pupils taught by the diagram method might reasonably be expected to show, with an equal time expenditure, a knowledge of subject matter which would be sufficiently greater than that learned by the conventional method to be statistically significant. It must be kept in mind, however, that the conventional method gives valuable training in written expression, which the diagram method does not, and that, therefore, a use of both methods of reporting laboratory exercises would probably offer the pupils better training than the use of either method exclusively."

In summary, the significance of these investigations of methods of reporting laboratory exercises lies, we think, chiefly in the evidence

---

[4] Moore, Fred W.; Dykhouse, Claude J.; and Curtis, Francis D. "A study of the relative effectiveness of two methods of reporting laboratory exercises in general science." *Science Education,* 13:1929, 229-235. Also Curtis, *op. cit.,* Vol. II, 119-122.

which they present indicating that briefer methods of reporting laboratory exercises may be substituted for the formalized essay type of report with equal effectiveness in certain respects and with considerable saving of time. It should be kept in mind, however, that every method of reporting probably offers the pupil unique and essential values. The skillful teacher, therefore, will provide in every laboratory course some opportunities for reporting by the conventional method, along with much more extensive opportunities for reporting by the diagram method and by various other short-answer methods.

LABORATORY DRAWINGS

Ayer[5] made an elaborate investigation of the relative merits of representative drawing, verbal description, and analytical drawing as these techniques are used by pupils in connection with their laboratory reports. He reached the conclusions (1) that representative drawing; that is, "one which reproduces as accurately as possible the exact appearance of an object," encourages bad habits of analytical study which are opposed to the interests of scientific thinking"; (2) that it interferes with the memory of scientific concepts; and (3) that analytical (diagrammatic) drawings "should be used wherever adaptable to the laboratory exercise." He concludes further (4) that "description is a desirable record of the work of the pupil," but that "it is necessary . . . to supplement and direct pupils' attempts at description." He also (5) advocates the practice of requiring the pupil to draw from memory.

Ayer's conclusions with respect to the relative merits of representative and diagrammatic drawing were later substantiated in large part by a similar investigation by Bryson.[6]

In a study to determine whether pupils are better able to remember details of zoölogical structures and to make comparisons and analyses when they construct and label representative drawings of the structures than when they merely locate the same structures on the specimens without drawing them, Ballew[7] reached the conclusion that the con-

---

[5] Ayer, Fred C. *The Psychology of Drawing with Special Reference to Laboratory Teaching.* Baltimore, Maryland: Warwick & York, Inc. 1916, pp. 107-168. See also Curtis, *op. cit.,* Vol. I, 37-39.

[6] Bryson, Olive F. *The Extent to Which Drawings Contribute to an Understanding of Scientific Facts.* (Master's Thesis Unpublished, University of Chicago.)

[7] Ballew, Amer M. "A comparative study of the effectiveness of laboratory exercises in high-school zoölogy with and without drawings." *School Review,* 36:1928, 284-295. See also Curtis, *op. cit.,* Vol. II, 195-199.

struction of representative drawings does not aid the pupil in making analytical observations of material under study, nor does it aid him in remembering observations made in the laboratory. He also concluded that "it would be advisable to omit representative drawings from laboratory procedure and to replace them with supplementary work, thereby enriching the course."

Using as his subjects a university freshman class in zoölogy, Colton[8] investigated various factors affecting improvement in making laboratory drawings. He concluded that in general those students who, at the time of entering the course, are able to observe and record make no further effort at improving their technique and in some cases even fail to maintain the same degree of excellence, and that even a small amount of training in drawing results in great improvement on the part of those less capable in this respect.

Huebner[9] investigated the relative effectiveness of model, chart, and teacher's drawing as aids to the teaching of botanical structures in high-school classes. She concluded (1) that the pupils as a whole gained a greater factual knowledge with the aid of models and of teacher's drawings than with charts, (2) that "the value derived from good diagrams can be made to approach closely the value derived from models, which are frequently very expensive," and (3) that "proper training tends to increase the pupils' ability to interpret diagrammatic blackboard drawings."

In his extensive study of biology notebooks, Baird[10] concludes: "Probably too much of the pupils' time is devoted to drawing and possibly much of this time is spent in copy work. . . . There is evidence of time wasted in trying to display artistic skill and in unnecessary coloring of some of the drawings."

From an investigation to determine whether the drawings for high-school biology should be made in pencil or made or finished in ink, Cooprider[11] concludes that in general pupils retain a somewhat better

[8] Colton, Harold S. "Drawing, a factor in the training of students in a course in general zoölogy." School and Society, 28: 1926, 463-464.

[9] Huebner, Dorothy E. "A comparative study of the effectiveness of models, charts, and teacher's drawings in the teaching of plant structures." School Science and Mathematics, 29: 1929, 65-70. See also Curtis, op. cit., Vol. II, 200-207.

[10] Baird, Don O. A Study of Biology Notebook Work in New York State. New York: Teachers College, Columbia University, 1929. See also Curtis, op. cit., Vol. II, 202-207.

[11] Cooprider, J. L. "Shall the drawing be inked?" School Science and Mathematics, 25:1925, 62-73. See also Curtis, op. cit., Vol. II, 192-194.

factual knowledge of the material covered by the drawings when they finish the drawings in ink. He attributes the superior results secured from inking the drawings to the assumption that "clear, definite lines tend to foster that pride which is much desired of students in their work."

One may be justified in making the following summary of some of the practical values of these various studies of laboratory drawing: (1) Simple diagrams, clearly labeled, should replace most of the representative or picture drawings in our laboratory courses in the secondary school; even in biology, in which the practice of making representative drawings is most strongly entrenched, there should be a far greater proportion of diagrams than is commonly found. (2) Skill in making and interpreting diagrams is not gained fortuitously; teachers must train their pupils to make and to interpret diagrams just as they must give specific training in every other skill which they wish the pupils to acquire. (3) Teachers should perfect their own skill in making diagrammatic drawings, as a means of improving their instruction. (4) Teachers should abolish the practice of requiring pupils to copy drawings and should discourage all attempts of pupils to embellish their laboratory drawings in purely artistic ways. (5) Only essentials should be included in a laboratory drawing, to the ends that pupils may the more quickly, easily, and completely understand it, and that much time may be saved for use in presenting additional materials of instruction or in providing further illustration of principles and drill on essentials already studied.

Correlating Class Work and Laboratory Experimentation

Bagby[12] made an extensive and carefully controlled study of the relative values of three plans of correlating class work and laboratory work in high-school chemistry: (a) that in which the performing of the laboratory exercises precedes the class work, (b) that in which a one-day preview precedes the work in the laboratory, and (c) that in which all class work is completed before the performance of the laboratory exercise. While she discovered no statistically significant differences with respect to immediate and delayed recall of subject matter in favor of any one of these methods over another, she pre-

---

[12] Bagby, Grace. "The correlation of laboratory and classroom work in the teaching of high-school chemistry." *Journal of Educational Research*, 19:1929, 336-340. See also Curtis, *op. cit.*, Vol. II, 314-316.

sents data to favor her conclusion that for pupils of low or medium intelligence the preview followed by the experiment and then by the classwork is best of the three methods investigated; but that for pupils of high intelligence the preview is of negative value, since these pupils made better scores with each of the other two methods than with the one providing a preview.

THE INDIVIDUAL VERSUS THE DEMONSTRATION METHOD OF PERFORMING LABORATORY EXERCISES

At the beginning of this century the prevailing practice in the majority of American secondary schools was to conduct laboratory experimentation on the individual basis. This practice remained fairly satisfactory and practicable so long as the numbers of pupils enrolling in the various courses in science remained relatively small. Chiefly as a result, however, of the so-called 'high-school movement,' which, beginning about 1892, has continued to bring into the secondary schools enormously increasing numbers of pupils, it became obvious that the rapidly mounting cost of apparatus and equipment adequate for individual pupil experimentation prohibited the continuance of that method exclusively, especially in the more widely-elected or required elementary courses, such as general science and biology.

Two alternative plans suggested themselves as possible substitutes for the individual method: (1) the group method, by which two or more pupils performed the laboratory exercises together with one set of apparatus but made their reports individually; and (2) the demonstration method, by which a pupil or the teacher performed the laboratory exercise before the class while the pupils made their reports of the exercise individually. Both of these methods possessed certain obvious advantages over the older individual method. The group plan promised substantial reductions in equipment costs while the demonstration method insured even greater economies and, in addition, promised a considerable reduction in the time required for performing the laboratory exercises.

The attention of leaders in the field of research in the teaching of science became focused, almost from the beginning of investigation in this field, upon the problem of determining experimentally the values of the demonstration, or lecture-demonstration, method and the individual-laboratory method as compared with each other and with various other classroom and laboratory methods. The first published investigation of the values of the demonstration method (called by the investigator the "experimental method") was that of Mayman;[13] the first published investigation of the relative values of the lecture-demonstration and the individual laboratory methods of instruction in science was that of Wiley.[14] Since the appearance of Wiley's report a considerable number of investigations of the relative merits of these two methods have been reported; in fact, probably more research has been devoted to this than to any other problem dealing with the teaching of science.

It is not surprising that those responsible for providing instruction in various science courses in the secondary schools watched for the results of these pioneer investigations with the keenest interest. When these early results were rather generally interpreted as indicating that the demonstration method insured learning values at least as good as those secured from the individual method, if not indeed even better, many administrators willingly became convinced that the demonstration method should supplant the individual method as rapidly and as completely as possible. This policy was carried out with enthusiasm and in some cases with such complete thoroughness that certain large city high schools were constructed with no provisions whatever for individual experimentation by pupils.

Such a change of administrative policy, despite its popularity with taxpayers, would have been justified only if there had been conclusive evidence of the superiority of the demonstration method over the individual method. But an accurate evaluation of these pioneer investigations, convincing to the careful student of research, was rendered difficult by a number of factors, prominent among which were these: (1) the experimental and statistical techniques employed were to a considerable extent faulty and inadequate; and (2) the lack of reliable and valid objective tests for measuring instructional outcomes other than retention of subject-matter knowledge rendered the results in the main unconvincing. Therefore, while students of research in the teaching of science welcomed all evidence which might reasonably be

---

[13] Mayman, Jacob E. *An Experimental Investigation of the Book Method, Lecture Method, and Experimental Method of Teaching Elementary Science in Elementary Schools.* New York: New York City Bureau of Educational Research, 1912. See Curtis, *op. cit.*, Vol. I, 30-33.

[14] Wiley, William H. "An experimental study of methods in teaching high-school chemistry." *Journal of Educational Psychology*, 9:1918, 181-198. See Curtis, *op. cit.*, Vol. I, 42-45.

interpreted as indicating positive values to be derived from the use of the demonstration method, at the same time they sounded a warning against a complete substitution of the demonstration method for the individual method on the strength of the investigational evidence available. In support of this statement it is interesting to note quotations from three critical summaries and evaluations of the results of the earlier investigations of these two methods of teaching science:

In his discussion of the techniques and findings of eight investigations of this problem prior to 1925, Downing[15] includes these statements among his conclusions: "The lecture-demonstration method of instruction yields better results than the laboratory method in imparting essential *knowledge* and is more economical of time and expense. This is true for both bright and dull pupils and for all types of experiments. *The last two points need additional experimental confirmation.* . . . The lecture-demonstration method appears to be the better method for imparting skill in laboratory technique in its initial stages and for developing ability to solve new problems. *Again, these two items are tentative conclusions, and further experiments will be required to establish them.*"[16]

Discussing five of these same investigations and two others published in 1925, Riedel[17] states: "Now it is one thing to say that one or the other of the above methods of teaching is superior—if, in fact, that were a safe assertion in view of the limited number of studies, admittedly small populations in most cases, inadequate statistical treatment in all cases except one, and the general lack of reporting of details so that the results are verifiable. It takes a lot of assurance and an utter disregard for the cautious, laborious, and oft-repeated observations such as those in physical science or even biometry to give science teachers the impression that anything at all has been proved on such meager evidence. And this is said with all deference to those science research students who have had the courage and wisdom to venture into this most worthy pioneer work."

[15] Downing, Elliot R. "A comparison of the lecture-demonstration and the laboratory methods of instruction in science." *School Review,* 33:1925, 688-697. Cf. his *Teaching Science in the Schools.* University of Chicago Press, 1925, pp. 120-128.

[16] Italics not in original report.

[17] Riedel, F. A. "What, if anything, has really been proved as to the relative effectiveness of demonstration and laboratory methods in science?" *School Science and Mathematics,* 27:1927, 512-519, 620-631.

Curtis ends a brief discussion of this problem with these statements:

> Some of the obstacles in the way of an early answer to this question are indicated by a consideration of three of the most important objectives of laboratory work:
>
> 1. *Teaching the pupil to manipulate, i.e., 'learn by doing.'* The chief objective of some exercises is to permit the pupil to 'learn to do,' in the sense of learning to manipulate. With such exercises it is of paramount concern to keep very clear the fundamentally important distinction between knowing, and thus being able to describe what manipulations are appropriate to a certain exercise, and being able, with dexterity, assurance, and dispatch, to perform those manipulations. Both objectives are desirable phases of 'learning to do,' but while the pupil may learn by observing demonstrations to know and describe appropriate experimental techniques, or even to make simple elementary manipulations more or less effectively through imitation, it is difficult to believe that he will acquire any considerable degree of manipulatory dexterity and skill except through the individual laboratory method.
>
> 2. *Teaching the pupil to interpret experimental data.* At times the objective is reasoning or interpreting rather than manipulating. The attainment of this objective is usually sought in physics, chemistry, and biology, at least, through individual pupil experimentation. But in seeking the solution of some problem which has arisen in connection with reading or some vicarious experience, the pupil may find manipulation a hindrance rather than a help to interpretation. His interest and attention may become so absorbed in the details of the investigation that he may lose sight entirely of the main problem to be explained. When reasoning is the prime objective, therefore, experience gained through actually doing may give a less effective basis for interpretation than that gained vicariously through a demonstration, during the performance of which the teacher directs attention to the pertinent, reifying elements.
>
> 3. *Teaching the pupil the concept of scientific method.* Again, in a few exercises the objective may be to afford training in the method of the research experimenter, which demands both ability to manipulate and to interpret. It is conceivable that either the individual laboratory method or the demonstration method may further the achievement of this objective, but the objective itself may be of less value than the preceding ones in a program of liberal unspecialized education.

These quotations from three critical analyses of the results of the earlier investigations into the relative merits of these competing methods indicate clearly the unwillingness of students of the teaching of science to accept the early experimental evidence as conclusive that the demonstration method is a satisfactory substitute for the individual method. In fact, even one of the earlier investigations, and several of the later studies, did reveal some findings which their investigators interpreted as relatively favorable to each of the two competing methods. Kiebler and Woody[18] found that although "the results secured through the use of the demonstration method were as good [as those secured with the individual method] if not better, . . . the individual method tended to be superior in those experiments that are especially difficult to perform or in which great care needed to be taken to see the exact procedure." They conclude further that "such facts suggest that the most effective method depends upon the nature of the experiments themselves and suggest the need for scientifically classifying them."

Analyzing the results of his experiment, Johnson[19] states, "In the light of the S.D.'s in the scores attained by the various methods, there appears to be a tendency toward a wider deviation by the individual method than by either of the others. The individual method, therefore, seems to provide greater opportunity for the exercise of individual differences." The investigator states further, however, that "although . . . it cannot be exclusively stated that it is superior, since the obtained differences were not found to be statistically significant, . . . it is apparent that the demonstration method of laboratory instruction may be expected to yield, if not larger, at least equal returns in primary learnings when compared with the . . . individual method. This [fact] becomes significant in view of the saving in laboratory equipment."

Pruitt[20] secured investigational results which he interpreted as favoring the individual method. He states: "The demonstration method has the smallest S.D. and the individual method the greatest S.D. This is a significant fact as it indicates that the demonstration method . . . tends toward making the group homogeneous. The individual method seemingly tends to allow more free play for individual differences."

---

[18] Kiebler, E. W., and Woody, Clifford. "The individual laboratory versus the demonstration method of teaching physics." *Journal of Educational Research*, 7:1923, 50-58. See also Curtis, *op. cit.*, Vol. I, 85-90.

[19] Johnson, Palmer O. "A comparison of the lecture-demonstration, group laboratory experimentation, and individual laboratory experimentation methods of teaching high-school biology." *Journal of Educational Research*, 18: 1928, 103-111. See also Curtis, *op. cit.*, Vol. II, 189-191.

[20] Pruitt, Clarence M. *An Experiment on the Relative Efficiency of Methods of Conducting Chemistry Laboratory Work.* Master's thesis (unpublished), University of Indiana, 1925. See Curtis, *op. cit.*, Vol. II, 289-292.

Knox,[21] however, presents evidence which he interprets as indicating the superiority of the demonstration method in effectively providing for individual differences. He states: "From the standpoint of the coefficients of correlation, it appears that the demonstration method provides superior opportunity for adaptation to individual differences in mental ability so far as teaching for immediate retention, delayed retention, and method of attack are concerned."

In their doctor's dissertations, Carpenter[22] and Horton[23] employ a scope and a refinement of experimental and statistical technique far in advance of that employed in any other investigations of the individual and the demonstration methods.

Using 34 different classes in chemistry in 23 widely scattered schools in an elaborate rotation investigation, Carpenter arrives at these conclusions:

> The results of this experiment point to the conclusions that the majority of pupils in high-school laboratory chemistry classes, taught by the demonstration method, succeed as well as when they perform the exercise individually, if success is measured by instruments which measure . . . specific information and ability to think in terms of chemistry. . . . On the whole the intelligent pupil will succeed no matter what method of presentation is used in the laboratory and . . . his success will be greater than the usual success of those of lower intelligence. In the eight classes in which intelligence scores of pupils were available, the pupils of medium and lower intelligence seem to profit on the whole a little more from a good demonstration than when they themselves perform the exercises individually, when success is measured as indicated above.

It is Carpenter's analysis of the significance of his findings, however, which is of chief interest:

> It is not the opinion of the author that individual laboratory work in high-school chemistry should be eliminated, or that buildings in future contain no laboratories, but rather that a larger number of laboratory exercises be offered by demonstration by the teachers and a smaller number be performed by the pupil, and that the increase in the number of demonstration exercises be greater than the decrease in the number of exercises performed either by groups or individuals.

---

[21] Knox, W. W. "The demonstration method versus the laboratory method of teaching high-school chemistry." *School Review,* 25: 1927, 376-386. See also Curtis, *op. cit.,* Vol. II, 295-299.

[22] Carpenter, W. W. *Certain Phases of the Administration of High-School Chemistry.* New York: Teachers College, Columbia University, Bureau of Publications. 1925. See also Curtis, *op. cit.,* Vol. II, 282-289.

[23] Horton, Ralph E. *Measurable Outcomes of Individual Laboratory Work in High-School Chemistry.* New York: Teachers College, Columbia University, Bureau of Publications. 1928. See also Curtis, *op. cit.,* Vol. II, 299-311.

It is the conclusion of the author, then, that instead of curtailing the work in chemistry in our high schools we increase the efficiency of our teaching by taking advantage of methods of presentation requiring less time and material in developing certain skills and abilities, in order that more examples and a wider range of subject matter may be presented in that same available time. . . .

The type of laboratory work must further be controlled by the objectives set up for the course. Demonstration will succeed in imparting information and in developing thinking in terms of chemistry; it cannot be expected to develop the manual skills.

Horton contributes to the attack upon this problem, not only a carefully controlled experimental technique, but also a battery of ingenious tests designed to measure objectively, desirable outcomes of laboratory experimentation not measured by earlier tests available. From the results of these tests the experimenter found certain substantial advantages of the individual laboratory method over the demonstration method in teaching chemistry. The following detailed quotations from his findings seem especially worthy of inclusion in this discussion:

The order of preference of the methods studied, in the light of all the outcomes measured, appeared to be: (1) individual laboratory work *without directions,* the so-called 'problem method'; (2) individual laboratory work following directions, but with these directions consciously generalized; (3) individual laboratory work following directions from a manual—the regular method of previous practice; (4) demonstration of all exercises by the teacher.

We need not expect individual laboratory work to assist the pupils much in gaining abilities to succeed in written tests. Demonstration work appears to give results almost as acceptable and requires less time and material.

If there is to be further study of chemistry in college laboratories or elsewhere, individual work without directions—or even with directions —may be recommended in preference to demonstration work for at least one period per week. If problem-solving and ability to do tasks in the laboratory are important, *practice* in doing similar tasks in the laboratory by self-direction seems to attain this end best.

The discontinuance of the individual laboratory work and the substitution of demonstration . . . after a preliminary period of training appear justified and feasible.

If ability to do experimentation or to solve perplexities of a chemical nature is a desirable goal, practice in this experimentation—not practice in watching some one else experiment—is necessary; . . . practice in solving problems and in exercising judgment must be given and . . . neither demonstration nor individual laboratory work following printed or other directions does give the opportunity for such practice; . . . to obtain such outcomes the evidence points to individual self-directed experimentation in problematic situations, as the method offering the best possibilities of success.

The results of Horton's investigation can be summed up as furnishing objective evidence of a convincing sort in support of Dewey's statement, "We learn to do by doing"; that is, they afford experimental confirmation of the opinions expressed by earlier investigators and critics that the laboratory method which is employed in the teaching of high-school chemistry in the secondary school should be selected in terms of the specific objective to the attainment of which the laboratory exercise is expected to contribute.

Further investigation of the merits of a method much like the problem method of Horton has recently been made by Walter[24] with laboratory groups in high-school physics. The report of this study loses much of its value and authority, however, because of its incompleteness. Using approved experimental technique, the investigator attempts to determine the relative values of the "individual-manual" method, the demonstration method, and the "individual-no-manual" method. His "individual-manual" method is the conventional individual laboratory method by which "the pupil followed the direction in the manual and performed the exercise individually under the direction of the teacher"; the "individual-no-manual" method is a problem method, by which "the pupil was simply given the material and told to prove or test a law. He was given suggestions which, with the apparatus supplied, limited him to practically the same procedure [as that] outlined in the manual, and followed by the other groups."

The results of this investigation lead the investigator to conclude that the "individual-no-manual" method is superior to the other two methods, both with respect to "ability to observe and remember" and "ability to think." The investigator interprets his data as indicating, moreover, that the latter method "seems to be best adapted to drill work where the pupil sees easily the meaning of the problem before he performs the exercise," but that "teacher-demonstration seems most appropriate where information is to be gained from the exercise."

---

[24] Walter, C. H. "The individual laboratory method of teaching physics when no printed directions are used." *School Science and Mathematics*, 30:1930, 429-432. See also Curtis, *op. cit.*, Vol. II, 231-232.

Approaching the problem from a different angle, Watkins[25] reaches a conclusion of considerable practical significance to administrators, especially administrators of schools in which the funds for science equipment are limited and inadequate: "There is little evidence to show that these schools are better equipped to do demonstration work than they are to do laboratory instruction. . . . It would seem almost hopeless, under present conditions, for most of the schools in the whole group studied to build up an adequate laboratory for individual laboratory instruction *of the type now expected of schools.* If this is true, it seems wise, on the basis of simple economy and expediency, to recommend that such schools spend their limited funds for more satisfactory demonstration apparatus rather than trying to spread the funds thinly over inadequate individual laboratory equipment."

One other investigation of the demonstration method seems worthy of mention before closing this discussion. Cooprider[26] reports a controlled investigation in which he attempts to measure the relative effectiveness of laboratory demonstrations by the teacher and by pupils in the class. The conviction which his data might otherwise carry is somewhat diminished by his failure to permit the pupil-demonstrators to perform an assigned exercise before the class met, although he did permit the pupil-demonstrator to study the directions in advance and to look over the apparatus before making his demonstration. Cooprider found that the average percentage score was on the whole slightly better with the teacher-demonstration than with the pupil-demonstration, and that the former method was preferred by most of the pupils. He concludes, moreover, that "where the teacher very closely supervises," the pupil-demonstrators seem to "obtain about as good results as the teacher"; also, that the abler pupils secure about as good results with their demonstrating as the teacher and at the same time require less supervision in their demonstrating than less able ones.

The practical significance of these and other investigations of the relative merits of the individual laboratory method and the demonstra-

[25] Watkins, Ralph K. "Equipment for teaching physics in Northeast Missouri high schools." *Science Education,* 13: 1929, 199-210. See also Curtis, *op. cit.,* Vol. II, 263-265.

[26] Cooprider, J. L. "Teacher versus student demonstration in high-school biology." *School Science and Mathematics,* 26: 1926, 147-155. See also Curtis, *op. cit.,* Vol. II, 186-189.

tion method, supplemented by such advice as this Committee believes to be sound, might be briefly summarized thus:

1. Each method offers training in certain knowledges, skills, and habits not offered by the other.

2. In the interests of economy both of time and of money, it seems desirable to perform more laboratory exercises by the demonstration than by the individual method.

3. At the beginning of every laboratory course there should be a sufficient use of the demonstration method to acquaint the pupils with apparatus and with some of the accepted methods of experimentation. Following this period of orientation, the pupil should be allowed to perform some exercises individually in order to acquire, early in the course, desirable manipulatory skills and laboratory techniques and habits.

4. The time saved in each course by the use of the demonstration method should be used for other types of learning exercises, which might include additional laboratory exercises, reading projects, individual investigations, observations, and drill upon essentials.

5. Among the exercises to be demonstrated in each course should be those which are dangerous if performed carelessly or unskillfully, at least some of those requiring delicate manipulation and accurate observation, and those requiring special expensive apparatus.

6. In general, especially with the more elementary courses and the younger or less capable pupils, demonstrations by the teacher are likely to prove more effective than those by pupils, unless the teacher supervises the demonstrations very closely.

Performing Laboratory Exercises in Pairs or in Groups

The investigational attack upon the problem of the relative values of laboratory experimentation by pupils individually or by pupils in pairs or in groups has not been extensive. Carpenter[27] investigated the relative values of the method of experimenting individually or in groups of two. He secured data from which he concludes that the majority of pupils in laboratory classes in high-school chemistry succeed less well when performing exercises in groups of two than when each performs the exercise individually. He states, however, that "the practical difference between results obtained, . . . while significant,

---

[27] Carpenter, *op. cit.*

may not justify the additional expenditures of equipment and materials for individual work." He states further that "pupils of medium and lower intelligence . . . do not as a whole do quite so well when working in groups of two as when working individually, but the difference is very slight."

Johnson[28] compared the relative achievements of pupils in groups of four or five when they, themselves, manipulated the apparatus (and also when they observed the demonstrations by the teacher) with those of other pupils working individually and in large demonstration groups. He states, "There appears to be no significant difference between results obtained from the group and individual methods." As stated earlier in this discussion, he found the demonstration method somewhat superior to either the individual or the group methods.

To summarize, we believe that, although the results of these two investigations do not justify the condemnation of the practice of allowing the pupils to perform laboratory exercises in pairs or in small groups, and although it seems logical to assume that pupils may gain much informational knowledge from observing other pupils perform the exercises, it seems certain, nevertheless, that other desirable outcomes of laboratory work, such as those investigated by Horton, are unlikely to be gained by the pupils except by individual experimentation. It is the judgment of this Committee, therefore, that the practice of permitting the pupils to perform laboratory exercises in groups or in pairs is inadvisable and should be discontinued.

LABORATORY TEACHING AT THE UNIVERSITY LEVEL

Some of the investigations which exemplify the highest degree of refinement of experimental and statistical technique are studies of laboratory teaching at the college level. Working with university students who were studying inorganic chemistry, Noll[29] made an elaborate series of controlled experiments (1) to compare the achievement of two groups receiving instruction identical in all respects except for the amounts of laboratory work, and (2) to compare the achievements of two groups whose instruction is identical except that the time devoted to laboratory experimentation by one of the groups is reduced by sub-

---

[28] Johnson, *loc. cit.*

[29] Noll, Victor H. *Laboratory Instruction in the Field of Inorganic Chemistry.* Minneapolis: The University of Minnesota Press, 1930. See also Curtis, *op. cit.*, Vol. II, 399-408.

stituting for part of it some other method of instruction. Among his general conclusions are these which merit especial attention:

> The most important problem in this study has been the question of the value of individual laboratory work in chemistry. Supplementing this was the problem of finding something that could be substituted for some of the laboratory work without loss to the student. As far as any measures used in this study are concerned, two hours of laboratory work out of five per week do not seem indispensable. The fact that students can be deprived of these two hours without significant loss would appear to be rather important evidence on this point. As for substitutes for laboratory work, of the two that were tried, recitation or oral quiz seems a fairly profitable substitute, but outside reading does not. It may be that a different plan for the outside reading or a different selection of topics would show results different from those found here.

> Oral quiz and recitations seemed to be somewhat more effective than laboratory work during the experimental period, and apparently the salutary effect carried over to sequent courses. This seems to be a rather important fact from the administrative point of view. It needs further experimental verification before being accepted unqualifiedly.

Hurd[30] made several elaborate investigations of problems of science teaching in the University of Minnesota. Among these problems were (1) the substitution of assigned library work for part of the laboratory work, (2) the substitution of some laboratory work on a distantly related subject for part of the regular laboratory work in human physiology, and (3) the effect of class size upon the achievement of students in college physics.

With the first of these three problems, the investigator finds "some evidence to indicate that seven and one-half hours of laboratory work in human physiology . . . produce measurable achievement in excess of that produced by five hours of laboratory work plus two and one half hours of library work." With the second, he discovers no significant results in favor of either of the two methods. With the third, he finds "no definite proof that . . . class size is a significant factor in achievement in elementary [college] physics under present instructional conditions. Achievement seems to be a matter of individual incentive, capacity, and effort."

---

[30] Hurd, A. W. *Problems of Science Teaching at the College Level.* Minneapolis: The University of Minnesota Press, 1929. See also Curtis, *op. cit.*, Vol. II, 385-393.

CHAPTER VIII

INVESTIGATIONS RELATING TO THE CONTENT OF SCIENCE COURSES*

During the past quarter century several factors have operated in modifying instructional materials in science, especially those for the secondary school. Prominent among these influences are (1) the 'high-school movement,' which, beginning about 1892, brought into the secondary schools enormously increasing numbers of pupils, and therefore reduced to a marked extent the degree of selection; (2) a resulting diminished emphasis upon the college-preparatory aim, which combined with other factors to render progressively less satisfactory and less appropriate the earlier type of textbook that comprised merely a somewhat simplified revision of materials written by university teachers for college and university classes; (3) important trends in educational psychology, prominent among which were a discrediting of the current extreme theories of general transfer and discipline and of serial and saltatory development and a growing acceptance of the functional point of view and of the theory of gradual and concomitant development; and (4) the beginnings of modern educational research, which has been contributing findings of increasing scope and refinement.

Until about twenty years ago, however, opinion was the only available means for determining course content. Only small, though promising, beginnings have yet been made through research toward determining what material not now adequately represented should be brought into the various courses; and practically nothing of practical value, outside of the field of elementary science, has yet been produced in the way of determining objectively the grade placement or the sequence of various units within the different courses.

WHO SHOULD DETERMINE THE CONTENT OF SCIENCE COURSES

Opinion with respect to course content, as well as of all other problems in education, is valuable only to the extent to which it is based upon a sound and thorough understanding of all existing factors

---

* For the Committee, by Francis D. Curtis.

and conditions. Until recently, and indeed even yet with respect to certain courses in the science curriculum, the content has been determined to too great an extent by the opinions of college and university teachers. These men have brought to the task a profound and valuable knowledge of subject matter, but at the same time their remoteness, both in experience and training, from the practical classroom situations in which their textbooks were to serve has rendered their products to a considerable extent inappropriate and ineffective.

The recent attempt to bring about an improvement of teaching materials by impressing upon administrators and classroom teachers the responsibility for revising and constructing courses in the light of the local situation has doubtless proved salutary. It has very often resulted in the selection of subject-matter materials that are more appropriate to the interests and needs of the pupils; and it has, in general, improved instruction, because the teachers have had an increased interest in presenting well the course materials in the selection and arrangement of which they themselves have had a share. On the other hand, the emphasis upon the construction of courses by teachers has not been wholly beneficial. In many situations administrators and teachers have placed too much emphasis upon the production of courses which are unique in content and have therefore discarded from consideration materials the values of which have been proved through continued use in a wide variety of situations and over a long period of years; also, there have been too many situations in which the responsibility for constructing entirely new courses in physics, chemistry, general science, and biology has been assigned to, and cheerfully accepted by, young teachers who have possessed no adequate background, either of subject matter or of classroom experience.

It is the opinion of this Committee that neither the university specialist nor the classroom teacher alone can produce the most effective classroom materials. Authors of textbooks and syllabi should take into consideration the points of view of three groups: (1) subject-matter specialists who insure that the materials are accurate and up-to-date, (2) classroom teachers and supervisors who refine the materials in the light of their appropriateness of content and difficulty, and (3) specialists in the teaching of science who contribute a knowledge of developments in the field with respect to educational research. There is much encouragement to be derived from the fact that several recent science textbooks obviously present the results of such intimate coöperation.

The Need for Guidance in the Selection of Content

Those interested in the teaching of science in secondary schools have been alarmed by the increasing voluminousness of textbooks and syllabi produced in this field. The attempt on the part of the conscientious teacher to teach all of the material in a modern science textbook to every pupil in the time available inevitably results in a degree of attainment of objectives and aims far short of the extent desired. While it is obvious that the instructional materials in any science course should be up-to-date and sufficiently extensive to meet the needs of the ablest pupils, it is equally obvious that in every course there will be pupils for whom the course is appropriate but who will nevertheless find impossible the mastery of a major portion of the textbook or syllabus provided. There is need for guidance, therefore, with respect to the relative importance of instructional materials, in order that optimal provision for individual differences may be made. Some guidance of this sort is found in the results of several investigations, and these are being increasingly used by makers of syllabi and authors of textbooks to indicate minimal essentials and additional goals appropriate to varying levels of industry and ability within the class. The selection of materials and the relative emphasis to be given them, however, is not thus permanently determined but must be modified in the light of further investigations as rapidly as these reveal more clearly the learning experiences that contribute directly to the attainment of objectives accepted as appropriate for particular grade and ability levels. The determination of the content which is likely to serve best the needs of pupils in varying situations and of varying abilities and the reduction of course content sufficient to make practicable the optimal attainment of desired objectives of science teaching are among the major problems which confront the curriculum specialist in this field.

Sources of Content Material for Courses in Science

In the space here available an attempt will be made merely to indicate some of the more valuable sources of materials for courses in science, such as outstanding reports of curriculum committees and of educational research in which the findings are presented in sufficient detail to be useful for purposes of course construction.

1. Elementary Science

In the elementary field several investigators have produced data which are of undoubted value. Palmer[1] has for many years been collecting questions relating to nature asked by children in the rural schools of New York. He has tabulated and classified these questions, and though he has nowhere published the detailed results of his findings, he has used them in determining the content of the *Cornell Rural School Leaflet.* Containing, as these do, not only authoritatively accurate subject matter but also practical teaching suggestions, they are of great value and importance to all teachers of science and especially to teachers in the elementary school.

Craig,[2] working upon the problem of an integrated program in elementary science (as distinct from nature study) for the first six grades, employed a number of research techniques which are described in detail in Chapter IV. His detailed results are of paramount interest and importance.

Both Palmer and Craig, together with Hillman,[3] attempt a solution of the problem of grade placement of materials, which is one of the most important as well as perplexing problems in the entire field of science teaching.

2. General Science

General science has from its beginnings offered an interesting field of investigation. One of the earliest textbooks in this field was based largely upon a study of children's interests as indicated by their questions. The content of several later books was seemingly determined by the results of their authors' analyses of the content of earlier textbooks in the field. An objection to this latter method of determining content of a textbook is that it is based upon the assumption that the content of the earlier books includes the material which is most appropriate and suitable to the subject. An acceptance of this assumption

---

[1] Palmer, E. Laurence, in the issues of the *Cornell Rural School Leaflet* for each September beginning with 1922. Brief digests of this extensive study appear in Curtis, *A Digest of Investigations in the Teaching of Science,* I, 204-207, and II, 36-40.

[2] Craig, Gerald S. *Certain Techniques Used in Developing a Course of Study in Science for the Horace Mann Elementary School,* (Contributions to Education, No. 276.) New York: Teachers College, Columbia University, 1927. (See also Curtis, *op. cit.,* II, 40-52.)

[3] Hillman, James Elgan. *Some Aspects of Science in the Elementary Schools* (Contributions to Education, No. 14). Nashville, Tennessee: George Peabody College for Teachers, 1924. (Curtis, *op. cit.,* II, 29-35.)

permits no provision for the introduction of new materials; consequently there is the danger that the course will become standardized, its content consisting chiefly of those elements that the opinions of the earlier authors dictated as most important and appropriate.

Recently, extensive research has produced materials which are of decided importance to writers of textbooks and syllabi in general science. The most extensive and elaborate of these studies is that of Curtis,[4] who combined the topics found in three outstanding syllabi with the subject-matter elements revealed by fourteen published and one unpublished analyses of materials appropriate for inclusion in the course on general science. The study resulted in a list of 1850 topics with their relative values as determined from the statistical technique employed.

Using a simpler technique, Harap and Persing[5] combined the results of five curriculum studies and the analyses of five textbooks of general science with the topics found in eleven courses of study. This synthesis resulted in a list of 275 subject-matter objectives with their relative values.

Cureton[6] analyzed the findings of previous research and combined the findings of previously reported curricular studies with the topics from nine courses of study in general science and with the results of his own analysis of two forms of one standard test and three forms of another, and of thirty-six textbooks and laboratory manuals in general science. From this synthesis he obtained a list of 548 topics and problems. In his published report of this investigation he lists 245 of the most important topics as determined by the statistical technique which he employs.

Attacking the problem of course content of general science from a different angle, that of determining the basic principles which the course should develop, Downing,[7] with the assistance of several graduate students, has produced materials of the greatest importance. These should be given increased emphasis in forthcoming textbooks and

---

[4] Curtis, Francis D. *A Synthesis and Evaluation of Subject-Matter Topics in General Science.* Boston: Ginn, 1929.

[5] Harap, Henry, and Persing, Ellis C. "The present objectives in general science." *Science Education,* 14: March, 1930, 477-497. (Curtis, *op. cit.,* II, 97-100.)

[6] Cureton, Edward E. "Junior-high-school science." *The School Review,* 35: December, 1927, 767-775. (Curtis, *op cit.,* II, 87-91.)

[7] Downing, Elliot R. "An analysis of textbooks in general science." *General Science Quarterly,* 12: May, 1928, 509-516. (Curtis, *op cit.,* II, 72-79.)

syllabi in this subject, since the development of these principles is a necessary step in the pupils' understanding of major generalizations, the attainment of which this Committee considers to be a major goal of science teaching.

3. General Biology

The content of general biology is less clearly defined than that of any other course in the science curriculum for the secondary school. Research in this field has been done largely within the last ten years. A pioneer investigation by Finley and Caldwell[8] emphasizes among other important findings the importance of the homocentric approach. Richards[9] publishes a list of 35 topics which he secured from an analysis of textbooks. Presson[10] gives the relative importance of forty-five biological topics as determined from this elaborate analysis of seven textbooks, 9053 teachers' examination questions, 371 questions of the College Entrance Examination Board, and 976 examination questions of the Board of Regents for the State of New York. A more limited list of topics, with their relative importance, is reported by Hill[11] from his analysis of 861 magazine articles.

Ruch and Cossman[12] published an extensive list of biological topics, with their relative importance determined from their analysis of more than two thousand teachers' examination questions.

Among the important committee reports on biological content are those of the committee appointed by the University of Illinois[13] in 1921 and of the Cleveland Biology Club.[14]

---

[8] Finley, Charles W., and Caldwell, Otis W. *Biology in the Public Press.* New York: Lincoln School of Teachers College, 1923. (Curtis, *op. cit.*, I, 259-264.)

[9] Richards, Oscar W. "The present content of biology in secondary schools." *School Science and Mathematics*, 23: May, 1923, 409-414. (Curtis, *op. cit.*, I, 233-237.)

[10] Presson, John M. *Achievement Tests in Biology for Secondary School Use Based upon an Analysis of the Content of the Subject.* Philadelphia: University of Pennsylvania, 1930. (Curtis, *op. cit.*, II, 143-147.)

[11] Hill, Harry A. "A comparison between the biological content of certain periodical literature and the Kansas high-school course of study." *Science Education*, 14: January, 1930, 430-436. (Curtis, *op. cit.*, II, 147-149.)

[12] Ruch, Giles M., and Cossman, Leo H. "Standardized content in high-school biology." *Jour. of Educ. Psychol.*, 15: May, 1924, 285-296. (Curtis, *op. cit.*, II, 141-143.)

[13] Hunter, George W. (Chairman). "The report of the Committee on One-year Fundamental Course of Biological Science." *School Sci. and Math.*, 23: October, 1923, 656-664. (Curtis, *op. cit.*, I, 254-259.)

[14] Persing, Ellis C. (Chairman). "Report of the Committee on Reorganization of the Biological Sciences appointed by the Cleveland Biology Teachers Club." *School Sci. and Math.*, 24: March, 1924, 241-246. (Curtis, *op. cit.*, 271-278.)

The recent report of the North Central Committee on Biology[15] is of especial significance since it includes the results of extensive research under the direction of its chairman, Downing, for the purpose of determining the important principles which should be developed in the course.

4. Physics

Valuable suggestions for a modification of the content in physics are found in several investigations and committee reports.

Though many might challenge the benefits to science teaching derived from the work of the College Entrance Examination Board, nobody will question the profoundness of their influence in establishing the content of textbooks and syllabi. An earlier study, which therefore demands consideration in determining the content of physics, is that of Glenn and Brookmeyer.[16] These investigators made a careful and exhaustive analysis of all of the questions in physics of the College Entrance Examination Board from 1911 to 1922. The extensive report of their findings includes the topics found in the examinations and the number of times each topic appeared.

Watson[17] attempted to determine the practical values of the content of our physics courses to adults in various occupations. From an analysis of three textbooks, he determined a list of 174 topics which he submitted to several hundred parents of pupils who were studying physics in 75 high schools of Kansas. These adults were asked to indicate the items which were worth while for themselves to know about and understand, those of doubtful value to themselves personally but of probable value to their children, and those of practically no value to themselves. An extensive list of topics was secured from 659 usable replies. The investigator draws two interesting conclusions: "There is evidence which indicates that there are numerous items treated in physics texts which possess little knowledge value for the majority of the adult population and that there are numerous pertinent items of recognized value which are not included." "Occupational life makes

---

[15] Downing, Elliot R. (Chairman). "Teaching units in biology—an investigation." *North Central Assoc. Quarterly,* 5: March, 1931, 453-470.

[16] Glenn, Earl R., and Brookmeyer, Ivan L. "An analysis of the College Entrance Board examinations in physics." *School Sci. and Math.,* 23: May, 1923, 459-470. (Curtis, *op. cit.,* I, 237-252.)

[17] Watson, Charles Hoyt. "A critical study of the content of high-school physics with respect to its social value." *School Rev.,* 34: November, 1926, 688-697. (Curtis, *op. cit.,* II, 209-210.)

less difference than has been commonly supposed in the selection of subject matter for high-school courses in physics."

Of commanding importance is the synthesis by Downing[18] of the results of four investigations of the principles appropriate to the course in physics. The author lists thirty-two principles which appear in two or more of these studies and indicates the relative importance of each principle in each study.

An earlier committee report which aimed to present an outline of physics, the elements of which were selected from the point of view of life situations, is that of the North Central Association of Science and Mathematics Teachers.[19] Unfortunately, while the voluminous outline undoubtedly consists of items which would lend themselves to classroom development from the point of view of life situations, the manner in which many of them are stated differentiates them little, if at all, from topics which are likely to be developed ordinarily from the extremely academic point of view.

The reports of the Committee on Physics for the North Central Association[20] are of very great value and importance, combining, as they do, not only a carefully worked out syllabus of materials but also considerable experimental evidence showing the practical value and effectiveness of these materials when taught in the typical classroom.

5. Chemistry

Several investigations have been reported which have an important bearing upon the content of chemistry. Gerry[21] analyzed twenty-eight sets of examination questions in chemistry issued by the College Entrance Examination Board from 1916 to 1920. He lists thirty-eight topics and shows the frequency with which each appeared in these examination questions.

---

[18] Downing, Elliot R. "Techniques for the determination of basic principles in science courses." *Science Educ.*, 14: November, 1929, 298-303. (Curtis, *op. cit.*, II, 211-214.)

[19] Vestal, C. L. (Chairman). "Report of the subcommittee of the Central Association of Science and Mathematics Teachers (1920) on the content of high-school physics." *School Sci. and Math.*, 21: March, 1921, 274-279. (Curtis, *op. cit.*, I, 160-168.)

[20] Hurd, A. W. (Chairman). "Progress report on the development of teaching units in high-school physics." *North Central Association Quarterly*, 4: September, 1930; also "Additional studies relating to physics." *Ibid.*, 5: March, 1931, 471-493.

[21] Gerry, Henry Lester. "College Entrance Examination Board questions in chemistry." *School Sci. and Math.*, 20: December, 1920, 845-850. (Curtis, *op. cit.*, I, 149-153.)

Powers[22] made an elaborate study of the extent to which high-school pupils and university students master the conventional content of chemistry which they have studied. Using a battery of twelve tests in a large number of schools during a period of several years, he secured results which led him to make these conclusions and recommendations:

There is need for curricular studies looking to larger unit divisions than units of physics and chemistry. The organization of science should be such as to include science from many fields in an earlier fundamental course but each succeeding course should be related to and built upon the preceding courses.

Much of the work (and the textbook material in chemistry) is adapted only to the ability levels of the best 50 percent of the pupils.

The standings of some of the schools were so low as to suggest the entire futility of much of the high-school work which is being attempted in chemistry.

These findings emphasize the necessity for reducing the amount of ground to be covered in chemistry, to the end that the materials may be mastered.

From an extensive investigation of the overlapping of high-school and college courses in chemistry, Koos[23] arrives at these conclusions:

Although there are some differences between high-school and first college courses in chemistry, they are remarkably alike.

If the materials presented in high-school courses may be presumed to be secondary in character, there is relatively little in these first college courses not purely secondary. Moreover, if a student takes the course in general inorganic chemistry in college after having had the high-school course, which is often done, he is repeating almost all of it. Even in that relatively small proportion of higher institutions where such a student enters upon a course in general inorganic chemistry presumed to be administered for those who offered the high-school unit for admission, there must be a large amount of repetition.

Two recent studies of chemistry content by Sites[24] and by Nuser,[25] under the direction of Downing, merit consideration in the construction

[22] Powers, S. R. *A Diagnostic Study of the Subject Matter of High-School Chemistry*. New York: Teachers College, Bureau of Publications, 1924. (Curtis, *op. cit.*, I, 313-317.)

[23] Koos, L. V. "Overlapping in high school and college." *Jour. of Educ. Research*, 11: May, 1925, 322-330. (Curtis, *op. cit.*, I, 293-298.)

[24] Sites, J. T. "Chemical principles, concepts, and technical terms used in science magazines." Master's Thesis (unpublished), University of Chicago, 1930. (Curtis, *op. cit.*, II, 267-276.)

[25] Nuser, Arlee. "A study of the chemistry found in agricultural periodicals." Master's Thesis (unpublished), University of Chicago, 1927. (Curtis, *op. cit.*, II, 276-278.)

of all textbooks and syllabi in the subject. Of special value are the lists of principles and topics,[26] with their relative importance as indicated by the analyses.

There is little doubt that the most important recent influence upon the selection of instructional materials in high-school chemistry has been exerted by the Committee of Chemical Education of the American Chemical Society. As an expression of authoritative opinion by a distinguished group of university and high-school teachers, the outline is worthy of the highest commendation. It is unfortunate, however, that in reporting their work[27] the committee failed to report the technique used by them in improving their original outline. They state that at their April meeting, 1924, they "revised the 'Standard Minimum High School Course in Chemistry' so that it was as near as possible in accordance with the 30,000 criticisms which had been made available . . . during the past six months." A subsequent revision of this outline has resulted in substantial improvement, especially in reduction of material; there seems little doubt, however, that the outline still contains far too much material, in spite of the commendable practice of the committee in indicating "essential," "supplementary," and "additional" topics.

The work of the Committee on High-School Chemistry for the North Central Association of Colleges and Secondary Schools[28] is an illustration of another approach to the determination of content for high-school chemistry.

6. Miscellaneous Fields of Science

Several types of curricular studies have appeared that apply to no course exclusively but have a more or less pertinent application to every course in science. These are studies of interests, for example,

[26] These principles and topics are published only in Curtis, *op. cit.*, II, 271-275 and 277-278.

[27] Gordon, Neil E. (Chairman). "Report of the Committee of Chemical Education of the American Chemical Society." *Jour. of Chemical Educ.*, 1: May, 1924, 87-93.

[28] Lancelot, W. H. (Chairman). "The course in high-school chemistry: a progress report." *North Central Quarterly*, 5: March, 1931, 471-493.

those by Downing, Pollock, and Curtis;[29] studies of magazine and newspaper science by Curtis, Hopkins, and Searles and Ruch;[30] and a study of the consumption of food, shelter, clothing, and fuel by Harap.[31] Because of their necessarily limited scope and treatment it would not prove advisable to construct a course merely upon the items revealed by any or all of these studies, alone; the value of the findings of these various studies, therefore, probably lies chiefly in the modifying influence which they should exert on subsequent textbooks, courses, and syllabi.

---

[29] Downing, Elliott R. "Children's interest in nature materials." *The Nature Study Review*, 8: 1912, 334-338. (Curtis, *op. cit.*, I, 129-131.)

Pollock, C. A. "Children's interests as a basis of what to teach in general science." *Ohio State Univ. Educ. Research Bulletin*, 3: January 9, 1924, 3-6. (Curtis, *op. cit.*, I, 265-267.)

Curtis, Francis D. *Some Values Derived from Extensive Reading of General Science*. New York: Teachers College, Columbia University, 1924 (Out of Print). (Curtis, *op. cit.*, I, 326-333.)

[30] Curtis, Francis D. "A study of the scientific interests of dwellers in small towns and in the country." *Peabody Jour. of Educ.*, 5: 1927, 22-34. (Curtis, *op. cit.*, II, 343-348.)

Curtis, *op. cit.*, I, 318-325.

Hopkins, L. Thomas. "A study of magazine and newspaper science articles with relation to courses in science for high schools." *School Sci. and Math.*, 25: 1925, 793-800. (Curtis, *op. cit.*, II, 334-338.)

Searles, Albert H., and Ruch, Giles M. "A study of science articles in magazines." *School Sci. and Math.*, 26: 1926, 389-396. (Curtis, *op. cit.*, II, 339-342.)

[31] Harap, Henry. *The Education of the Consumer*. New York: Macmillan, 1924. (Curtis, *op. cit.*, II, 332-334.)

CHAPTER IX

CURRICULAR DEVELOPMENTS IN THE TEACHING OF SCIENCE*

I. BASES FOR DETERMINING THE CURRICULUM

The curriculum of science,[1] as well as the materials for the courses that make up the curriculum, must be determined on one of three bases: (1) best opinion regarding what sequence of courses should comprise the curriculum and what elements should make up these courses; (2) the results of such researches as shed light upon these questions; and (3) a combination of opinion and the results of research.

Despite the relatively recent origin of educational research, a creditable number of extensive and valuable investigations are already available that contribute to the solutions of problems of curricular content and sequence. These investigations are largely analyses of present practices by means of questionnaires and surveys. However, it seems likely that little progress can be expected from analyses or surveys of conditions which now exist or have existed earlier; such studies of curricular trends are primarily of historical interest. Until studies of other types—for example, learning studies and various psychological investigations—have been produced in sufficient number, the question of the selection and sequence of the courses within the curriculum must be decided chiefly by authoritative opinion.

II. THE SCIENCE CURRICULUM IN 1900

At the beginning of this century, chiefly because of the influence of the so-called 'scientific movement' of the preceding half century, there was nothing approximating a generally accepted sequence of science courses in the secondary school. Courses in bewildering variety and of an astonishing degree of technicality were found in every grade from

---

* For the Committee, by F. D. Curtis.

[1] Throughout this book, the Committee has tried to be consistent in its use of *program of studies* to designate *all* of the curricula offered in a school; of *curriculum* to designate each group of closely related courses, as those in science, mathematics, etc. The program of studies, therefore, is composed of several curricula, each of which in turn is composed of a group of related courses.

the ninth through the twelfth. Because of the lack of a generally recognized introductory course that should present facts and principles fundamental to the study of other sciences, it became necessary in each school to incorporate into the ninth-grade course—physics, chemistry, botany, zoölogy, physiography, physiology, or whatever else it might be—some materials to serve as a foundation upon which to build in the courses offered later in that school. None of these introductory courses, however, acceptably served the purpose of orienting the pupil in the field of science at large. Dissatisfaction with each of them as a foundational course spread; attention became more and more sharply focused upon the need for an introductory course of an essentially different type. Contrary, therefore, to the frequent assertion that general science was introduced into the science curriculum by enthusiasts and propagandists, the subject developed in response to this urgent need for an elementary course that should be free from obligations to any special subject and that might therefore be molded into a satisfactory introductory course for all special sciences.

III. The Development of the Course in General Science

Toward the close of the first decade of this century, therefore, courses named 'elementary science,' 'introductory science,' and 'general science' began to appear here and there as the initial courses in the science curriculum of progressive schools. These pioneer courses inevitably exhibited wide variation in content and in organization; they often conspicuously lacked in integration and in balance of materials selected from the contributing sciences. These same defects are exhibited in most of the earlier textbooks, those that began to appear about 1910. Much progress toward a solution of the problem of effective integration of materials has been shown in later textbooks and syllabi, but the present course in general science remains, like the earlier ones, disproportionately weighted in favor of the physical sciences.

1. Its Handicaps

Ever since its introduction into the curriculum general science has had to make its way in the face of decided difficulties and handicaps. Thus, there is probably no subject in the high-school program which has so frequently been assigned to inadequately prepared or totally unprepared teachers—"anybody can teach general science" has been the conviction of many administrators. Moreover, administrators who have recognized the necessity for entrusting the teaching of general science only to teachers thoroughly qualified to present it have frequently been forced to assign it to inadequately prepared teachers because no better prepared ones were available.

Considering these handicaps, together with those which inevitably arise in the process of developing a subject through the crude formative stages, it is no wonder that the results secured from general science were often disappointing; it is no wonder that administrators, as well as many teachers of science in high schools and especially in universities and colleges, regarded the subject with doubt or suspicion or open hostility. In spite of all adverse influences, however, the growing popularity of general sciences is evidenced by its rapid spread and by the increasing numbers of pupils studying it.

From the first introduction of general science its opponents have declared that its values were minor or even negative; its proponents have voiced equally emphatic opinions of the opposite nature. Such a controversy can never be settled on the basis of opinion; objective evidence must be secured. Until the educational research movement had developed sufficiently, it was impossible to secure such evidence. Within the last ten years, however, a number of investigators have attacked the problem of determining what specific values, if any, may be derived from the study of general science. Their commendable efforts have resulted in a considerable array of data which, imperfect and fragmentary as it necessarily is, nevertheless offers the best answer now available to the question, "Is the study of general science sufficiently worth while to merit a place in the science curriculum?" A very brief summary of the results of six investigations of the values of general science follows.

2. Objective Data on Its Value

From an analysis of subject matter in various textbooks of science as a means of determining the overlapping of the subject matter of general science with that of other science courses taught in the high school, Leker[2] draws this conclusion: "No other subject can give the boy or girl who quits school as much usable knowledge as general

---

[2] Leker, W. R. "The articulation of general science with special science." *School Sci. and Math.*, 25: 1925, 724-737, and *General Science Quarterly*, 9: 1925, 158-173. See also Curtis, F. D. *Second Digest of Investigations in the Teaching of Science.* Philadelphia: Blakiston, 1921, 67-70.

science in the time that is given to its teaching. On the other hand, should the pupil continue through the high school, he will have the elementary fundamentals of the special sciences and can continue in biology, chemistry, and physics just where he quit in general science."

From an investigation of the value of general science as preparation for later courses in science, Carpenter[3] reaches the conclusion that the gain in physics and chemistry for the group which had preceded the study of these subjects with the study of general science was definitely greater than the gain in English, Latin, and intermediate algebra for the same group. "It may be inferred, therefore, that this gain in physics and chemistry is due to the general science preparation, since other variables are eliminated."

Hurd[4] made a study of the mean ratings of pupils from scores in unit tests on high-school physics to compare those who had studied general science with those who had not. He reaches this conclusion:

> It seems, on the whole, that it helps to have had general science in some fields, notably electric lighting and heating, ventilating and humidifying. In more unrelated fields, there is apparently less indication. There seem to be no general abilities gained from a pursuance of general science which carry over into the field of physics. These data also show no selective function of general science to sort out students of superior ability. Any indications point merely to the seeming truth that if a group have studied certain topics, they evidence more knowledge of the field and are able to maintain the supremacy through a subsequent course in the same field.

Dvorak,[5] using tests on subject-matter knowledge of general science, investigated the relative achievement of pupils who had studied general science and other pupils who had not. He concludes: "Pupils who have not had a course in general science acquire considerable general-science information in courses in specialized sciences. Differences in central tendencies continue, however, in favor of those pupils who have had general science. . . . Achievement in the general science test shows uniformly higher scores for pupils who have had a course in general science."

---

[3] Carpenter, Harry A. "Success in physics and chemistry in relation to general science and biology." *Science Education*, 14: 1930, 589-599. (Curtis, *op. cit.*, II, 129-133.)

[4] Hurd, A. W. "Progress report on the development of teaching units in high-school physics." *North Central Assoc. Quarterly*, 5: 1930.

[5] Dvorak, August. "A study of achievement and subject matter in general science." *General Science Quarterly*, 5: 1925-1926, 289-310, 368-396, 445-474, and 525-542. (Curtis, *op. cit.*, II, 122-125.)

In an investigation of the relative achievement of ninth-grade pupils who had studied general science during the preceding year with that of other ninth-grade pupils who had not, Ashbaugh[6] found that the former group possessed a knowledge of subject matter, as revealed by scores on standardized tests, only slightly greater than the knowledge possessed by the latter group.

Cramer[7] reports an extensive investigation to determine whether general science functions in promoting the success of pupils in subsequent courses in science. He concludes:

> Pupils who have had a course in general science have more scientific information than do similar pupils who have had no such course. . . . Success in general science tends to be followed by a like success in the special sciences. . . . In this study, the . . . conclusions would imply this [that "the success of the subsequent science is caused by success in general science"] . . . The significant point for this study is the fact that there is a superior achievement in each one of the special sciences that is apparently attributable to a previous study of general science.

In sum, these researches indicate a justification for the introduction of general science into the science curriculum, since in each investigation the pupils who had previously studied general science showed measurable superiorities[8] over those who had not.

IV. The Development of a Definite Science Curriculum

The rise of general science had a marked effect upon the science curriculum. The success of the subject helped in two ways to bring about gradually a definite science sequence: first, it practically eliminated as introductory courses many subjects, conspicuously physiography, physiology, hygiene, and astronomy, that earlier had had extensive trial with unsatisfactory results; second, it concentrated and therefore intensified the competition of other science courses in the three upper years of the secondary school. In consequence it enabled

---

[6] Ashbaugh, E. J. "General science in the eighth grade or not?" *Educ. Research Bulletin, Ohio State University*, 9: 1930, 503-597. (Curtis, *op. cit.*, II, 124.)
In considering the evidence from this study it should be kept in mind that the tests were administered in October of the year following that in which the experimental group had studied general science; that is, from about four to about twelve months had elapsed since the portions of subject matter upon which the respective test items were based had been studied.

[7] Cramer, W. F. "A study of some achievements of pupils in the special sciences—general science versus non-general science groups—in the high schools of Kansas City, Missouri." *Science Education*, 14: 1930. (Curtis, *op. cit.*, II, 125-129.)

[8] With the exception of the Ashbaugh data as previously explained.

the three subjects—biology, physics, and chemistry—that demonstrated greater survival values (possibly because they were thought to possess more practical contact with everyday life, or because they were already more strongly entrenched or were more vigorously and militantly supported) gradually to reduce, almost to insignificance, the representation of all other subjects in the science curriculum of the secondary school.[9]

General science was only one factor which operated toward the establishment of a definite science sequence. Its influence cannot be separated from that of the evolving junior high school, since the rise of general science has been practically coincident with that of the junior high school, and since, moreover, the subject has been developed with an increasing regard for the aims and needs of that school.

A third factor which powerfully influenced the development of a definite science sequence is general biology, which came into the science curriculum at about the beginning of this century.[10] The history of this subject is similar to that of general science. It developed chiefly in response to a demand for an introductory course that would make possible an integration of materials selected from various biological courses, and that would therefore afford a satisfactory orientation in the field of biological science, a purpose which the introductory courses in botany, zoölogy, physiology, and hygiene had failed to fulfill. Like general science, it met with stubborn opposition from the start and has been vigorously opposed by many administrators and subject-matter specialists in high schools and especially in universities and colleges; but also like general science, it has thrived because of a growing conviction of its merits and has now firmly established its place in the science curriculum. "The special biological subjects (botany, zoölogy, and physiology) are decreasing in the number of schools offering them and in proportionate numbers of pupils registered in them. The loss in these special subjects is more than compensated by the gains in the numbers of pupils taking courses in general biology and courses in general science, of which latter subject a large part concerns biology."[11]

---

[9] It should be noted, however, that there has recently been a slight increase in the number of large school systems in which botany, zoölogy, physiology, and other specialized courses are offered in the junior and senior years.

[10] Finley, Charles W. *Biology in Secondary Schools and the Training of Biology Teachers.* New York: Teachers College, Columbia University, 1926. (Curtis, *op. cit.,* II, 137.)

[11] Finley, *op. cit.* Curtis, *op. cit.,* II, 138.

The chief results of these three influences upon the content of the science curriculum in the secondary school are indicated in the findings of an extensive study by Hunter,[12] who reports the emergence of a fairly well established sequence in the four-year senior high school by about 1920; this sequence, moreover, consisted of general science in the ninth grade; general biology, as definitely distinct from separate years or semesters of botany and zoölogy, in the tenth; and physics and chemistry, offered in either the eleventh or twelfth grades.

The establishment of this definite sequence was, however, considerably retarded by confusion resulting from the curricular needs which have developed with the evolution of the junior high school, and which have affected chiefly the placement of general science. In the 8-4 organization general science and biology have rapidly strengthened their positions in the ninth and tenth grades, respectively. In the junior-high-school grades in school systems organized on the 6-6 or 6-3-3 plans, however, there is manifest a growing tendency to offer science in all three grades, though in these schools practice varies greatly with respect both to the grade or the semester in which the work in science is begun and to the number of years or half-years of science which are required. Undoubtedly much confusion has resulted from the earlier lack of acceptable instructional material for use in the seventh, eighth, and ninth grades. It is only recently that textbook writers have recognized the opportunities offered by these grades. The tendency that has been most in evidence in the junior high school has been to accept for the seventh and eighth grades the texts in general science that have been written for the ninth grade and to accept for the ninth grade the texts in general biology that have been written for the tenth grade. It is clear that such a program is not acceptable to this Committee. Courses developed for the senior high school cannot be accepted as satisfactory for the junior high school.

V. The Committee's Recommendations for Grades Seven, Eight, and Nine

The Committee recognizes two important functions in the course in science for Grades VII, VIII, and IX: first, to give such a background of learning that it will enable the pupil to adjust himself intelligently to the phenomena of experience; second, to furnish an

---

[12] Hunter, G. W. "Is there a sequence in secondary science?" *School and Society*, 20: 1924, 762-766. (Curtis, *op. cit.*, I, 309-312.)

introduction to the major fields of science, to the end that the pupil may become so well acquainted with these fields that he will be able, with some assurance, to determine in which branch or branches he may later desire to do more specialized work. In order that these functions may be served, it is essential that the work in science for these grades be so organized that these functions are definitely recognized. As stated in Chapter I, the work of these grades should be so organized as to develop for the learner the largest possible understanding of the principles and generalizations of science that function in human thought and behavior. In developing instructional materials for these grades, textbook writers must focus attention upon the needs of the children and on the functions to be served by the schools designed for this level.

It is unfortunate that the content of the present course in general science remains, as it has been from the first, largely physical in nature; that the forces of conservatism and inertia have thus far rendered ineffective all attempts to bring about in this subject a more even balance between the physical and the biological sciences. The course throughout these grades should offer more opportunity for a study of living things in their physical environment. With the constantly increasing demand for a three-year integrated sequence for the seventh, eighth, and ninth grades, the opportunity is offered for an enrichment of the present content of general science to include more biological material.

The Committee wishes again to emphasize its recommendation in Chapter I that the work of the seventh, eighth, and ninth grades be organized as an integrated sequence and that the same point of view be followed in planning the work for these grades, irrespective of whether the school is organized on the 8-4 or the 6-6 plan. Recognition of the special subjects, such as biology, physics, and chemistry, does not offer a proper criterion for the selection of content for the intermediate school. The challenging phenomena of experience arise from observation of living things (of which the pupil is one) in a physical environment. The work in science that is offered below the level that marks the beginning of specialization (the tenth grade) should be organized about those principles and generalizations of science, knowledge of which contributes directly to understanding of the adaptations of living things to their physical environment.

VI. The Committee's Recommendations for Grades Ten, Eleven, and Twelve

The point of view that is guiding in the planning of the public-school system and the trends in curricular developments support the foregoing recommendations. The science curriculum of the first nine grades deals with unspecialized science. The objectives of these grades are selected so that their progressive attainment gives to the pupil an increasingly enlarged ability (1) to interpret the scientific phenomena of common experiences, (2) to think clearly in problematic situations in which ideas from the field of science are used, (3) to use as need arises the methods of study that have been developed in the field of science, and (4) to gain some appreciation of the scientific attitudes that have functioned in freeing mankind from fears and from the errors in thinking that stand in the way of happiness and rich living.

The offering in science for the tenth, eleventh, and twelfth grades is one of electives. The objectives of each elective science are selected from a special field of science. The subjects most frequently recognized are general biology, physics, and chemistry. General biology is the first specialized course in biological science, and physics is recommended as the first specialized course in physical science. Chemistry should follow physics and these two courses should be planned so that at least in some features they may constitute an integrated sequence. Where it is practicable to offer in the senior high school more than one year of biological science, the values of courses in botany, zoölogy, or physiology are not questioned. It should be recognized, however, that such courses are of value primarily to the pupil who already possesses an extensive, even though elementary, knowledge of the entire field and who desires to pursue the subject further with more highly specialized work. These specialized courses in botany and in zoölogy are, therefore, coming to be offered only as advanced work for which the course in general science and general biology are prerequisite.

In the larger high schools equipped to offer an extensive and varied science curriculum, courses in astronomy, physiography, botany, zoölogy, physiology, or geology may profitably be added to the more conventional list of courses, which includes general science, biology, physics, and chemistry. The former courses should be planned for pupils interested in securing a more intimate acquaintance with a limited field of science; they should in all cases be elective, and should be available only to pupils in the twelfth or perhaps in the eleventh and twelfth grades; in no cases should their election be permitted as a substitute for biology, physics, or chemistry in fulfilling the requirements for a two-year or a three-year science sequence.

In smaller school systems it is frequently impracticable administratively to offer both physics and chemistry in the same year. It is therefore recommended that in such schools these courses be offered in alternate years.

In most schools it is impracticable to limit the enrollment of pupils in a given science course to one grade. This Committee, therefore, recommends that general biology be open to election by pupils in the tenth, eleventh, and twelfth grades, and that physics and chemistry be elective in the eleventh and twelfth grades. For the pupil desiring a year both of physics and of chemistry, it is believed preferable to elect physics before chemistry.

In some schools the practice is followed of offering general science as a substitute 'college-entrance' subject in lieu of one of the specialized science courses, such as general biology, physics, or chemistry. In these schools these introductory courses are administered in the same manner as the more advanced, specialized courses, even in some cases to the extent of a provision for seven periods per week (including two double laboratory periods). The Committee disapproves this practice, which it considers contrary to the aims and purposes of this elementary and introductory course. It is the opinion of the Committee that general science or junior-high-school science should be required of all pupils, whether or not they continue their education beyond the years in which this science is offered, and that it should be considered as a foundation, but never as a substitute, for general biology, physics, chemistry, or any other specialized course.

The Committee condemns the practice followed in some secondary schools of allowing pupils in the tenth, eleventh, or twelfth grade to elect general science after they have studied one or more of the three advanced science courses. This introductory course can provide little of value to the pupil who elects it after having studied one of the specialized sciences.

Realizing the administrative difficulties which accompany the offering of courses of more than five periods per week, this Committee recommends that in all schools in which the periods are at least fifty-five minutes 'in the clear,' the courses in advanced biology, physics, and chemistry be offered only five periods per week.

This Committee voices its unqualified condemnation of the practice, followed in certain schools organized on the 8-4, 7-4, and 6-6 plans, of assigning the teaching of general science in the seventh and eighth grades or in the eighth grade to the regular eighth-grade teacher who is without adequate subject-matter preparation and who is in some cases even without any subject-matter training in science whatever. The course in general science which is given under these conditions is commonly merely a reading course, without demonstration or experimentation of any kind, and can in no sense be considered a satisfactory or desirable course in science; in fact, from the standpoint of desired objectives of science work, such a course would better be omitted entirely from the program of studies. The Committee also condemns the practice, too frequently noted, of assigning a course in biology to a teacher who has had obviously insufficient or no subject-matter training in the field of biology.

CHAPTER X
THE PROGRAM OF SCIENCE IN THE ELEMENTARY SCHOOL*

In Chapter III the educational values of science are discussed. In Chapter IV the objectives of science for a program of general education are defined and discussed. In these chapters may be found statements of values of science, many of which conform to the purpose of the elementary school.

In the past there has been a tendency to restrict the curriculum to the so-called 'fundamentals,' or '3 R's.' At present there is a definite trend in industrial nations toward the inclusion of liberal training in the program of studies for the elementary school. This is illustrated in courses of study of recent issue in the United States[1] and in the new combine schools of Russia, the modern *Volksschule* of Germany, and the Decroly type of school in Belgium. The present movement is towards including science as a part of this liberal training in universal education.

The Necessity for Selecting Content for Science Teaching

The first task in developing a course of study in science for the elementary school is the problem of selection of content. It is obvious that not all of science can be taught. The curriculum-maker must select the science with a realization of the place and function of the elementary school in modern society.

The primary purpose of science in the elementary school is like that of other subjects—that of assisting boys and girls to become educated laymen. The acceptance of this purpose assists greatly in defining the content of science. In the past great stress has been placed upon the vocational side of science. Some have insisted on directing the instruction towards training boys and girls to become naturalists and scientists; some have pointed to the values of courses in elementary agriculture; others have insisted on giving the sort of material which would assist children in vocations closely allied with science.

* For the Committee, by Gerald S. Craig.
[1] For example, in New York, New Jersey, Pennsylvania, Baltimore, St. Louis, Cleveland, and the Horace Mann School of Teachers College.

Periods of unemployment and the realization that production has surpassed consumption indicate the futility of making the elementary school into a vocational training school. Children of ages six to twelve are unable to choose their vocation, and superintendents or educational advisors can scarcely select their life work for them. In Russia, a country in which an attempt is being made to become industrialized in a short space of time, there may be justification for the training of skilled workers in the elementary grades. There we find an unprecedented demand for workers of all kinds. If Russia does attain that purpose, it is quite likely she will have to modify her elementary schools thereafter.

In the United States, at any rate, we must consider what boys and girls need in becoming educated laymen. What is the function of science in the lives of educated people?

OBJECTIVES DERIVED FROM THE GREAT CONCEPTS OF SCIENCE

It is not only to the physical side of our living and the benefits and comforts that have been attained by man that we must look for our curricular material. Science is more than just a body of knowledge; it has developed concepts the effects of which are not limited to the field of science itself. Some concepts, because of their direct relations to human interest and human welfare, have modified thinking in many fields. Many of these concepts, when understood, greatly modify the thought reactions of the individual. The breadth of view of an individual and his attitude toward everyday problems are often changed when he comprehends certain scientific generalizations. These concepts are of fundamental importance to laymen as well as to scientists. Many of them have been secured as a result of infinite toil and even actual persecution. The race had been thousands of years in development before it discovered them. They are a part of the priceless heritage that must be passed on to future generations, and they are fundamental to intelligent living. They should not be treasured away in libraries, known only to a few specialists, but rather should be understood by the masses.

From these considerations we may secure our first criterion for selection of objectives for the elementary school, as follows:

Certain objectives that are selected for elementary science should conform to those conceptions (1) that greatly influence the thinking of the individuals who learn their meaning, and (2) that have modified thinking in many fields outside of science.

The following statements[2] will illustrate this criterion:

1. The earth is very old as measured in terms of our units of time.
2. The surface of the earth has not always had its present appearance and is constantly changing.
3. Space is vast.
4. The earth has been developed as a result of the action of natural forces.
5. The sun is the original source of energy for the earth.
6. The earth's position and relation to the sun and moon are of great importance to the life of the earth.
7. All life has evolved from very simple forms.
8. Species have survived because by adaptations and adjustments they have tended to become better fitted to the conditions under which they live.
9. The physical environment has great influence, not only upon the structural forms of life, but also upon society.
10. Man has modified plant and animal forms through a knowledge of methods found in nature.
11. Through interdependence of species and struggle for existence there tends to be maintained a balance among the many forms of life.
12. Chemical and physical changes are manifestations of energy.

The studies by which these statements have been selected and evaluated are described in Chapter IV. Most of them are as suggestive of objectives in the junior high school as in the elementary grades.

At first thought, it would appear that these concepts of science could have no part in the elementary-school program. Examination, however, reveals in many of them essential meanings that are distinctly upon elementary-school levels. For example, "Species have survived because by adaptations and adjustments they have tended to become better fitted to the conditions under which they live,"[3] involves such matters as migration, hibernation, parental care, and social life of animals.

Migration becomes not a mere matter of instruction concerning birds flying south, but rather of how migration is a means of adaptation to the environment. Parental care becomes not only an observation of how certain animals take care of their young, but how parental care has assisted some animals to survive. Each essential meaning is

---

[2] In order to simplify the discussion, the objectives of science teaching in the elementary school are stated as declarative sentences. See Footnote 1, Chapter IV.

[3] A more detailed analysis of this is given in Chapter XI.

directed towards the larger concept. This concept is large enough to provide learning on all levels, including those of adult life. One may continue to learn new facts about the concept of adaptation even though he study all his life. There can be continuous growth for the individual in the direction of the increasingly enlarged understanding of this concept.

Migration, social life, hibernation, parasitism, and coloration, then, may be considered as biological themes which form an integral part of the larger concept of adaptation. The content of these themes becomes more challenging in learning as it becomes directed toward this larger objective; the teacher has improved her technique of teaching when she causes the children to see the theme in relation to the concept, and the principle or meaning involved becomes associated with its various aspects and in turn becomes a means of interpreting many new phenomena. The real aim should not be to teach the child facts about life habits of animals, but rather to make the basal concepts acceptable and challenging to the child, to cause them to emerge more clearly, and to give opportunity for their use in the interpretation of new phenomena.

It may seem to those who have little experience with this point of view in elementary science that directing the learning in each grade toward the larger concepts is a more or less visionary notion; they forget that the concept is really inherent in each of these themes. In a treatment of seasonal change in the primary grades the challenge, in the language of the child, may be "How do plants and animals prepare for winter?" This is a challenge pointing directly to adaptation and adjustment. It takes no botanist or zoölogist to see the association that is essential to the development of this theme. The same is true with such topics as "How animals care for their young" or "How some animals coöperate with each other." The teacher may never use the terms 'adaptation' and 'adjustment'; rather the discussion involves bulbs, leaf-coloring, leaf fall, leaf scar, hibernation, migration, building homes, nursing young, etc. These latter are concrete examples of the concepts that lie within the observations and experiences of children, but the children should be directed in their studies, to the end that the relationships become apparent. Directing the activities of children towards the significant and profound concepts of modern life is not visionary. It is being achieved by many classroom teachers at the present time.

Certain objectives may be listed which are closely associated with the development of scientific attitudes.[4] Seven illustrations are:

1. Man's conception of truth changes.
2. It is desirable to have confidence in the scientific method.
3. Nature's principles are invariable.
4. There is a cause for every effect.
5. Much knowledge remains to be discovered.
6. Conditions favorable to life are apt to persist on the earth for a very long time; no catastrophe for the entire earth is probable for immense periods of time.
7. Man has become an important determining factor of the environment of many forms of life. His continued existence and advancement are dedependent upon his wise modification and control of the environment.

These seven principles are next discussed in order and in relation to learning experiences in which they may be illustrated.

(1) One can hardly expect an individual fully to accept "Man's conception of truth changes" without being open-minded. Frequently the instruction of the elementary school, and probably of all levels, has carried with it the implication that it was the truth for all time. The teachings of Aristotle were considered for centuries to be the truth, even to the point of defying the individual to doubt them. One of the greatest discoveries of science has been that our concepts may change. What may seem to be true to-day may not seem to be true to-morrow. In science instruction, teachers should teach the facts, principles, and hypotheses which are most acceptable to scientific authorities; at the same time, the pupils should realize, as a result of the instruction, that many of our concepts have changed in the past and will probably change in the future.

There is a large body of content for this objective. It may be clarified through a study of any number of topics such as:

How should we ventilate our schoolroom?
Why do birds migrate?
What is the atmosphere?
How do scientists explain the formation of the earth?
Is the earth moving?

Indeed, almost any body of content in science can be used in developing this concept. It should permeate science instruction in the elementary school. Children should realize that some of the explanations of natural phenomena taught them in the school may not be acceptable

---

[4] An outline of scientific attitudes is given in Chapter IV.

at a later time. In this lies one of the great contributions of elementary science to society.

(2) The child should have confidence in the scientific method, not only for his own good, but also for the welfare of society of which he is a part. There is plenty of contemporary and historical content to use in developing this confidence in scientific method. Thus, the work of such scientific agencies as the United States Weather Bureau and the United States Biological Survey can be emphasized. Children should be taught the importance of getting information from reliable sources. This instruction can be associated with many topics, of which the following are a few:

How to be healthy.
How we may decide whether a plant or animal should be protected or exterminated.
Gardening.
Extermination of pests.
Introduction of new species.
The balance in nature.
Weather.

(3) "Nature's principles are invariable." There is order in nature. The principles operate, not because of luck or omens or superstitions, but because of natural causes. This objective can be associated with almost any science unit in the elementary school.

(4) "There is a cause for every effect." Science in the elementary school is concerned with interpreting natural phenomena, and the child in the early grades becomes acquainted with certain natural forces operating as causes and associates them with various phenomena that may be seen as effects. As he comes to accept the relationship of cause and effect, he no longer looks to magic and superstition in explaining the events that occur about him. Although he will probably explain but a small part of the natural environment, still he comes to the very important understanding that there is a natural cause for everything.

(5) "Much knowledge remains to be discovered." The child can look forward to a future when man will know more about himself and his environment. The teacher need not hesitate to say that there are many things that the scientist has not explained satisfactorily to himself. This objective is obviously related to the attitude of open-mindedness.

(6) and (7). The last two objectives bear directly upon the scientific attitudes in reference to man's own possibilities and potentialities. Man has been pessimistic about the future of the earth and the future of mankind. He has been constantly prophesying doom for the entire earth. The volcanos or the shooting stars have been seen as demons of destruction in punishment of sins. But now the geophysicist studies the interior of the earth and the astronomer studies the heavens, and neither foresees destruction for the entire earth for immense periods of time. There is no evidence that the cosmos is filled with demons that are unfriendly to man's welfare. By the study of natural phenomena man can utilize natural forces for his own well-being. Man probably has ample opportunity for working out whatever good is in him.

All of these concepts related to attitudes have a part in the work of the elementary schools. They are, of course, not to be taught verbatim or learned as catechisms. They may be made acceptable to the child through a variety of content, including the study of the air, the stars, plants, animals, and the earth. These concepts are so important that they should be introduced into the early grades. Many primary teachers, in fact, have had considerable success in introducing these ideas to children. The content of science, then, can be useful in developing scientific attitudes, and it is in this field that the elementary-school teacher will undoubtedly develop a new chapter in education.

OBJECTIVES FUNCTIONING IN ESTABLISHING HEALTH, ECONOMY, AND SAFETY

A second criterion may be stated as follows:

Certain objectives that are selected for science in the elementary school should conform to those goals (information, skills, and habits) in science that are important because of their function in establishing health, economy, and safety in private and public life.

This criterion has been acceptable as an aim in education. Much of elementary science is basic to the health knowledge that is needed by the individual. It is not sufficient to give the child the rules of health. He must have some of the scientific background of the rules and he must know the reasons for obeying them.

Science has a very close relation to the economic problems that have faced man within recent years. Man has become an important determining factor in the environment of life. His continued existence and advancement are dependent upon his wise modification and control of the environment. In a few centuries he has greatly changed the North American continent. He has drained swamps, cut down forests, built cities, introduced exotic species, exterminated certain indigenous ones, built artificial lakes, changed the course of streams, and altered the original balance of nature. Not all of these things have been done wisely; some of them have brought disasters. In many cases it is after the damage has been done that man has sought scientific advice.

The future will demand a utilization of science in the multitude of problems that involve the life of man. He cannot continue to be ignorant of the web of life in which, as one of the species of animals, he is by nature involved. The change from a haphazard development of natural resources must eventually give way to an intelligent plan, backed by accurate scientific information. Little can be accomplished until the masses of the people have a feeling of confidence in the scientific method. This is a task for the elementary school and can be done by instruction in the relationship of the animate and inanimate, of the extensive linkages and interdependence of living things, and the importance of accurate information in dealing with the world's problems.

Some of the objectives which satisfy this criterion are the following:

1. Man has become an important determining factor in the environment of many forms of life. His continued existence and advancement are dependent upon his wise modification and control of the environment.
2. The earth has been developed as a result of the action of natural forces.
3. Species have survived because by adaptations and adjustments they have tended to become better fitted to the conditions under which they live.
4. The physical environment has great influence, not only upon the structural form of life, but also upon society.
5. Man has modified plant and animal forms through a knowledge of nature's methods.
6. There is a very great variety and range in the size, structure, and habits of organisms.
7. Through interdependence of species and struggle for existence there tends to be maintained a balance among the many forms of life.
8. Life is dependent upon certain materials and conditions.
9. All life comes from life.
10. Efficient living is dependent upon knowledge of the principles of health and sanitation.
11. The earth and its life are greatly affected by the ocean of air which completely surrounds it.

12. In industry and in the home man can accomplish more in less time by the use of machines.
13. Heredity is responsible for many of the differences between parents and offspring as well as the resemblances.

OBJECTIVES DERIVED FROM CHALLENGING CONTENT

A third criterion may be stated thus:

Certain objectives that are selected for elementary science should conform to those facts, principles, generalizations, and hypotheses of science that are essential to the interpretation of the natural phenomena that commonly challenge children.

Studies of children's interests reveal the challenge that comes from the interpretation of natural phenomena. The wise teacher will utilize these interests. A study of them reveals certain principles, an understanding of which is essential for interpretation of the challenging phenomena. The teacher will need to guide the child in his attempt to interpret his observations and experiences, and she will best be able to do this by having knowledge of the accepted principles of science.

Some of the concepts or generalizations that satisfy this criterion and that have not been listed already under the first and second criteria are:

1. There are fewer than one hundred elements.
2. Every substance is one of the following: (a) an element, (b) a chemical compound, (c) a mechanical mixture.
3. Light is indispensable to life. The phenomena that have been discovered concerning light and the applications that have been made are important to man's continued progress.
4. Sound is caused by waves that are produced by a vibrating body and that can affect the auditory nerves of the ear.
5. Gravitation is the attraction between bodies. It has profound influence upon the movements of astronomical bodies.
6. Any machine, no matter how complicated, may be analyzed into a few simple types of machine.
7. The properties of the different elements depend upon the number and arrangement of the electrons and protons contained in their atoms.
8. All matter is probably electrical in structure.
9. The applications of electricity and magnetism in the home and industry have revolutionized the methods of living of many people.

Some of these generalizations will probably have little application prior to the junior high school. Even so, there is much knowledge and there are certain attitudes that can be acquired in the elementary school that are fundamental to the understanding of these principles in the higher school grades.

Interpretation of Phenomena Rather Than Object Lessons

Courses of study in elementary science have frequently consisted of items which are very indefinite as to the amount of learning involved. Characteristic items of this type have been names of animate and inanimate objects, such as 'insects,' 'food,' 'sun,' 'soils,' 'trees,' 'minerals,' and 'frogs.' Unfortunately, such topics have been frequently used as the constructional units with which the courses of study in elementary science or nature study have been built. They are indefinite because they are not specifically related to the children's needs and can scarcely be considered challenging either to teachers or children. As listed they might as easily imply a treatment on the college as on the elementary-school level. The teacher needs to know what phases of such topics may reasonably be expected to come within the range of the child's experiences and what ones are essential to his development.

Listing objects in that way, instead of essential meanings, as the constructional units of the course of study has encouraged the continuance of the object-lesson and of 'busy work' in the elementary school. The word 'beaver,' for instance, does not imply a definite objective. The lesson might deal with the physiology of the beaver, the structure of the beaver, the habitat of the beaver, the economic value of the beaver or the social life of the beaver. This bare listing of objects to which we are objecting is in part a result of object-lesson teaching and in part a result of the attempt to emphasize the identification of objects in the environment of the child.

Some persons seem to take for granted that children cannot generalize and cannot interpret, that they can only make an acquaintance with their environment, and hence that only in the maturer high-school years should the interpretation of nature's principles take a place in the curriculum.

But children do draw conclusions, though, to be sure, they are not conclusions of the adult level. The teacher can assist the child to make correct generalizations instead of allowing him to absorb current unscientific conceptions and superstitious ideas. Adults have not appreciated the intrinsic value of the child's simple generalizations just because they are so elementary; yet, in terms of the child's own growth, the simple interpretation may be just as significant as some complicated fact learned in adult life. The simple generalizations of childhood are, moreover, frequently fundamental to basic scientific conceptions.

The fundamental purpose of elementary science as expressed in this material is to guide the child in interpreting the phenomena of the environment in the broader sense. The course of study should utilize elements of learning involving interpretation or meanings, and should state these elements in the form of declarative sentences. The advantage in using declarative sentences is that the curricular element is then made specific as to the learning involved.

The wise teacher can appreciate the growth of the child, even though the stages of growth may be minute as measured by adult standards. The curriculum-maker has here an opportunity of service to the elementary school by making teachers conscious of the stages of growth in interpreting natural environment, by use of such meaningful statements as:

Stars are suns.
Stars are in the sky during the day as well as at night.
Some birds fly south in the autumn.

These define the content and assist greatly in grade placement, not a small matter at a time when the elementary curriculum is overloaded and the classroom teacher is expected to teach all the subjects. This point of view of elementary science does not deny the importance of identification and observation, but it recognizes them only as means to the end in view, the interpretation of phenomena. We must not, then, be content in the elementary school with the mere naming of objects and the mere observing of them.

Studies that have been made of laymen's judgments and children's questions (Chapter IV) indicate the great value of interpretation. Children's questions are not necessarily concerned with the trivial; frequently they involve the profound questions that scientific authorities cannot always answer. *It is quite likely that the lack of recognition of natural science in the elementary school has been due to the inanity of the activities proposed by our courses of study and by the lack of any challenge in the content that has characterized so much of our subject matter.*

DETERMINING THE ESSENTIAL MEANINGS

The curriculum-maker, having selected and evaluated the objectives, must translate them into terms suitable for the elementary school. The first task is to analyze the objective to find what is involved in it—what its constituents are. The component parts or elements can then be studied in terms of the child's needs, experiences, observations, and abilities. These constituent parts of the larger objective may then become the learning elements of the elementary-school curriculum.

Source treatises written by authorities in developing the concept or principle that one is analyzing may be studied to determine what central, or key, meanings the author discloses or implies. Some of these key meanings are extremely elementary, so simple that no previous learning elements are essential to their comprehension, and they may be acquired by simple observations that the child may make. These elements may be elementary enough to go into the primary grades.

Thus, if one analyzes the concept, or larger objective, "space is vast"[5] in authoritative treatises, one will find such simple elements of learning indicated as the following:

1. Of all the heavenly bodies, the sun and the moon are the most easily seen from the earth.
2. During the day we see the sun, sometimes the moon.
3. At night we see the stars and sometimes the moon.
4. The sun gives heat to the earth.
5. The sun gives light to the earth.
6. Light comes to the earth from the moon.
7. The lighted portion of the moon that we see gradually grows smaller after the period of the full moon.
8. The sun, moon, and stars rise in the east and set in the west.

These elements are exceedingly simple. They may be based on observation; no previous knowledge of astronomy is essential to their understanding; indeed, they were not even established by an astronomical science. One might say that they are statements of phenomena as they appear to the untutored. They have meaning to the child as well as to the astronomer. Such elements of learning can be placed in the primary grades.

Most of the key meanings secured by analysis of the astronomical treatises are not so simple as those just illustrated. Observations alone will not necessarily convince the child that the sun and stars are larger than the earth or that the earth rotates. To the child the earth seems

---

[5] The analysis of this objective into meanings, from simple and elementary ones that are suggestive of primary work to those which are more complicated and difficult and suggestive of junior-high-school work, is illustrative of what can be done with other objectives.

larger than any other object and the center about which all other bodies revolve. It took man many centuries to arrive at certain of our fundamental truths. Our terminology of common celestial phenomena, coming down as it has from the days of geocentric ideas, may now prove confusing to children, as for example, 'sunrise' and 'sunset.' Great emphasis upon Agassiz's advice to study nature, not books, as the essential method of nature study has been at times unfortunate. Thus the child will hold a geocentric conception of the universe if he be left to base his interpretations upon his own individual observations. There is a place in the science program of the elementary school for supplementary books, visual instructional material, and a well-informed teacher.

The child will not discover many of the great scientific truths by himself. Isolated and untrained observations cannot be relied upon for the development of dependable understandings; we cannot rely upon the folk lore of nature, and accept such assertions as that toads cause warts or that horse hairs in water troughs develop into snakes. It is not likely that children will discover for themselves the great heritage accumulated by the race.

The child must realize that there is a great body of tested knowledge, and he must appreciate the importance of seeking information from reliable authorities. One function of the school is to give the child the method of securing precise information.

We find, then, in the key truths developed by the scientist a number of elements which may be made acceptable to children but which cannot be based on empirical observation. The following are examples of this type:

1. The sun is much farther from the earth than is the moon.
2. The light on the moon comes from the sun.
3. Our sun is a star.
4. The sun is larger than the earth.
5. The earth revolves about the sun.
6. Day and night are caused by rotation of the earth on its axis.
7. The stars are separated by very great distances.
8. Some stars are very much larger than our sun.

Listing of these elements of learning which are essential to the understanding of the larger principle or concept gives an array which is very suggestive to both curriculum-maker and teacher. Certain meanings must be learned earlier than others. Some of these may be less involved and will require less previous learning. They are challenging to children. Some of them may be basic to the understanding of others. Three examples follow:

The statement, The earth rotates upon its axis, defines a basic element for the understanding of a number of meanings, among which are the following:

1. The earth rotates on its axis every twenty-four hours, causing day and night.
2. The stars seem to move from east to west during the night because of the rotation of the earth on its axis.
3. The rising and setting of the sun and moon are due to the daily rotation of the earth on its axis.
4. On an average, the moon rises about fifty minutes later each day.
5. Time differs in different parts of the earth.

A knowledge of the approximate shape of the earth is basic to the comprehension of many meanings, of which the following are examples:

1. When it is day on one half of the earth, it is night on the other half.
2. Only one half of the earth can be lighted by the sun at one time.
3. The earth rotates on its axis once every twenty-four hours, thus causing day and night.

The concept of one body revolving about another is fundamental to a complete understanding of a number of meanings. The following are a few of this type:

1. Phases of the moon are due to its revolution around the earth.
2. The moon rotates on its axis in the same length of time in which it revolves around the earth.
3. The same side of the moon is always toward the earth.
4. The moon follows the earth around the sun.
5. Change of seasons is due to the revolution of the earth around the sun and to the tilting of its axis toward the path that it follows as it revolves around the sun.
6. The earth is one of a number of heavenly bodies that revolve around the sun.

An analysis of this astronomical objective illustrates the fact that there is a natural order in the learning elements in science. The analyses of other objectives reveal a similar array. Some meanings must precede others because they are basic. The arraying of these elements from the simple and elementary ones to the complicated and more difficult assists greatly in grade placement.

Function of Essential Meanings

There has been a recent tendency in the elementary school to condemn the teaching of information. This has been due in part to the effort to break away from the unfortunate practice of considering the child's mind a storehouse to be filled with information which he might need at some future time. Attitudes, appreciations, and methods have been proposed as more satisfactory goals for the elementary school. It is unfortunate that with the attempt to break away from the process of pouring in content, there has come an attempt to minimize significant content itself.

We need to discriminate between meanings and facts. In science, meanings are keys to the interpretation of phenomena. They may be made acceptable to the learner through a body of context or facts. The facts may or may not be important to the learner. The meanings, however, are functional in a number of situations. One may be ignorant of some of the context. The central meaning, however, may be very essential in a liberal education.

The fact that the earth rotates is an essential meaning. It unlocks an entire series of everyday phenomena.[6] They are equally worth-while in Maine and California. The meaning can be made acceptable through its function in interpreting phenomena. It takes on perma-nence in the thought reactions of the individual as a result of giving new experiences which are to be interpreted in its terms. In this lies the opportunity for exercise. It is not enough to introduce and make acceptable the explanation of evaporation and condensation in the intermediate grades. There will be numerous experiences arising during the year in which the children may have opportunity to use their learn-ing in order to explain events in the schoolroom. The teacher should see that the new experiences involving condensation and evaporation are utilized as opportunities for the exercise of the learning elements that have already been made. With the simple interpretations of natural phenomena dealt with in the elementary school, the teacher can provide for frequency of occurrence.

SELECTION OF ILLUSTRATIVE MATERIAL

Emphasis on meanings and elements of learning as the blocks, or constructional units, out of which the curriculum should be built, in-stead of objects, animate and inanimate, raises the question as to the place of plants, animals, rocks, and stars in such a program. The an-swer is that they form the illustrative material for the elements of

---

[6] Downing, Elliott R. *The Supervision of Nature Study.* "The Supervision of Elementary Subjects." Appleton, 1929, p. 487.

learning. Each meaning is illustrated by something in nature, frequently by a host of materials. It becomes the curriculum-maker's task to acquaint the teacher with the type of illustrative material best suited to the meanings to be developed. It becomes the task of the teacher to manipulate the environment in such a way as to utilize the illustrative material efficiently in assisting the children in the learning process.

Considerable discussion has been raised as to the use of exotic materials in the elementary grades. Some have contended that no illustrative material should be used except that which is in the natural environment of the school. This seems to be a very narrow interpretation of illustrative material. In this age in which the child listens to events happening in Antarctica or other far parts of the earth, in which his environment is spreading out so that the whole world comes into his home in one way or another, to restrict the illustrative material to local, indigenous objects seems, indeed, to be inexcusable.

There is no reason why both indigenous and exotic material should not have their part to play in the elementary school. There is every good reason why the thing at hand, the familiar example, the thing which the child can experience, should be utilized in illustrating scientific meanings. But to limit the city child to the animals of his native environment is depriving him of what is indeed very challenging. Some of the most interesting animals to the child are the prehistoric ones which cannot possibly be seen alive by the child and can never enter the classroom.

Material illustrative of meanings in science can be selected on the basis of study. This is the task of the curriculum-maker. He can suggest illustrative material best suited to develop the various meanings in the course of study.

For example, "The Social Life of Animals" is a theme that appears in courses of study. This theme must be illustrated by animals. The first task is to find what is involved in the social life of animals; that is, its various aspects. One must turn, at this point, for help to the authorities in this particular field. By analyzing their reports and writings, one will find certain meanings which may be developed. The following are illustrative of these meanings:

1. Some animals lead social lives.
2. In some cases this social life aids them to protect themselves against the weather.

3. Some animals unite in fighting and protecting themselves against their enemies.

4. Some animals unite in establishing homes, such as quarters for winter or homes for rearing young.

5. Some animals unite in gathering food for common use.

6. Some animals unite for entire life periods.

7. Some animals live together but do not help each other (mere toleration).

8. Community life has probably aided some animals in the struggle for existence.

9. Many animals live a great portion of their lives alone—such animals are called 'solitary.'

Having secured the meanings inherent in the theme, "social life," the curriculum-maker may next select the illustrative material satisfactory for the development of the theme for the child. Analysis of the writings of the authorities of social life of animals will indicate various animals illustrating each of the meanings.

In this case, there are certain animals which are indigenous, and some of these may be brought with impunity into the classroom. Observation bee-hives and ant hills may be installed, since bees and ants illustrate various meanings listed above.

It is important in choosing illustrative material that the negative illustrations be represented. In the case of community life, it is the so-called 'solitary' animals. It is not enough to teach only the animals which fully illustrate the central theme. It is important that more than one aspect of the theme be represented. Otherwise the child may get the idea that the theme is applicable to all animals.

Similar analysis of treatises by authorities[7] concerning means of protection among animals reveals the illustrative material for "How Animals Protect Themselves."

In this case the curriculum-maker will mention such means as protective coloring, hiding, escape by hopping, jumping, dodging, flying, ferocious appearance, sudden hop, reproducing abundantly, life spent underground, small size, peculiar shape, hard wing and exterior, distasteful odor, night activity, stinging, biting, clawing, defense in colony organization, selection of isolated and protected places for homes, behavior of parents by attracting enemies away from young, assuming death-feigning attitudes, and acute senses, such as hearing and smelling. Most of these can be illustrated by animals within the environment of the child, but the exotic should be utilized when it illustrates the theme more meaningfully than the indigenous.

An analysis of the theme, "How Animals Care for Their Young," discloses a number of aspects. Some animals care for their young in

---

[7] Pearse, Arthur S. *Animal Ecology.* McGraw Hill: New York, 1926.

one way; others utilize other methods. Some may take little care, others great care of their young. Some of the meanings which may be developed are the following:

1. Some animals take little care of their young.
2. Some animals take great care of their young, even teaching them how to care for themselves.
3. In the case of some animals there are many young, and these receive little or no care from their parents.
4. Some animals produce only one or very few offspring at one time, which they care for very carefully, feeding and protecting them until they are able to care for themselves.
5. Animals which have milk glands for feeding their young are called 'mammals.'
6. In the case of some animals, only the males care for the young.
7. In the case of some animals, only the females care for the young.
8. In the case of some animals, both parents care for the young, sharing the duties between them.
9. In the case of some animals, the young are carried about after they are born.

Such meanings as these will indicate to those making syllabi in elementary science the kinds of animals needed for illustrating a central theme.

It is important that information about man be used to illustrate the themes of science. Man prepares for seasonal change, cares for his young, protects himself, and lives in communities. The themes will be enriched by illustrations within the child's own personal experience.

The teacher should bear in mind, in selecting illustrative material, that the important thing is to develop the meanings rather than the giving of object lessons. The skillful teacher will give opportunity for the child to choose illustrative material.

A Continuous Program of Science Through the Grades

In the Third Yearbook (1904) of this Society, W. S. Jackman called attention to the break between the elementary and secondary schools. He indicated that true nature study of the elementary school was natural science and its methods were truly scientific. He urged that, throughout the course from the kindergarten to the university, every step taken by the pupil be a substantial preparation for the next one.

Jackman's recommendation was not widely accepted; on the contrary there has been widespread insistence that science could have no part in the curriculum prior to the high school. This latter point of view has grown out of the tendency to think of science as only a body of technical content organized about its various fields and as having little or no value to children.

With the growth of general science as a junior-high-school subject, the interest of the laymen in the contributions of science, and the realization that science is one of the great factors in our contemporary civilization, it no longer seems wise to deny the child the educative values that science has to offer him.

Another difficulty in the past has been that adults have not appreciated the intrinsic value of the child's simple generalizations.

Again, the tendency to distinguish between nature study and elementary science has hindered the administration of instruction. At a time when there is a growing demand for fewer categories of instruction in the elementary school, it is wise to introduce instruction of natural phenomena under one term.

There seems to be no reason to continue the discussion of the relative merits of nature study and elementary science. It is difficult to distinguish the practices that have been in operation under these two names. Many who now use the term 'nature study' really conform to what is considered good practice by those who teach 'elementary science.' The important question is not what we shall call this subject, but rather what service is to be rendered the child.

This Committee approves a continuous science program, beginning with the kindergarten and continuing every year through the elementary and secondary schools. There is no reason why this program should be called by any other name than 'science' prior to the years of actual specialization in the secondary school. The only basis for differentiating between the science offered in different grade levels is the increasing maturity of the children.

There has been a tendency to substitute geography or health for science in the intermediate grades. It is hardly necessary to show why this cannot be called progressive practice. There is no reason why any of the social sciences should be substituted for natural science in any of the grades of the elementary school or vice versa. The child cannot secure the contributions science has for him in a brief acquaintance between ages 6 and 9. As administrators and teachers become aware of the opportunities that are inherent in a continuous program of science through the grades, they will doubtlessly remedy this situation. Examination of recent courses of study indicates a definite development of a continuous program of science through the grades of the elementary school.[8] Similar developments are under way in other states and cities in which courses of study have not as yet been published.

The tendency to introduce 'biological nature study' in the kindergarten and primary grades and 'physical science' in the intermediate grades has had its defenders. But the child is not conscious of these scientific fields, much less of their boundaries. As far as careful studies indicate at the present time, his interest is distributed among all of the major scientific fields, and he needs elementary, although fundamental, instruction and experience in a well-balanced science. The teacher should provide such a program in science instead of teaching one adult-divided scientific field, such as biology, to the exclusion of others.

Elementary science may be considered as derived from the major science fields of astronomy, biology, chemistry, geology, and physics. However, the teacher should consider her task that of guiding the child in interpreting natural phenomena rather than that of introducing the child to these special fields. She need not be concerned over the fact that the children may use materials from several sciences in the course of one activity; she need be aware of the separate content fields only when she finds it necessary to look up source materials.

One attendant weakness noted in the content and objectives of some current offerings in nature study has been the failure to develop a well-balanced program. The nature study that has been introduced in many schools represents only a small segment of the whole field of natural science, and this small segment has not, in most cases, been fundamental to the child's present or future experiences.

Children Need Truthful Interpretations of Phenomena

It is important that teachers in all grades of the elementary school, either by direct explanation or by implication, guard against causing the children to accept animistic explanations of natural phenomena. Many supplementary books used in the elementary school are characterized by such distortions, as animals talking, Nature planning, and the plant and animal world conferring. There is no intent here to condemn the use of such material for general reading, but it is evident

---

[8] See, for example, courses of study in elementary science in the states and cities mentioned in Footnote 1.

that the work in the study of science in the early years should be concerned with the observation, manipulation, and explanation of natural phenomena, always in truthful, even if elementary, fashion. Every effort should be made in the science activities to interpret phenomena for the child in a manner that will strictly avoid satisfying childish curiosity by explanations smacking of the mystic. There has prevailed so marked a tendency to feed the child on nature myths that he often does not know what is truth about nature and what is myth.

Teachers who know the field will not find it necessary to follow such undesirable practices in order to secure interest, though admittedly teaching truths about nature is not an easy matter. The technique of teaching science without the personification of abstract forces and inanimate objects has not been generally acquired. In the past many have felt that nature study must be diluted with fairy tales in order to make it intrinsically interesting to the child, but studies of children's questions indicate that children are interested in truthful explanations of natural phenomena.

Primitive man explained causes of phenomena on the basis of an anthropomorphic philosophy. Frequently he ascribed human qualities to plants and animals. The teacher will have difficulty in preventing the same sort of idea developing in her instruction. Some of the adjustments and adaptations of plants and animals to the environment are so marvelous in character as to cause one upon superficial consideration to wonder whether they were not thought out and planned. At present, the teacher may find it necessary to use certain otherwise splendid reference books which err in this respect. If such material is used with her pupils, she should make sure that, if the books do state untruths, they are presented in such a manner as to appear obviously false to the children. The point involved here is decidedly important. To take a concrete case: if a ten-year-old reads an interesting story in which a fox talks with a boy, he is not for an instant mislead; but if he reads that kind Mother Nature covers the ground with leaves each fall to protect tender bulbs from the winter's cold, he may readily form from this sort of personification a decidedly misleading idea of purpose and of human traits in natural objects and events.

Nature study to many implies more outdoor work than elementary science. It is unfortunate if elementary science should become associated only with indoor classroom study. There seems to be no reason why excursions and living materials cannot be utilized as efficiently under a program of elementary science as under one of nature study. In some of the public schools in Hamburg, Germany, science is placed as the last subject in the day's program. This permits the teacher to take the children on a field excursion and to dismiss them without returning to the school.

Excellent manuals for outdoor work may be secured. Professor E. Laurence Palmer of Cornell University has developed field books[9] that make it possible for elementary-school teachers and children to study material of the out-of-doors. These field manuals are organized about some of the significant principles and meanings of science. Such material enriches the teaching of science and deserves even greater use than it has at present.

The school garden may become a laboratory for the study of many of the objectives of science. It will offer children opportunity for acquaintance, demonstration, and experimentation. The purpose of the elementary-school garden is not so much to give a beginning in elementary agriculture as it is to help the child to become acquainted with growing plants and to provide an experience that every boy and girl needs, regardless of future vocations.

WHO SHALL TEACH ELEMENTARY SCIENCE?[10]

A question most frequently asked by school systems desiring to introduce or extend elementary science is: "Who shall teach elementary science?"

There are many elementary schools in which, either because of inadequate financial provision or because of the lack of specialists, the regular classroom teacher must introduce science if it is taught at all. Administrators in such schools frequently raise the question whether they should expect these teachers, considering their poor training in this field, to teach science. The answer can be secured by examining the accomplishments of the classroom teacher in the field. Throughout the United States there are many classroom teachers who have had but little training in science and yet are doing successful work in teaching it in the primary and intermediate grades. The classroom teacher,

---

[9] Palmer, E. Laurence. *Field Book of Nature Study.* Comstock Publishing Company: Ithaca, N. Y., and *Cornell Rural School Leaflets.* The New York State College of Agriculture: Cornell University, Ithaca, N. Y.

[10] A program for the training of elementary-school teachers is given in Chapter XVIII.

because of her proximity to the child, has an opportunity to integrate the learning in science with the classroom activities that is not afforded a specialist who comes into the classroom only at stated periods. An organized program in which the outcomes are so well expressed as to afford the teacher an opportunity to prepare herself for the task of teaching science can do much to assist her; she should be provided with syllabus material containing a background of information and suggested procedure.

In the past there has been little encouragement for the classroom teacher to attempt any instruction in nature study or science. This in part has been due to the insistence of some of the leaders, particularly in the field of nature education, who have set such requirements for the instructors of these subjects as would eliminate the majority of the elementary teachers. The assumption that, in order to be a successful teacher of nature study, one must be a unique individual differing in character and personality from other elementary-school teachers has never been proved. No one need be deprived of the opportunity of becoming a successful teacher of science because of innate character-istics any more than he need be of becoming a teacher in any other field. The claim that a teacher of these subjects must be both a naturalist and a scientist is unwarranted. The extravagant demands that have sometimes been listed for teachers of nature study are probably due to confusion of the duties of 'nature guides' in summer camps and those of teachers of science.

One reason that elementary teachers feel their own dearth of sci-entific knowledge lies in the difficult questions often asked by chil-dren. Children's questions cover a wide field, and many of their ques-tions have never been answered by the scientists. Hence, the elemen-tary teacher need not feel chagrined when the children ask questions she cannot answer, but she has reasons for feeling her instruction has not achieved its goal if she continually fails to utilize their questions to motivate their work. They should not be discouraged in raising the questions that spontaneously interest them. The wise teacher will strive to improve her methods of using the interests of children.

A number of schools have introduced the departmental organization of instruction in science. A few administrators despair of having classroom teachers that are capable of teaching science in an adequate way along with remedial reading, art, music, social science, and all of the other subjects of the elementary school. In parts of Germany,

Czecho-Slovakia, Poland, and Russia, no apology is made for departmental instruction in the years corresponding to our intermediate grades.

In the departmental program science is taught by a specialist, usually at periods set aside. There are a number of advantages in this kind of organization of instruction. In particular, the instruction is likely to be more accurate than that of the regular classroom teacher.

But along with its advantages, this type of instruction presents certain disadvantages. Science tends to become a subject that is locked away in a tight compartment, unrelated to other categories or activities. It tends to be integrated only with the instruction of the departmental specialists, although there may be scores of opportunities for integration with the classroom activities and the life experiences of the child. In the mind of the child, science becomes a subject to itself, separated from its natural contacts. Frequently departmental instruction, taught as it may be once or twice a week, becomes fragmentary, disjointed, and unconnected with life situations. The experience of many specialists has been that, to be really effective, departmental instruction must take place as many as three or four times a week.

In some schools the instruction in science is vested in both the classroom teacher and the science specialist. The specialist is both a teacher and an adviser. The specialist is responsible for the development of a course of study and of informational materials and also assists the teacher, actually teaching the children at those times when the classroom teacher, because of lack of knowledge of science, is unable to do so. The specialist does not take over the entire instruction in science but assists at difficult places, perhaps in starting units, in pointing out the meanings that are essential in a given study, securing books, information, or visual materials. Some of this work may be done in conferences with the teacher, some by actual instruction. In this way the specialist's efforts in science are multiplied many times over; the teacher secures accurate information and actual training in service.

At all times when the specialist is teaching the children, the classroom teacher should be present. Too frequently, under departmental work, the classroom teacher uses the science period as a time for rest or recreation. Soon she finds she knows less about some of the topics in science than the children and as a result the children may fail to discuss the science activities with her, and she is then unable to use to the utmost the many incidents and activities that would vitalize the work. The classroom teacher should participate in all the activities of her pupils; she should be the agent who utilizes the specialists, and should be responsible for the achievement in science in the classroom.

The Function of a Course of Study in Progressive Practice

The course of study has a definite function to perform in the elementary school. This is just as true for the progressive school that employs large units, or activities, that integrate one or more subject-matter fields in a problem as it is for the school that divides the week's program into definite subject-matter periods.

There has been widespread acceptance of the view that nature study in the schools should be placed on an incidental basis. An incident had to arise in order to produce a lesson in nature study. If the child happened to bring a frog to school, there was a lesson on frogs. There was no suggestive organization of learning elements through the grades. An organized program was alleged to kill all spontaneous expression on the part of teachers and pupils. To observe and be able to identify these objects, then, became the objective of the natural-science work. The teacher was expected to be an expert naturalist and to identify and make interesting object lessons of what came to hand. In this way a few teachers developed a most interesting technique of teaching. Successful teaching was usually due to the fact that the teacher had had a splendid training in science, or had at least, a large store of information, but apparent success was achieved by some who had a fund of bits of interesting nature lore about many objects.

The teacher who was unprepared to teach on the incidental basis blocked the possibilities of any incidents arising. In many cases where time was allotted for nature study, the time was used for drill work or other purposes in subjects in which the organization was at least apparent and on which the accomplishments of the child could be more readily measured. Thus, in many schools, nature study tended to become merely a disconnected series of object lessons, a subject that was planned from day to day; it became incidental, and even accidental, in the school program when it was not completely ignored.

Lack of prearranged organization and the prevalence of the 'incidental' theory of teaching have unquestionably interfered with the successful teaching of science. With this point of view there could be no definite criteria for selection of material to be used in teacher-training courses and it is clearly impossible for normal schools to train teachers to meet all the emergencies that might arise in object lessons taught incidentally. The task of the teacher-training institution is discerned more clearly by a suggested organization of instruction in science for the elementary school in which the major emphasis is placed on meanings rather than on objects.

Some of the advantages of having a sequential organization of essential meanings, of having a course of study indicated through the grades, are:

1. It assists the teacher-training schools by giving them a definite task—a course to be professionalized.
2. It places the emphasis on meanings rather than objects.
3. It provides the teacher with the guidance which comes from research and study. Undoubtedly most elementary teachers have had little acquaintance with one or more subjects or fields they are expected to teach. The course of study is suggestive to the teacher of possibilities that she may otherwise never discover.
4. It suggests learning elements at grade levels appropriate for their learning.
5. It provides for proper balance rather than a narrow segment which might result if the teacher followed her own interests and preferences.
6. It provides for setting up new situations in later grades which may cause previous learning elements to be needed.

A definite course of study need not infringe on children's interests, on the use of incidental material, or on the pursuance of activities. The incident may become something that may be utilized in developing learning elements indicated in the course or in opening up new activities. The incidental material and interests of the children are particularly functional if the teacher is aware of the possibilities that are opened up by them. She needs the advice of the specialist. The specialist can render much of this assistance through courses of study and other source material.

If the teacher is conscious of the larger meanings, she can make a far richer use of the incidental material and of children's interests. Many elementary teachers place in their pre-plans for units the meanings that might be developed. The situations that rise spontaneously, the questions that challenge the children's interest, the incidents that were unforeseen, become more meaningful because the teacher is conscious of the worth-while goals and can direct the instruction in those directions.

RELATION OF SCIENCE TO AN ACTIVITY PROGRAM

Activities that integrate one or more subjects need not interfere with a functional program in science. Instruction through activities is unquestionably securing excellent educational approval. Supervisors of science can do much to improve the activity instruction by assisting the teacher to realize the possibilities of science study that lie in the activities. Too frequently the activities only explore the subject-matter field in which the teacher feels her greatest competence. The children may emerge from the elementary school with their training warped by teachers who have in one way or another harped on their own hobbies. This is at present one of the greatest weaknesses of the activity program. The fundamental subject, such as reading, writing, and arithmetic, in which accomplishments can be more readily measured probably do not suffer so much in this particular as do aspects of liberal education, such as the social and natural sciences.

Courses of study should offer to those elementary schools that organize their instruction about the activity program a means of checking to determine whether the year's program of activities is properly balanced in the various fields. The elements of learning should be arrayed in the course of study or other curricular material in such a way as to be accessible to the classroom teacher. In case the teacher finds that certain themes, or elements of learning, with a high evaluation in the syllabus have not been considered, she can provide for new activities.

Teachers of elementary schools are sometimes made to feel that all activities undertaken by the children must involve a number of subjects. This frequently results in actually pulling in content from the various fields, tearing it out of its natural context and logical setting, and putting it in strange and extraneous habitats. There is undoubtedly too much forced correlation in the elementary school.

It is desirable that some activities in the elementary school be largely science activities. Teachers will frequently find it advisable to have some projects that do not ramify into other fields. A course of study in elementary science is suggestive of many purposeful activities or units that may be largely, if not entirely, science. There is a danger at present that the desire to integrate the fields may become a boomerang that will destroy some of the constructive results of recent educational progress in the subject-matter fields.

The tendency to subordinate science to the social-science field is a very common practice. In this practice the classwork is organized about social science units. The only natural science considered is that which is contributory to the social science units. The fault in this practice is easily apparent; science is dragged into settings that are unnatural. Examination of typical integrating units shows that such instruction as is labeled 'science' cannot be defended as accurate or worth while. Science has a contribution of its own for the child. It need not enter the curriculum through the back door. A study of Africa need not be introduced in order to study dryness and evaporation, when evaporation is a phenomenon occurring in the everyday life of children. Nor is a study of Holland necessary to introduce bulbs nor a study of Syria essential to initiating work on air, a medium which constantly surrounds the child. The attempt of certain educators to subordinate natural science to social studies is without real support. It results not infrequently in fastening a pseudo-science onto the social studies. Those constructing such units are frequently ignorant of the place of science in life situations and in the elementary-school curriculum.

Science can have a place in connection with social studies units. There is a relationship that is real, and integration is to be encouraged. But the real contribution of elementary science will probably never be secured by introducing science only through social-study units. Social studies at times may be integrated into units that have been vitalized through science, where there is a real opportunity for integration. On the other hand, science may be integrated with social studies or there may be activities which integrate both. There is no need of making a fetish of integration to the extent that the children fail to secure the meanings they need, and that values of science in elementary education are lost because of its subordination to other subject-matter fields.

Courses of study should make teachers conscious of the best context for learning elements. This can be done by giving a background of information and suggested procedure for teachers. Elements of learning should be learned in connection with the context that will prove challenging and satisfactory for their real mastery. Obviously much of this context is to be found in the observations and experiences associated with the subject-matter field from which the learning elements are derived.

Teachers who organize their work about large units of work sometimes attempt topics in science for which children are unprepared. Courses of study may assist the teacher by indicating the types of units that are recommended for each grade as well as the order of the learning elements that are involved. In this way the teacher may determine what learning is essential to the study of a given topic and be guided in the final selection of a unit.

There are undoubtedly too many individual categories in the elementary-school program. The curriculum at the present time is overloaded, causing teachers and pupils to rush from one subject to another. This difficulty is especially significant in elementary science, since there has been no allotment of time for it in many schools and it must then be introduced as an additional subject. Projects, activities, or larger units integrating a number of subject-matter fields have been proposed to remedy this condition. Schools utilizing this latter type of program are frequently less hesitant about introducing science than those which have the traditional subject-matter divisions. There is need that the units of activity programs be evaluated in order to determine whether the major contributions that are inherent in the separate subject-matter fields for elementary education are being achieved.

SUMMARY

Science has become a subject deserving of a place in the elementary school because of its fundamental and far-reaching contribution to the child and to society, and because it conforms to the purposes and ideals of the elementary school.

The Committee recommends a continuous program of science beginning in the kindergarten and extending through the elementary and secondary schools.

The science of the elementary school should be well-balanced and derived from the major fields of science. It should, however, not be organized or treated about the separate sciences, but rather about the problems and situations which are challenging, many of which may integrate the separate fields.

The objectives of science should be carefully selected, with the contribution of science to the child and to society as guiding principles. The work from grade to grade should be directed towards those objectives and, in terms of the *Third Yearbook* of this Society, "every step taken should be a substantial preparation for the next throughout the course from the kindergarten to the university."[11]

Teacher-training institutions should plan and introduce courses designed to train teachers to teach science in their classrooms. Administrators and supervisors should encourage and assist teachers to secure training while in service.

---

[11] Jackman, W. S. *Loc. cit.,* p. 14.

CHAPTER XI

THE TECHNIQUE OF ANALYSIS TO DETERMINE CONTENT IN THE ELEMENTARY SCHOOL*

In the organization of curricular materials in science the fundamental learning experiences will be directed toward the realization of large scientific principles.[1] In the development of these principles an understanding and interpretation of environmental phenomena will be acquired which will enable the learners to meet new situations intelligently. The learners will be prepared in this way to react wisely to those situations common to their level of development, and at the same time will acquire a background of understanding which is fundamental in meeting future needs. These scientific principles may be used as guides in the selection and organization of teaching materials.[2] Their development and understanding may serve as objectives, or goals, toward which the work is directed. In harmony with the general nature of education in elementary schools those scientific principles will be emphasized which are fundamental in giving the environment a broad interpretation.

Examination of various large principles of science indicates that they are too far-reaching in their importance to be developed completely in any one grade. Their development will continue as the learner advances from one grade level to the next. In such a gradual development the interpretation of natural phenomena will expand progressively and will contribute to the continuous enlargement of the understanding of the guiding principle. This enlargement will continue as the learner progresses through the elementary school, secondary school, college, into the research laboratory, and on through life.

AN ILLUSTRATIVE PRINCIPLE

The following scientific principle has been selected to illustrate the way in which science in the elementary school may be directed toward the attainment of large general truths:

---

*The Committee is indebted for this chapter to Dr. Florence Grace Billig, Detroit Teachers College, Detroit, Michigan.

[1] The term 'principle' is here used to designate a general truth in science toward which the work in science may be directed.

[2] Powers, S. R. "Research in science teaching," *Teachers College Record*, 30:1929, 334-342.

Living things survive because they are fitted[4] to conditions under which they live and in which their structures and ways of living enable them to attain adult life and to leave offspring.

The validity of this guiding principle for a course in science for elementary schools is supported by the study made by Craig[3] to determine and evaluate the 'objectives' of science for Horace Mann Elementary School, and by the study made by Florence G. Billig[4] in the analysis of outlines of science in use in elementary schools and the analysis of books for specialists and lay readers that have been written by authorities in the fields of science.

A study of this guiding principle indicates that it is too extended in its significance to be understood fully as it stands. It may be analyzed into subordinate principles, which in their turn may be further analyzed into constituent parts, or elements, that give it more specific meaning appropriate for a course in science for elementary schools.

In developing an outline of study for elementary schools, the elements of learning derived by means of the suggested analysis may form the bases upon which to build increasingly larger and larger conceptions, which in their turn may serve as simple learning elements. These relatively simple learning elements may form more and more complex associations,[5] so that step by step an understanding and interpretation of the guiding principle may be developed in the minds of the learners.

To secure the learning elements which are of importance in developing this illustrative principle, an analysis was made of literature written for the specialist and for the lay reader by authorities in the several fields of science. By means of this analysis those elements were derived which experienced authorities consider important in developing the principle from the point of view of the specialist and layman. A survey of outlines of science in use in elementary schools in different sections of the country gave the elements which, on the basis of experience and judgment, educators consider suitable for use in elementary schools.

The subordinate principles derived by the survey of literature and outlines of science may be stated as follows:

---

[3] Craig, G. S. *Certain Techniques Used in Developing a Course of Study in Science for Horace Mann Elementary School.* Teachers College Contributions to Education, No. 276, 1927.

[4] Billig, F. G. *A Technique for Developing Content for a Professional Course in Science for Teachers in Elementary Schools.* Teachers College Contributions to Education, No. 397, 1930.

[5] See Powers, S. R., *loc. cit.*

I. There are limiting factors in the environment of living things.
II. The environment of living things changes continually.
III. Living things respond to stimuli in their environment.
IV. Living things have structures, functions, and habits which enable them to attain adult life and to leave offspring.
V. A balance in nature is maintained through interrelations of plants and animals with each other and with their physical environment.
VI. Through long ages there has been persistence of life upon the earth.

Analysis of each of these subordinate principles was continued until learning elements appropriate for elementary schools were derived. The results of analysis of Subordinate Principle IV are given in the following outline (stated in terms for the teacher):

IV. Living things have structures, functions, and habits which enable them to attain adult life and to leave offspring: The activities of plants and animals are directed toward the preservation of the individual and the species.

A. Plants

1. Only green plants make carbohydrate foods.
   a. Green plants secure the raw materials for photosynthesis from air, soil, or the medium in which they grow.
   b. The process of photosynthesis takes place in nature only in the presence of sunlight.
   c. In the process of photosynthesis light energy is transformed and stored in food made by green plants.
   d. Some food made by green plants is used immediately and some is stored in stem, root, fleshy leaf, bud, fruit, etc.
   e. Storage of food by plants seems associated with tiding over an unfavorable period.
   f. The green leaf is the chief organ of photosynthesis.
   g. Plants synthesize fats.
   h. Plants synthesize proteins.
   i. The leaf is the chief organ of respiration in most plants.
   j. Fibro-vascular bundles conduct plant materials through the stem to and from roots and leaves.
   k. Roots of plants absorb water and dissolved mineral substances used in the process of photosynthesis. The absorbing surface of roots is increased by root hairs.
   l. Water absorbed by roots and not used in carrying on plant processes and in keeping cells distended is transpired.
      (1) Plants wilt when they do not take in water enough to carry on plant processes, keep cells distended, and provide sufficient water for transpiration.
      (2) Some plants have structures which help protect them from excessive evaporation.
         (a) Some leaves have a thickened epidermis.

  (b) Some plants have bloom on their leaves.
  (c) Some plants have reduced leaf surface.
  (d) Some leaves have hairs.
  (e) Some plants produce resin, wax, or mucilage.
2. Plants perpetuate their kind.
  a. Some plants reproduce asexually: In asexual reproduction all offspring have the same inheritance as the parent.
    (1) Some plants are reproduced by bulbs.
    (2) Some plants are reproduced by underground stems.
    (3) Some plants are reproduced by roots.
    (4) Some plants are reproduced by runners.
    (5) Some plants are reproduced by cuttings.
    (6) Some plants are reproduced by fleshy leaves.
    (7) Some plants may be reproduced by budding and grafting.
  b. Many plants reproduce sexually: In sexual reproduction, all offspring inherit from two parents.
  c. The flower is the reproductive organ of many plants.
    (1) Stamens produce pollen and the pistil produces ovules.
    (2) Pollen is carried to the stigma by various means.
      (a) Wind carries pollen of many plants.
      (b) Insects carry pollen of many plants.
      (c) Humming birds carry pollen of some plants.
      (d) Some flowers are self-pollinated.
    (3) Many plants have structures which aid in pollination.
    (4) An ovule fertilized by a pollen grain develops into a seed.
  d. A seed is an immature plant that has stopped growing for a time.
  e. Seeds provide for the survival of a species over an unfavorable period.
  f. Seeds of some plants are distributed over wide areas by various means.
    (1) Many seeds are distributed by wind.
    (2) Many seeds are distributed by animals.
    (3) Some seeds are distributed by water.
    (4) Some seeds are distributed by man.
3. Many activities of plants seem associated with seasonal rhythms.
  a. Plants grow when temperature, sunlight, moisture, and soil conditions are favorable.
  b. The fruiting season follows the active growing season of plants.
    (1) Spring is a period of rapid growth for many plants.
    (2) Summer and early fall is the fruiting period for many plants.
    (3) Winter is a period of dormancy for many plants.
  c. Many activities of plants during summer and fall seem associated with tiding over an unfavorable period.
    (1) Leaf coloration seems to be associated with the approach of unfavorable conditions.

(2) Leaf fall seems to be associated with the approach of unfavorable conditions.

(3) Seed production seems to be associated with tiding over an favorable period.

(4) Storage of food seems to be associated with tiding over an unfavorable period.

B. Animals

1. Animals need food to renew the supply of energy which they use in performing their work and to provide materials which become a part of their bodies.

2. By the process of digestion insoluble food is changed into soluble forms which can be used directly by the organism.
   a. Man and other higher animals have definite structures which aid in digestion.
   (1) Mouth, stomach, and intestines aid in digestion.
   (2) Various glands secrete fluids that aid in digestion.

3. Digested food of many animals is carried to various parts of the body by blood and lymph.
   a. Blood is carried to various parts of the body through blood vessels and sinuses.
   b. Blood is forced through arteries and veins by action of the heart.
   c. Lymph is a fluid that acts as an intermediary between the blood stream and body cells.

4. Animals need oxygen to live.
   a. Oxygen is necessary for oxidation.
   b. Energy released by the process of oxidation is used in performing various body activities.
   c. Animals with lungs secure oxygen from the air.
   d. Animals with gills secure oxygen from that dissolved in water.
   e. Some animals secure oxygen through their body surfaces.
   f. Oxygen reaches the various parts of the insect body by means of extensively branched tubes or tracheae. Spiracles are openings of tracheae.
   g. The circulatory system of higher animals carries oxygen from lungs or gills to various parts of the body and returns carbon dioxide to the lungs or gills.
   h. Animals give off carbon dioxide as a waste product of respiration.

5. Animals have some means of removing waste products from the body. Waste products resulting from body activities are removed through skin, kidneys, lungs, and intestines.

6. The nervous system controls the reactions of many animals to their environment.

7. Many activities of animals seem associated with seasonal rhythms.
   a. Some animals are permanent residents in a given locality.
   (1) Some animals lay up stores of food for use during winter.

(2) Some animals vary the type of food eaten with the change in season.

(3) During summer and fall some animals build homes for winter.

(4) Some animals show seasonal coloration that makes them inconspicuous in their surroundings.

(5) Many mammals develop a thicker coat of fur during the fall.

b. Many animals are not so active during winter as during summer.

c. Some species of insects are decreased in number as winter approaches.

(1) Insects live over the winter in adult, egg, larval, or pupal stages.

(2) Only the females of some species live through the period of dormancy.

d. Some animals hibernate during a part of each year.

(1) During hibernation breathing is scarcely perceptible; heart action is faint; excretion is slight; and animals go without food and drink.

(2) Environmental factors associated with hibernation are scarcity of food, low temperature, and drought.

(a) Hibernation is characteristic of many animals in cold countries.

(b) Some animals that normally hibernate show no tendency to hibernate if food and warm temperature are available.

(3) Some hibernating animals are heavy sleepers and some are light sleepers.

(4) The period of hibernation of different species of animals varies in length.

(5) Some hibernating animals become fat with the approach of winter.

(6) Many 'cold-blooded' animals hibernate.

(7) Insects pass the winter in egg, larval, pupal, and adult stages.

(8) Hibernation is a racial characteristic as well as an individual reaction.

e. Some animals migrate.

(1) Some birds migrate.

(2) Some insects migrate.

(3) Some fish migrate.

(4) Some mammals migrate.

(5) Some animals have long migratory routes.

(6) Much has been learned about bird migration by means of bird-banding.

(7) Migration is a racial characteristic as well as an individual reaction.

(8) Many theories have been advanced to explain migration.

(9) The causes of migration are not definitely known.

(10) Some migratory birds are protected by migratory bird treaties.

f. Many animals mate and produce young in the spring.
g. Many animals show great activity in caring for young during spring and summer.
8. Many animals have inherited means of protection against enemies.
  a. Some animals defend themselves and young by means of armor, antlers, rapid running, rapid flight, agility, kicking, striking, stinging, nocturnal habits, discharging disagreeable odors, discharging secretions of mucous, etc.
  b. Some animals seem to be protected by disguise and mimicry.
  c. Some animals seem to be protected by coloration.
  d. Some animals are protected by an exoskeleton.
9. Many animals form temporary or permanent associations which aid in preserving the individual and the species.
10. Animals reproduce their kind.
  a. All living things are derived from living things.
  b. Some animals reproduce asexually: Only one parent is involved in asexual reproduction.
  c. Most animals reproduce sexually.
    (1) Two parents are involved in sexual reproduction.
    (2) In sexual reproduction, offspring inherit characteristics from each parent.
    (3) Every living thing produced sexually begins life as a single cell.
  d. Some animals pass through a metamorphosis in their life history.
  e. Many animals at birth look much like their parents and do not pass through a metamorphosis.
  f. Breeding habits of animals are related to reproduction.
  g. Some animals show secondary sexual characteristics.
    (1) Many male animals are distinguished by brilliant color or ornamental structures.
    (2) Some male birds develop special breeding plumage.
    (3) Males of some species develop horns, tusks, antlers, excessive growth of hair, etc.
    (4) Many males are larger than the females of the same species.
    (5) Some females are larger than the males of the same species.
  h. Animals give varying amounts of parental care to their young.
    (1) Some animals give little or no care to their young.
      (a) Some animals place eggs in conditions in which development is favored, but give no further attention to them.
      (b) Some animals leave their young to care for themselves as soon as they are born.
      (c) Some animals carry their young about with them.
      (d) Animals that produce many young usually give little or no care to their offspring.
    (2) Some animals give much care to their young.
      (a) Some animals care for their young until they are able to care for themselves.

  (b) Some animals build nests, remain with their eggs, and care for their young.
  (c) Mammals feed milk to their young.
  (d) Animals that produce few young usually give much parental care.
  (e) Animals that have a long period of infancy usually receive much parental care.

This detailed outline embodies fundamental truths relating to the guiding principle that may serve as goals, or objectives, for science work in elementary schools. These basic truths have general significance in interpreting environmental phenomena. They are valid for a school located in a city as well as for one in a rural community, whether the school is situated in the eastern, central, or western section of the country.

Further analysis of the elements in the outline gave a large number of illustrations that may be used as teaching materials in developing the principle. The illustrations used in any school will be selected, in most cases, from those in the local community. Whether the meadowlark, robin, or cardinal is studied as an example of a permanent resident or as a migratory bird depends upon the section of the country in which the school is located. Whether the toyon, azalea, or trailing arbutus is used as an example of a plant that is in need of protection depends upon the part of the country in which the teaching is being done. Forms common in a community will be used in most cases to illustrate and to develop the fundamental general truths. Those forms having the broadest application will be used in preference to the occasional ones. On the other hand, the fundamental ideas to be developed will be the same for any section of the country; they are general in importance.

ILLUSTRATIVE ARRANGEMENT BY GRADES

To illustrate a way in which materials included in this outline may be arranged for use in the elementary grades, the following suggested organization[6] is given. The subordinate truths developed to show this organization are the following two:

Many activities of animals seem associated with seasonal rhythms.
Many activities of plants seem associated with seasonal rhythms.

---

[6] There is need for extended study relating to grade placement of topics. The placement indicated in this outline is based upon the judgment and experience of educators.

SUGGESTED OUTLINE FOR GRADES ONE TO SIX

Grade I

I. Activities of animals and plants seem associated with the approach of fall and winter.
  A. Some animals become less abundant as fall advances.
   1. Insects become less abundant.
   2. Toads, frogs, turtles, etc., become less abundant.
   3. Birds become less abundant.
   4. Birds become less active as winter approaches.
  B. Some animals remain in a given locality during the winter.
   1. Some birds remain.
   2. Some wild animals remain.
   3. Some animals that remain store food for use during the winter.
  C. Leaves of some trees become brilliantly colored in late summer and fall.
  D. Leaves of some trees fall in autumn.
  E. Some trees keep their leaves throughout the year.
  F. Some plants die in the fall.
  G. Seeds of some plants ripen in late summer and fall.
  H. Seeds of many plants are distributed by wind.
II. Activities of animals and plants seem associated with spring: Spring is the awakening time of the year.
  A. Animal life becomes abundant.
   1. Some animals awaken from their winter's sleep.
   2. Some birds return to their summer homes.
   3. Insects lay eggs from which insects develop.
   4. Birds lay eggs from which young birds develop.
   5. Frogs and toads lay eggs from which young frogs and toads develop.
   6. Many animals are born in spring.
  B. Animals are busy providing for themselves and their young.
  C. Plants grow rapidly in spring.
   1. Buds of trees and shrubs develop into leaves, flowers, fruit, and twigs.
   2. Seeds begin to grow.
  D. Many plants produce flowers.
   1. Flowers develop from buds.
   2. Flowers develop into seeds and fruit.

Grade II

I. Activities of animals and plants seem associated with the approach of fall and winter.
  A. Some animals become less abundant during the fall.
   1. Insects become less abundant.
   2. Some insects live over the winter as eggs.
   3. Some insects live over the winter as pupae.
   4. Some insects live over the winter as adults.

   5. Toads, frogs, and turtles bury themselves in the ground, where they remain during the winter.
   6. Some birds leave their summer homes.
B. Some animals remain in their home locality during the winter.
   1. Some animals search for food much as they did during the summer.
   2. Some animals store food for use during the winter.
   3. Many animals develop a thicker coat of fur during the fall.
C. Man makes preparations for winter.
   1. Man puts on warmer clothing.
   2. Man stores and preserves food.
   3. Man stores fuel.
   4. Man provides shelter for himself and family.
D. Many plants ripen their seeds and fruit in late summer and fall.
E. Many vegetables mature in late summer and fall.
F. Some plants live over the winter as bulbs, tubers, roots, and seeds.
G. The appearance of the landscape changes as fall advances.
   1. Leaves of some trees fall.
   2. Leaves of some trees remain green.
   3. Leaves of some trees become red, yellow, brown, etc.
   4. Grass turns brown.
   5. Few wild flowers are in blossom.
   6. Many plants turn brown and die.
   7. Many plants go to seed.

II. Spring is the time of great activity among animals and plants.
A. Many animals return to their summer homes.
B. Many animals awaken from hibernation.
C. Many animals mate, build homes, and raise young.
D. Birds, many insects, and other animals lay eggs from which young hatch.
E. Plants grow rapidly during spring.
   1. Seeds begin to grow.
   2. Buds develop into leaves, flowers, fruit, and twigs.
   3. Many plants produce seeds and fruit.
F. The appearance of the landscape changes as spring advances.
   1. Leaves of trees become green.
   2. Fields become green.
   3. Many plants blossom.

Grade III

I. Many insects are common in fall.
A. Some insects are common around water.
B. Some insects are common around flowering plants.
C. Some insects are common around trees and shrubs.

II. Many animals build homes and lay up stores of food for use during the winter.

III. Many plants do not grow during the winter.
IV. Spring is the active growing time for many plants.
 V. Summer is the flowering and food-storing time for many plants.
VI. Many plants mature seeds and fruit in late summer and early autumn.
VII. Seeds of many plants are distributed in late summer and fall.
   A. Some seeds are distributed by wind.
   B. Some seeds are distributed by water.
   C. Some seeds are distributed by animals.

Grade IV

I. Animals respond to seasonal rhythms in various ways.
   A. Insects live over the winter in egg, larval, pupal, and adult stages.
   B. Some animals hibernate.
      1. Environmental factors associated with hibernation are scarcity of food, low temperature, and drought.
         a. Hibernation is characteristic of many animals in cold countries.
         b. Some animals show no tendency to hibernate if food and warm temperature are provided.
      2. During hibernation breathing is scarcely perceptible, heart action is faint, excretion is slight, and animals go without food and drink.
      3. Some hibernating animals are heavy sleepers and some are light sleepers.
      4. The period of hibernation of different species of animals varies in length.
      5. Some hibernating animals become fat at the approach of winter.
      6. Many "cold-blooded" animals hibernate.
      7. Hibernation is a racial characteristic as well as an individual reaction.
   C. Some animals migrate to other regions.
II. Plants grow when conditions are favorable for their growth.
   A. Plants require favorable temperature.
   B. Most plants require light.
      1. Some plants grow best in shady situations.
      2. Some plants grow best in full sun.
   C. Plants require moisture.
   D. Many plants require appropriate soil conditions.

Grade V

I. Many animals migrate in fall and spring.
   A. Many birds migrate.
      1. Migratory routes of some birds are definitely known.
      2. Some birds have long migratory routes.
      3. Birds encounter many dangers in migration.
      4. Birds travel the same migratory routes traveled by their ancestors. Migration is a racial characteristic as well as an individual reaction.

     5. Some migratory birds are protected by migratory bird treaties.

     6. Banding birds has enabled man to learn much about their migration.

  B. Some insects migrate.

     1. Some species of butterflies migrate each year.

     2. Some species of grasshoppers migrate.

     3. Migration of some insects is annual.

     4. Migration of some insects is not annual in occurrence.

     5. Migration of some insects seems to be associated with available food supply.

II. Storage of food by plants seems to be related to tiding over an unfavorable period.

  A. Plants store food in roots, stems, leaves, seeds, fruit, tubers, bulbs, etc.

  B. Plants store food in the form of sugar, starch, fat, and protein.

  C. Stored food enables plants to make rapid growth at the opening of the following growing season.

  D. Man uses food stored by plants.

Grade VI

I. Many animals migrate in fall and spring.

  A. Some fish migrate.

     1. Some adult ocean fish ascend to the headwaters of streams and rivers to spawn.

     2. Some adult lake fish ascend streams to spawn.

     3. Some fish ascend rivers at all seasons, but at some seasons they ascend in large numbers.

     4. The fishing season for some species is largely dependent upon their migration.

  B. Some mammals migrate.

     1. Many mammals have seasonal migrations.

     2. Migration of some mammals seems to be related to food supply.

     3. Migration of some mammals seems to be related to breeding habits.

     4. Some mammals migrate at irregular times but not seasonally.

     5. Some mammals have definite migratory routes.

     6. Many mammals follow the same migratory routes traveled by their ancestors.

     7. Some mammals rove at will but do not exhibit true migratory habits.

  C. Many theories have been advanced to explain migration, but the causes are not definitely known.

II. During spring and summer green plants are actively making and storing food.

  A. Environmental conditions of light, temperature, and moisture are favorable for making food.

  B. Activities of plants slow down with the approach of fall.

  C. Green plants make and store starch and sugar.

1. Green leaves are the chief organs for making starch and sugar.
2. Green coloring matter in plants absorbs energy from the sun which is used in making starch and sugar.
3. In the process of photosynthesis light energy is transformed and stored in food made by the plant.
4. Raw materials used in making starch and sugar are secured from air, soil, and water.
5. Raw materials used in making starch and sugar are assembled in leaves.
6. Plants use immediately some of the food which they make.
7. Plants store food which they do not need in carrying on their various activities.
8. Plants store food in roots, stems, seeds, fruit, tubers, bulbs, etc.
D. Food made by green plants is the source of food used by animals.

Comments on the Foregoing Outline

In this outline the subordinate principles are given that seem appropriate as goals, or standards of attainment, for the different grade levels. They are amplified by specific learning elements that contribute to the development of larger ideas, which in their turn point toward the attainment of the large principle of science under consideration. Illustrative materials to be used are not included in this outline, since such materials will be selected from those available in each community.

Because of variations in interests, experiences, and abilities of children there will be variation in the accomplishments of individual pupils and groups of pupils on the same grade level. Although this outline suggests no special means of providing for varying abilities, it is adapted to different levels of ability attainment. It may be expanded by an indefinite number of illustrations. The extent of this expansion is limited only by the capabilities of the pupils, the interests of pupils and teachers, and the amount of time available. It may be further extended by the use of marginal content[7] not included in the outline but closely associated with the suggested teaching materials.

The outline gives a sequence of topics for the different grades. The elements of learning are arranged so that the work in each grade will utilize, as a foundation, the knowledge and skills gained in the preceding grades. The elements are organized to show their various relationships and meanings.

---

[7] Suggested marginal content relating to the illustrative principle is given in Billig, Florence G. "A Technique for Developing Content for a Professional Course in Science for Teachers in Elementary Schools."

Classroom work will be developed by means of directed observations, either individual or class; by discussions resulting from observations made in field and laboratory; by experiments and demonstrations performed by individual pupils, groups of pupils, teacher, or a combination of teacher and pupils; and by various activities, such as growing plants, and providing proper homes, food, and general care of animals. Literature relating to the various topics will give additional information and will verify conclusions derived by careful observation and discussion. Pupils will be led to make accurate observations, organize and interpret results, and draw conclusions from data gathered. They will be encouraged to withhold judgment until sufficient information is available on which to formulate a conclusion.

At first glance there may seem to be much material in the outline that is common to the first two grades. However, the content suggested for the second grade will be developed as a continuation and extension of that suggested for the first grade. Different illustrations will be used in its development; new relationships will be emphasized; and an extended acquaintance with environmental factors will contribute to an enlargement and enrichment of the work begun in the first grade. This acquaintance with the environment is fundamental in understanding and appreciating natural phenomena. It is the foundation upon which future work is built. During these years the experiences of the learners will be enlarged, a consciousness and understanding of environmental factors will be developed, and interest in the out-of-doors will be extended and intensified.

The outlines presented in this discussion relate to the development of one large principle. A course in science would be directed toward the development of a number of principles[8] that establish goals for the work. These principles will relate to the physical as well as to the biological environment. The teaching materials used in developing them will be integrated so as to indicate the relationships and meanings expressed by the materials, to show the interdependence of living things to each other and to their physical environment, and to emphasize science as unified.

The plan suggested is valuable in that it is adaptable to a rural or city community regardless of the section of the country in which it is

---

[8] There is, of course, need for extended study to determine the principles of science toward the development of which a course in science for the elementary school should be directed.

situated, and adaptable to a minimum or maximum amount of time. The principles express fundamental truths in science that are general in their significance. Their development in different communities and in different sections of the country will differ only in illustrations used. If only a minimal amount of time is available, but a few illustrations will be used to develop the principles. On the other hand, if more time is provided, illustrations may be multiplied, thus enlarging the understanding of relationships and meanings expressed, which in turn will give an enriched appreciation of the natural environment.

CHAPTER XII

SUGGESTED CONTENT FOR THE GRADES OF THE ELEMENTARY SCHOOL[1]

The outline of science for the grades of the elementary school that is presented in this chapter is extracted from a number of recent syllabi of science and serves to illustrate the program that has been presented in Chapter X.

KINDERGARTEN

Courses of study of the rigid requirement type are not adapted for use in the kindergarten. On this level there should be provision for freedom of choice both on the part of the children and the teacher, and the syllabi should attempt to array the possibilities for the enrichment of the science instruction and to present the types of activities that have proved successful. Science in the kindergarten should consist of elementary identification, observation, and interpretation of the environment that surrounds the children. The teacher strives to make this environment a rich and varied one by selecting materials that make for worth-while experiences and learning. These activities should introduce the child to varied phenomena, such as those of the stars, the earth, the air, the change of seasons, day and night, simple appliances of the home and school, and a variety of living things.

In many kindergartens the instruction in science and the social studies is concentrated about a few major units, such as the study of airplanes. Teachers find in this type of program two limiting conditions. First, concentrating the entire year's work in a few units fails to provide for sufficient variety of experience and as a result the learning in science is developed in only one direction. Second, the study of the unit may demand considerable learning for which the children are unprepared. Airplanes may provide properly for some learning on the kindergarten level, but prolonged study of them must introduce elements that cannot, under ordinary circumstances, be mastered until the child has secured more experience with the basic phenomena involved.

A number of challenges may arise through plant and animal life as revealed in the aquarium, vivarium, desert gardens, out-of-door

---

[1] For the Committee, by Gerald S. Craig.

gardens, and excursions. Why can some animals breathe in water while others can not? In what ways do the various animals protect themselves? How do they move about and secure their food? What do plants and animals do in winter? How are seeds scattered about? Excursions may create interest in the effects of weathering and erosion. The children may learn that not all rocks are alike, that some rocks wear away faster than others, and that soil is made from rocks.

Simple experiments have a function in the kindergarten work. Toys of the children may be brought in and demonstrated. The child may learn some of the sources and uses of power. Excursions to places where machines are operating will vitalize and supplement this work.

Much more might be written about the program of science in the kindergarten. In this work the teacher should be conscious of the environment of the children and should make it as rich for learning in science as possible. She should have knowledge of the large concepts of science in order to make the environment more meaningful for children. The teacher will develop much of the learning through activities, actual experience, simple discussions, and excursions of the children. The learning should not be too involved. A variety of experiences with but very elementary interpretations should be the goal rather than long and complicated thought about one experience.

The child may gain a simple appreciation of the scientific attitudes by realizing the relation between cause and effect. He may find in his work that guessing about things does not explain them. In this he is making an early contact with science and is securing fundamental learning for later life.

First Grade
A. Change of Seasons
The meanings which may be developed in a study of this unit are listed in Chapter XI of this report.

B. An Effect of Cold Weather
1. Water fills more space when it turns to ice.
2. Freezing of water breaks up rocks.
3. Freezing would cause great damage to plants if they did not prepare for winter.

C. Using a Thermometer
1. A thermometer tells how hot or how cold it is. It is better to use a thermometer than merely to guess about the temperature.
2. Changes in weather cause people to change the kind of clothes they wear.

D. The Air about Us

1. Air surrounds man at all times.
2. Man breathes and lives in air.
3. There is water in the air.
4. Air is in motion in the winds and in the schoolroom.
5. The wind sometimes blows dust and sand.
6. Fire must have air.
7. If your clothing should catch fire, you should not run, because that gives the fire more air. The air should be kept away by smothering the flames with sand, with a rug, blanket, or a coat.
8. Fire sometimes causes great damage to property and life.

E. Where Plants and Animals Live

1. Many plants and animals live only on land.
2. Fish, tadpoles, and some insects live in the water.
3. Certain plants grow only in water.
4. A few animals burrow into the ground; for example, earthworms, woodchucks, common white grubs.
5. A few animals spend part of their time flying in the air; for example, some birds, some insects.
6. Some animals live on land and in water; for example, frogs, turtles.

F. Plants and Seeds

1. Plants produce seeds and thus there may be more plants.
2. Many plants blossom, and later seeds are produced from parts of flowers.
3. Many seeds are provided with ways by which they may be scattered.

G. Sun, Moon, and Stars

1. The sun, moon, and stars are heavenly bodies that we see easily.
2. The sun gives us heat and light.
3. The moon appears to change its shape from night to night.
4. We see the stars in the sky at night.

SECOND GRADE

A. Plants and Seasonal Change

1. The plant secures material from the soil.
2. The plants which grow from a seed are like the plant from which the seed came.
3. Plants do not grow so rapidly during the cold weather.

B. Animals and Seasonal Change

1. Some of our birds fly great distances in the fall and thus escape winter.
2. The birds find the kind of food they like and a warmer climate in the place to which they go.
3. Some animals hibernate most of the winter.
4. Some animals store food in their homes for winter.

5. Some animals become fat before winter starts.
6. Some animals build their homes during summer and autumn.
7. Some animals are white like the snow in winter time.
8. Some animals do not store food but forage or hunt for food during winter.
9. Man prepares for winter in several ways: (a) by having warmer clothing, (b) by storing food, (c) by heating his home, or (d) by moving to a warmer climate.
10. Man prepares for winter by thinking and planning.

C. Water, Ice, and Steam

1. Ice forms at the top of water.
2. Water freezes at 32° F.
3. Water appears in three different ways, or forms: one form is ice, which is solid; another form people drink, a liquid; a third form is steam, which is a gas.
4. Heat causes ice to liquefy.

D. Air and Weather

1. We are surrounded by air.
2. Air contains dust.
3. A fire must have air.
4. Air may hold moisture.
5. Weather influences our activities.

E. Heat and Light of the Sun

1. We receive heat and light from the sun.
2. The days grow shorter in the fall and longer in the spring.
3. We receive less heat from the sun in autumn than in summer.
4. Plants need sunlight in order to live.
5. The sun rises in the east and sets in the west.
6. We see the sun more hours a day in summer than in winter.

F. Magnetism

1. Iron nails are attracted by a magnet.
2. Paper, rubber, cloth, etc., are not attracted by a magnet.
3. A little force is needed to remove iron from a magnet.

G. Plants as Food

1. We eat the roots of certain plants.
2. We eat the stems of a few plants.
3. We eat the leaves of several plants.
4. We eat the flowers of plants in a few instances.
5. The fruit and seeds are eaten most frequently.

H. Things in Nature Not Just Alike

1. No two things in nature are just alike.
2. Some things in nature are alive, as plants and animals.
3. Other things are not alive, as rocks, stars, and soil.

I. Blossoming Time

1. Different plants bloom in the fall than in the spring.
2. Each plant has its time of blooming. For some it is short; for others it is long.
3. Seeds follow the blossom.

J. Some Ways Electricity Helps Us

1. Electricity is used for lighting.
2. Electricity is used to run a great many appliances in the home.
3. Electricity makes possible the radio, telephone, and telegraph.
4. Electricity travels along wires.
5. Dry cells will run some of our toys.
6. Wires must be connected to a dry cell in two places in order that electricity may flow.

THIRD GRADE

A. How Animals Protect Themselves

The essential meanings for this unit are given in Chapter X.

B. How Animals Care for Their Young

The essential meanings for this unit are given in Chapter X.

C. How Seeds Are Scattered

1. Many plants are scattered because their seeds are constructed in such a way as to be blown about by the winds.
2. Some seeds are scattered by animals.
3. Other seeds float and so are carried by water currents.

D. Mold

1. Some forms of life are tiny.

E. Magnetism

1. The magnetic needle of a compass points (nearly) north and south.
2. The magnet attracts iron nails when brought near them.

F. Air

1. Drops of water form in warm moist air when the air is cooled.
2. Plants give off water into the air.
3. Water gets into the air in several ways.
4. The air sometimes moves with force.
5. A fire cannot burn without air.

G. Floating Objects

1. Objects lighter than water float.
2. Objects heavier than water sink.

H. Light and Plants

1. Plants which have green leaves must have light in order to grow.
2. The sunlight is made up of many colors.

I. Cause of Day and Night

1. The sun lights one half of the earth all the time.
2. The earth rotates, causing night and day.
3. The side of the earth toward the sun has daylight; the opposite side has night.

J. The Sun and the Moon

1. The sun is very much larger than either the earth or the moon.
2. The moon is smaller than the earth.
3. Sometimes the moon can be seen in the daytime.
4. The sun is much hotter than any spot on the earth.

K. Food of Animals

1. Many mammals eat plants.
2. Many mammals eat other smaller animals.
3. Many insects feed upon plants. The young often eat more than their weight each day. They eat all parts of plants.
4. Insects often feed upon other insects and other animals.
5. Some birds feed largely upon insects. A few feed upon other animals.
6. Some birds eat fruit, seeds, and buds.

L. Man Needs Plants and Other Animals

1. Man is dependent upon plants and other animals for food and clothing.

FOURTH GRADE

A. The Earth We Live On

1. Things are drawn toward the center of the earth.
2. "Down" is toward the center of the earth; "Up" is away from the center of the earth.
3. The earth is made up of a solid, a liquid, and a gaseous part.
4. The earth moves around the sun.
5. The earth has one moon.
6. The earth is millions of years old.
7. The surface of the earth is constantly changing.

B. Economic Value of Animals

1. Many animals are of some value to man.
2. Most of the birds should be protected.
3. Many foolish statements which are mere superstitious ideas have been made about many animals.
4. One should seek the advice of scientists before destroying any kind of animal life.
5. Toads, frogs, and most of the snakes are beneficial to man.

6. Some insects are harmful.
7. One should kill animals only when there is good reason for doing so.

C. Social Life of Animals

The essential meanings for this unit are given in Chapter X.

D. The Ocean of Air

1. The surrounding air presses with force against all objects.
2. The blue sky is not a dome, but merely the effect of the atmosphere on the sunlight as it passes through it.
3. The atmosphere surrounds the earth like an envelope, growing thinner as the height from the earth increases. There is very little air above 100 miles.
4. Air expands when heated.
5. Over a source of heat, such as a radiator, a stove, or an open fire, the air rises.
6. Cold air is denser than warm air.
7. Cooler air pushes in toward a heated area and this causes the air currents and wind.

E. Soil

1. Water, wind, ice, and plants help to break up rock.
2. Wind and water are constantly eroding the land portion of the earth.
3. It took a long time for rivers to make their valleys.

F. Gardening

1. It is important to select a place for a garden with sufficient drainage and sunlight.
2. It is important to have good seed.
3. It is important to have soil well cultivated.
4. Weeds should not be permitted in the garden, since they will use certain soil elements and water that otherwise might be used by the plants.
5. The top crust should be broken from time to time.

G. Molds and Bacteria

1. Some plants do not have flowers, do not reproduce, or grow, from seeds.
2. Molds belong to this kind of plant life.
3. When left for some time in a damp place, foods, and clothing often become covered with mold.
4. Molds and bacteria produce spores which are like seeds.
5. The spores can be carried by the air and thus lodge upon food, where they start to grow.
6. It is important to care for food in order to prevent it from spoiling.
7. Food should be bought from stores in which it is properly cared for.
8. It is important to keep the body clean.
9. Some bacteria are helpful; some are very harmful.
10. One should keep his hands away from his nose and mouth.
11. One should not sneeze in another's face.

H. Electric Wiring

The following outcomes may result from a study of simple electric circuits:

1. A knowledge of the difference between insulated and bare wire in appearance and purpose.
2. Ability to recognize copper wire.
3. Ability to install a simple electric bell, a buzzer, or a small motor.
4. Ability to install a push button or simple electric switch.

I. The Sun and The Moon

1. The sun is the source of light, heat, and energy for the earth.
2. The sun is a tremendous globe of material that is so hot that it is gaseous.
3. The sun is visible because it is a source of light.
4. The moon is visible by reflected light that comes from the sun.
5. Objects are visible either because they are a source of light or because they reflect the light from other sources.
6. The earth is a very small body compared with the sun.
7. The earth revolves about the sun.
8. It takes a year for the earth to revolve about the sun.
9. The moon revolves about the earth once in a period of time covering a little less than one month.
10. The earth is much larger than the moon.
11. The rising and setting of the moon is due to the rotation of the earth.

J. A Plant's Means of Protection

1. Plants have means of protection from animals, weather, or other unfavorable conditions.
2. In wet weather the bark of trees prevents the entrance of water. In dry weather it prevents evaporation.
3. The scales of winter buds serve a similar purpose.
4. A few leaves have a covering of hairs which hinders evaporation.
5. Many plants have thorns that protect them from animals.
6. Some plants have a taste or an odor unpleasant to animals. This protects them from being eaten.
7. The dropping of the leaves of deciduous trees is a great protection against winter.

K. Fossils

1. There are fossil records of many plants and animals.
2. We can find out much about the history of the earth by studying these fossils. The earth is very old.

L. Protection of Wild Flowers

1. Many wild flowers must be protected if they are not to be exterminated.
2. When flowers are picked, seeds cannot be formed.
3. When flowers are picked, sometimes leaves are also taken. When this happens in the spring, it is impossible for the plant to manufacture or store food during that year.

M. The Importance of Water

1. Water is necessary for all forms of life.
2. Many plants take up water by means of their roots.
3. Water evaporates and becomes invisible.
4. Water evaporates more rapidly when heated.
5. When water boils, it turns into steam.
6. Steam has force. It is used to run engines, heat buildings, and for other purposes.
7. Water dissolves many substances.
8. Falling water is used to run mills and to generate electricity.

FIFTH GRADE
A. Hibernation

1. Some animals hibernate all winter.
2. Some animals hibernate part of the winter.
3. Some animals store food for winter use.
4. Some animals become fat before hibernating.
5. Many animals do not hibernate.

B. Migration

1. Some animals migrate from one environment to another.
2. Usually such animals return to their old homes for purposes of nesting and raising young.
3. Some birds migrate regularly.

C. Causes of Fogs and Clouds

1. Water evaporates into the air from rivers, lakes, and oceans.
2. In hot, dry places water evaporates very rapidly.
3. Leaves of plants give off moisture into the air.
4. Fogs and clouds consist of water vapor that has been partly condensed.

D. Stars

1. Our sun is a star.
2. Stars shine by their own light.
3. Stars are suns.
4. The earth is one of several bodies that move about our sun.
5. Many stars are much larger than our sun, but they are so far away they seem quite small.
6. Light travels at the rate of 186,000 miles per second, yet some of the stars are so far away that it takes the light several hundred years to reach us.
7. Shooting stars, or meteors, are not real stars.

E. Metamorphosis

1. Some animals change their forms and appearances during their life time as a part of their regular growth and development.

F. The Moon and Its Movements

1. The moon revolves about the earth.
2. The moon shines by reflected light from the sun.
3. At the time of the new moon a small crescent is made visible by the sunshine; then the first quarter, then half, and later the entire surface of the moon appears to be illuminated.
4. On the average the moon rises about fifty minutes later each day.
5. The moon does not have an atmosphere to support life, as does the earth.
6. The moon always presents the same side toward the earth.
7. The moon goes around the sun with the earth.
8. The earth has one moon. Some planets have more than one; some have none.
9. Of all the astronomical bodies the moon is the nearest neighbor to the earth.

G. Leaves

1. Green plants manufacture their own food.
2. Sunlight furnishes the energy that is used.
3. Water and carbon dioxide are two very important raw materials used.
4. Oxygen is given off by the plant.

H. Conservation of Forests

1. Forests may be of assistance in preventing floods.
2. Forests may be of assistance in protecting animals, gardens, and fields against storms.
3. The trees furnish homes for many of the birds.
4. The trees retard the erosion of soil.
5. Man uses lumber for many purposes.
6. Much damage has been done by careless campers.
7. Man must conserve his forests.

I. Insects: Their Place in Nature

1. There are many thousands of different species of insects.
2. A few insects are pests.
3. Some insects are beneficial to man.
4. Some of the harmful insects here are those that have come from other countries where they may do no great harm.
5. Scientists study insects in order to find out which are harmful and which are beneficial. The scientist finds ways to destroy the insects which are harmful.
6. Most insects multiply very rapidly when living under favorable conditions.

J. The Balance of Nature

1. Enemies, scarcity of food and water, storms, fires, diseases, and parasites, all assist in checking the number of any one species of plant or animal life.
2. Man has done much toward destroying many forms of life.

3. No plant or animal should be exterminated except as recommended upon a basis of careful study by scientists.
4. Wild flowers and plants should be picked only in the most economical manner; some should not be picked at all.

K. Protective Coloration

1. Many animals are concealed because of their coloration.
2. By means of this concealment animals frequently escape being discovered by other animals.
3. The coloration of animals assists them in capturing their prey.
4. In coloration and structure some animals greatly resemble a part of the background of the place in which they live.
5. The coloring of some animals changes with the seasons.

L. How Plants Grow

1. Plants require warmth, water, air, and food for growth.
2. Many plants produce seeds which can produce new plants.
3. Green plants are dependent upon the light which comes from the sun.
4. Some plants develop new parts, such as leaves, flowers, or seeds, during the process of growing.

SIXTH GRADE
A. The Story of the Earth

1. The earth has been developed as a result of the action of natural forces.
2. The climate of the earth in the past has not always been the same.
3. Many types of life that existed in the past are now extinct.
4. The surface of the earth has not always had its present appearance and now it is constantly changing.

B. The Solar System

1. The planets revolve about the sun.
2. The earth is a planet.
3. Nine planets have been discovered in our solar system.
4. Some of the planets have moons.
5. The planets shine by reflected light.

C. Reproduction in Plants

1. Any given kind of living thing can produce its own kind only.
2. Plants are reproduced in various ways.
3. Some plants produce bulbs.
4. Some plants produce runners.
5. Some plants produce root stocks.
6. Seeds start new plants.

D. Water: Its Importance to Life

1. Water is very widely distributed in its various forms.
2. Water is essential to life.

3. Water exists in three forms.
4. When water changes to ice it expands.
5. The melting point of ice is the same as the freezing point of water.
6. Pure water in small amounts is practically colorless.
7. Pure water is odorless.
8. Pure water is tasteless.
9. The freezing point of water is 32° F.
10. The boiling point of water is 212° F.
11. City water must often be purified to make it fit for drinking.
12. Water may become impure in many ways.
13. Evaporation is a cooling process.
14. Evaporation of perspiration makes a person feel cool.
15. Large bodies of water have a great effect upon climate.

E.   Air and Ventilation

1. Air has weight.
2. Air exerts pressure.
3. The higher one goes into the air, the lighter the air becomes.
4. Air contains dust.
5. Air is always in motion.
6. Air in living rooms should be kept suitable by ventilation.
7. Air is suitable for breathing when it is clean, at a proper temperature, and in motion.
8. Direct drafts should be avoided.
9. Air pressure can be used to operate many simple devices.
10. The ideal room temperature of air has been found to be from 65° or 66° to 68° F.
11. Overheated air has its influence upon susceptibility to colds, pneumonia, and other diseases.
12. Flues and ventilators should remain open wherever there is danger of poisonous gases. Especially is this true in garages where cars are running or in closed rooms in which there are fires.

F.   The Weather Bureau

1. The Weather Bureau, a branch of the United States Department of Agriculture, has official stations scattered all over the United States and West Indies, each a Key Station to weather changes.
2. Observations from each station are sent daily to Washington, D. C.
3. Weather maps are made by the Weather Bureau, and from them weather predictions are made.
4. The warnings sent out by the Weather Bureau have been of great benefit.
5. The annual saving of property exceeds, several times over, the total cost of the Weather Bureau.

G.   Oxygen and Fire

1. The air is made up of gases. It contains nitrogen (about four-fifths), oxygen (about one fifth), and small quantities of water vapor, of carbon dioxide, and other gases.

2. Water is a compound. It is made up of two elements, hydrogen and oxygen, in definite amounts.
3. Oxygen is necessary for burning.
4. Some fire extinguishers extinguish a flame by cutting off the supply of oxygen; some by cooling the fire below its kindling temperature.

H. Magnetism and the Earth

1. The earth is a terrestrial magnet.
2. A magnet has two poles, the one north-seeking and the other south-seeking.
3. A suspended or floating magnet will always come to rest in a certain position.
4. Similar magnet poles repel; unlike poles attract.
5. The earth is a magnet and has two magnetic poles.
6. The compass, a suspended magnet, is used to indicate directions.
7. The compass needle does not point true north in most places.

I. Electromagnets

1. A coil of wire carrying an electric current acts like a magnet.
2. An electromagnet is made by wrapping wire around a special iron core and then sending an electric current through the wire.
3. The electromagnet may be straight or horseshoe shape.
4. The wires of a horseshoe magnet are wound in different directions on the two arms of the horseshoe.
5. The strength of the electromagnet depends upon the amount of the current sent through the coil of wire and upon the number of turns of wire in the coil.
6. The electromagnet will act in whatever position it is held.

CHAPTER XIII
SCIENCE IN THE SEVENTH, EIGHTH, AND NINTH GRADES[1]

I. INTRODUCTION: SOME GENERAL PREMISES AND RECOMMENDATIONS

The science courses of the seventh, eighth, and ninth grades should be considered as an integral part of the program of science instruction for the periods of elementary and secondary education. The science on this level should, on the one hand, be built upon and comprehend the science of the first six grades; it should, on the other hand, serve as a basis for, and orientation into, the special sciences of the high school for those pupils who continue in school beyond the ninth grade. Above all else, it must provide the most worthwhile science experiences possible for the pupils on this level, and it must be in accord with the acceptable objectives of a liberal education for boys and girls from twelve to sixteen years of age.

In presenting this section of the Yearbook, the Committee accepts the thesis that seventh-, eighth-, and ninth-grade pupils should receive the same opportunities in science education whether they happen to be in a school system organized upon the 8-4 plan, upon the 6-3-3 plan, or upon any other administrative grouping of the school grades. So far as science instruction is concerned, the Committee recognizes no essential differences between the pupils in the seventh and eighth grades of the eight-year elementary school and the seventh- and eighth-grade pupils of the junior high school. While there exist differences in the training of teachers and in the availability of instructional materials in the various types of administrative organizations, it is the opinion of the Committee that such differences should be eliminated as rapidly as possible, to the end that the study of science may be equivalent for all seventh- and eighth-grade pupils. Similarly, the Committee advocates, upon the basis of the general thesis presented in this paragraph and also developed in the introductory chapters, that ninth-grade pupils should receive the same education in science whether they be in the ninth grade of the junior high school or in the first year of the four-year high school.

In general, it is the belief of the Committee that the work in science on any grade level should be built upon and comprehend the work of

---

[1] For the Committee, by Charles J. Pieper.

the preceding grade or grades and that there should be throughout the first nine grades an integrated program of science that, through ever-broadening experiences and activities, gradually expands the learner's abilities to understand more clearly, to enjoy more fully, to appreciate more deeply, to use more intelligently, and, so far as possible on any grade level, to adjust himself more effectively to the materials and forces of his environment. In a program of this nature it must be understood, of course, that the pupil will study himself as one of many biological organisms, as well as study the external forces and materials with which these organisms must interact.

The Committee advocates for grades seven, eight, and nine a three-year integrated program of science study, organized not on the basis of any special science or sciences, but rather upon the basis of large topics, problems, or units relating to the significant problems that arise out of present-day experiences.

There are in many sections of our country serious attempts to construct an integrated program of science study for all grades from one to nine. This Committee sanctions such experimentation, believing that out of these and other attempts there will develop not only a more defensible science program but also a richer education for intelligent participation in the activities of life in the modern environment. Until a thoroughly integrated program of science instruction shall be developed for our elementary schools and for grades seven, eight, and nine, it remains imperative for educators to continue the progress already made in the direction of effecting a sane science education for pupils on the junior-high-school grade levels. For the great majority of our future citizens this level provides at present the only opportunity to acquire those scientific knowledges, skills, interests, and attitudes essential to intelligent behaviors in a scientific age.

The 'general science' which was introduced into the first year of the four-year high school and which, in modified form, has found its rightful way into the junior high school, must serve for the present as the best safeguard against pupils leaving school without adequate means of meeting those situations in life to which even a meager science education may contribute intelligent thought and rational bases for action. The introduction of such 'general science' courses represents an outstanding educational experiment of the last twenty years. It has been, and is now, the basis of significant experimentation in curriculum-making and in methodology. The tremendous growth in the number of pupils pursuing general science, the numerous and optimistic recommendations of national and local committees calling for this subject as an introductory course in secondary science, and the wide acceptance of the subject by our schools confirm the faith of those whose foresight and courage led to its inclusion in the science curriculum.

II. The Objectives of Science in Grades VII, VIII, and IX

Causes That Led to the Introduction of General Science

The mere mention of the causes which led to the introduction of general science will suffice to give a perspective of certain social and educational forces and conditions which gave direction to the statement of the objectives of the subject when it was first brought into the secondary school. Among these causes are the following: (1) the tremendous growth of the high school and the cosmopolitan character of the school population which made of the high school a second school for the education of the masses; (2) the ever-increasing advances in pure and applied science, which more and more demanded on the part of the future citizen an understanding of and an adjustment to an environment modified by man's scientific discoveries and inventions; (3) the inadequate program of science instruction in the elementary school, which failed to fit boys and girls to live intelligently in the modern environment; (4) the formal, abstract character of the special sciences and the consequent relative decrease in the enrollment in these specialized subjects that fell so short of fulfilling the possibilities of science study in a complete educational program for life in a scientific age; (5) the low enrollment of pupils in the science courses offered during the first and second years of the four-year high school and the rapid elimination of pupils in these years, which resulted in a majority of our youth not receiving instruction in science before leaving school; (6) the lack of a sequence in science courses in the secondary school that would provide orientation and educational guidance for pupils in the field of science; (7) the tremendous gap between the nature study of the elementary school and the special sciences of the high school, and the resulting lack of provision for a transitional course between the two widely different types of science courses; (8) the changing aims of secondary education and the newer views of educational psychology, which made mandatory a change from the formal, special sciences to an organization and a technique of instruction that allowed pupils to solve the problems of science associated with their adjustment to the various aspects of the environment and to develop their abilities in scientific procedures through learning situations as nearly as possible like those of real life.

It is quite natural that the statements of the objectives of general science in its early days should have been made to some extent in terms of the previously accepted learning products of the special sciences. Undoubtedly such statements of objectives delayed the acceptance of the subject by school administrators and generalists in education. It was difficult for science teachers trained in the special sciences and in the old psychology to comprehend clearly and to advance effectively the real claims of the new subject in terms of the newer theories and philosophy of secondary education. Thus, we find among the early aims of general science, the following: (1) to prepare for later study of the special sciences; (2) to acquire a fund of information about nature and the sciences; (3) to develop observation, discrimination, imagination, and accuracy of thought.

At approximately the time when general science was being introduced into the schools, the junior high school came into being. The forces, theoretical and practical, which led to the junior-high-school movement were, in many cases, the same forces which brought general science on the scene. Eliot's address before the Department of Superintendence in 1888 and the recommendations of the Committee of Ten, of the Committee on College Entrance Requirements, of the Committee on Six-Year Courses, and of the Committee on Economy of Time aided in crystallizing the views of educators on matters of economy of time in education, of adapting the schools to the needs of a democratic society, of recognizing individual differences, of giving exploration and guidance to children, of giving opportunity to the pupil for earlier orientation and differentiation in the various major fields of human endeavor, and of retaining the pupils in the school. It was quite natural that general science, which had been considered as an orientation course in science, should, therefore, find its way into the junior-high-school curriculum, especially because its aims were so closely in accord with the major purposes of the junior high school.

The new points of view arising from the maladjustment of the high-school program of studies to modern life in a democracy prompted a reorganization of the secondary-school program. Simultaneously the recognition of the failure of the formal, special sciences led to marked changes in the science curriculum. The nature of the newer points of view and of the proposed reorganizations are elaborated in the reports of the various commissions of the National Education Association which appeared between 1915 and 1920. The report entitled *Cardinal Principles of Secondary Education*[2] and the report on *Reorganization of Science in Secondary Schools*[3] had a decided influence upon the science curriculum. The aims and purposes of general science, as well as of other sciences, were stated both in terms of six ultimate objectives to which the study of science should contribute and in terms of the more immediate objectives; that is, the knowledges, habits, powers, interests, and ideals which would lead pupils to the acquisition of the desirable, ultimate objectives in matters of health, home membership, vocation, citizenship, use of leisure time, and ethical character.

The Yearbook Committee recognizes the contribution of the report on *Reorganization of Science in Secondary Schools* and is in accord with the social philosophy of education expressed and implied in this report and in *Cardinal Principles of Secondary Education*. These reports constitute an excellent background for further development of the objectives of science teaching, particularly of the objectives of unspecialized science at the seventh-, eighth-, and ninth-grade levels. It appears now that we need to go much farther in the analysis of the more specific human behaviors to which a study of science on this level may contribute and then to determine in turn the specific knowledges, interests, skills, habits, and attitudes prerequisite to the specific behaviors.

Need for Further Analysis of Behaviors Affected by Science Teaching

These specific behaviors are in general of two kinds: (1) those which satisfy mental curiosity concerning phenomena and applications in the field of science—that is, the intellectual adjustments to the environment—and (2) those which represent the 'practical' tasks or activities met in everyday living—that is, the practical adjustments to the environment. It is understood that the desirable adjustments include those which pupils and adults actually do make or attempt to make in the unspecialized activities of life and also those which, upon the basis of education in science, they are able to make. In general, science on this level should emphasize the point of view of the con-

---

[2] Bureau of Educ. Bulletin, 1918, No. 35.
[3] Bureau of Educ. Bulletin, 1920, No. 26.

sumer. The study by Harap[4] has provided a technique for the analysis of the science that is of special value to the consumer and has presented some of the objectives of science instruction.

It is recognized that pupils and laymen cannot be expected, and should not attempt, to perform certain technical activities that require specialized training, as for example, the diagnosis of and prescription for major physical ailments. In all situations involving technical problems the science instruction should lead the pupil to respect and to call for assistance upon the expert. Thus we call on the physician for vaccination or inoculation; we turn to the weather forecaster for the weather report; we consult the agricultural expert for advice on soil fertilization; and we hire the electrical expert to wire our houses. Behavior of this sort on the part of pupils and laymen illustrates some of the important mental and practical adjustments referred to in the preceding paragraph.

Determination of the desirable specific adjustments in relation to the aspects of the environment which are most significant in everyday life offers the possibility of both a practical organization of a series of science courses for the three-year period under consideration and a set of attainable objectives. In accord with the plans of recent textbooks and courses of study in general science, a defensible basis for the determination of the specific adjustments seems to be provided by such aspects of our surroundings as the following materials, phenomena, and forces: food, water, air, clothing materials, materials of construction, fuels, plant life, animal life, heat, light, electricity, sound, machines, the weather, the climate, the sky, the crust of the earth, and the soil.

Each of these major aspects of the environment presents to us many problematical situations requiring intelligent adjustment. Thus we make certain mental and practical adjustments to food; for example, (1) some of us are engaged in producing food; (2) we select food materials at the market; (3) we prepare food for use; (4) we select a proper diet or ask the expert to do this for us; (5) we avoid deleterious foodstuffs; (6) we preserve foods; and (7) we aid in the conservation of the food supply. These are but a few of the specific adjustments which the intelligent citizen makes to this aspect of his environment. Adequate research to determine what are the significant aspects of the environment and further research to discover the im-

---

[4] Harap, Henry. *The Education of the Consumer.* New York: The Macmillan Company, 1924. 360 pp.

portant adjustments to each of these aspects will furnish us with a set of specific objectives defensible and worthy of instruction in science.

In such a program of research we must analyze the activities of the child (and of the adult) and learn from the scientist and the specialist what pupils should and should not do. This analysis must depend upon our present knowledge of science and the scientific methods that are available.

Criteria for Selecting Adjustments

It is obviously impossible to elaborate here all of the specific adjustments that should be acquired by pupils in the three years of the junior high school. It is in order, however, to suggest certain criteria that may be applied in selecting those adjustments which general science or junior-high-school science should seek to develop. When in each case all other things are considered equal, criteria should be applied that will assure that those adjustments selected are (1) universal in their application to life needs, (2) in accord with the findings of science, (3) in harmony with the best interests of society, (4) crucial in individual or social life, (5) conducive to the desire to make further worth-while adjustments, (6) of the proper order of difficulty for the seventh-, eighth-, and ninth-grade pupils, (7) highly satisfactory to the individual without giving harm to others or to himself, (8) desired by the pupils, (9) identifiable in their attainment, and (10) essential to the making of other desirable adjustments. If these ten criteria are applied, it is possible to state the specific adjustments that should constitute the objectives of the science courses for these grades in a liberal program of studies. The extent to which we may hope to have pupils attain these objectives must depend upon the background that they bring, upon the attitudes that can be instilled, and upon the knowledges, interests, skills, and habits that they are able to acquire during these three years of their school life.

Need for Determining Effective Items of Knowledge

Having prepared a defensible set of adjustments to be desired, it becomes necessary to discover those knowledges that will make the adjustments intelligent. Thus, if we would have pupils interpret how our foods are produced, select their foods properly, conserve the food supply, and engage in other activities relating to this aspect of the environment, it becomes essential to have them acquire certain ideas that will serve as a basis upon which they may act intelligently. They will need to build from a variety of real and vicarious learning experiences (observations, experiments, reading, and so forth) those generalized ideas concerning food and its relation to individual and social life that will help them to act intelligently in the situations of life that are concerned with the production, utilization, and conservation of the food supply. Among the larger ideas necessary to this end we may indicate the following, which are, of course, directly related to the larger principles or generalizations stated in Chapter IV:

1. Foods are substances which serve certain purposes in living things.
2. All foods come directly or indirectly from green plants, which manufacture them from inorganic materials.
3. The cultivation and fertilization of the soil provides conditions and materials necessary to plant growth.
4. Foods differ in their chemical composition.
5. The various classes of foods serve different purposes in living things.
6. A correct balance of different classes of foods is essential to a proper diet.
7. The waste products from different foods must be removed from organisms.
8. Foods are made harmful by the action of some micro-organisms.
9. Foods are preserved from the action of micro-organisms by heat, by refrigeration, by drying, and by addition of chemicals.
10. The available food supply of the world is limited by our means of production and transportation and by natural conditions.
11. The purity of food is controlled by local, state, and federal regulations.
12. Many national, state, and local organizations are attempting to solve the scientific problems relating to food.
13. Scientific information concerning various phases of the food problem can be obtained by consulting food experts.

In providing pupils with learning experiences through which they may gain the basic knowledges for intelligent action, it should be borne in mind that these generalizations, whether they are generalized facts, statements of cause and effect, or statements of relationship of any kind, should include both the ideas developed by pure science and the social implications of these ideas. For the seventh-, eighth-, and ninth-grade levels they should be largely qualitative and unhampered for understanding by the quantitative or technical considerations that are so common in the special sciences of the high school. It should also be planned that the generalizations become associated, as the course proceeds, into larger and larger ideas as the different aspects of the environment are considered and as newer relationships may come to light through learning. In such development of the learning outcomes the detailed facts, the terms for materials, forces, processes, and phenomena, and the associated ideas will be woven into a systematized, though small, group of generalizations, which will be those knowledges most usable in interpreting life situations and in assuring the desirable adjustments sought as the objectives of the work in science on this level.

The Committee wishes again to emphasize the desirability of coordinating the more specific items of knowledge set as the objectives of the junior-high-school science with the larger principles and generalizations designated in Chapter IV as justifiable bases for guidance in selecting specific objectives at all levels of elementary and secondary education. Only through such coördination can we hope to build at any level upon the previously learned facts and generalizations and to effect on the part of the pupils an ever-broadening understanding of the products of scientific study that have most direct and most comprehensive application to human welfare and human interest, from the point of view of both mental and practical adjustments to the environment.

It is impossible for pupils to acquire the essential knowledge and to reach the desirable attitudes and adjustments without at the same time developing the important skills, habits, and attitudes that are the elements and the means of effective methods of study in science. Only through these means can science experiences be real and educative. This makes imperative that the work in science on this level include a great variety of physical and mental activities, that pupils be made conscious of the elements and means of proper study procedures in these activities, and that they be given practice in applying the study skills in such ways and with such frequency as will lead to acceptable study habits and attitudes. The means and methods which scientists employ in acquiring information, in testing hypotheses, in arriving at defensible, tentative conclusions, in expressing the results of their study, and in applying their findings to human action suggest the variety of activities that should constitute the course. A suggested list of such activities will be found in Section V of this chapter.

Need for Attention to Attitudes

The combination of knowledges and of scientific skills, habits, and attitudes in science study do not suffice to insure the desirable behaviors that we have designated as the real goals of science teaching unless they are so acquired that they yield also the proper attitudes toward the environment. Thus we may know what constitutes a balanced diet, we may be skillful in interpreting dietary tables or in testing different foods for their ingredients, we may be open-minded in realizing that there is still much to be learned about proteins, and yet we may give little heed to the dangers of eating too much protein food. While the potential values of the knowledges and of the skills, habits, and attitudes of science study are recognized, it is important that teachers of science go beyond these instrumentalities and develop in children the attitudes toward themselves and their environment which will insure desirable adjustments. These interests, attitudes, and appreciations arise in pupils from seeing the individual and social implications of the knowledge and methods of science and from observing desirable behaviors in other human beings, particularly in teachers, in leaders of social life, and, in general, in their elders. The least that science teachers should do in this regard is to acquaint pupils with the values of desirable adjustments as exemplified in the lives of fellow human beings. It is in this connection that the study of the pertinent activities of the great past and present leaders in science, pure and applied, may aid in developing in youth those intellectual interests, desires, resolutions, and emotionalized standards that may well prove far more significant in their lives than the specific knowledges or specific study skills and study habits gained in the science course.

The fact that we have thus far done but little in measuring the results of science study in terms of these interests, attitudes, and appreciations should not lead us to overemphasize knowledges and skills as the significant goals. The emphasis on the more easily measured objectives has undoubtedly led to the unverified assumption that to know implies to do and to be. At all events, if science as taught on the seventh-, eighth-, and ninth-grade levels can contribute to desirable behaviors and to ethical character, as we believe it can, there needs to be made available objective evidence to show the nature of the contribution. Until such objective data are available, the teacher of science should certainly proceed upon the assumption that the science lesson for the day is filled with possibilities and opportunities for developing attitudes toward, interests in, and appreciations of, the relations of man to the materials and forces of his surroundings. Modern psychology bears out the view that every learning or reaction changes in some degree the entire personality and life of the pupil. Teachers of science, in planning their courses, should not neglect the import of this point of view.

Need for Articulation with Elementary-School Science

The Committee would point out once more the need for planning the objectives on the junior-high-school level in relation to those of the entire science program from the first to the twelfth grade. Such planning will consider adjustments, attitudes, study activities, and knowledges. The present conditions of science teaching in the elementary school must determine the objectives which can be attained on that level. The seventh-, eighth-, and ninth-grade science must be planned to articulate with the goals attained in the elementary school and must govern the organization and content of the sciences studied in later years. There are almost limitless possibilities for research in establishing a defensible sequence and articulation of science on the various grade levels.

The clarification of the science objectives for grades seven, eight, and nine will, moreover, aid in making more specific and more exact the objectives of the junior high school. Just how far can children's abilities, interests, and aptitudes be explored on this level? How far can we proceed in revealing the major specialized fields of human endeavor? To what extent may we meet individual differences? In what measure may we satisfy pupils' needs? What conscious applications of the principles of healthful living can we assure? These are some of the problems of the junior high school that may be answered in part by research in the field of science objectives.

III. The Selection and Organization of Learning Activities

We have pointed out in the preceding section that the subject matter and activities comprising the course in science in the seventh, eighth, and ninth grades should be chosen in terms of those aspects of the environment which, from the point of view of science, are most significant in the everyday life of individuals and of society. It may not seem out of place to trace very briefly the evolution of ideas concerning the selection and organization of the content of general-science courses and thus to clarify the point of view which this Committee holds.

Among the early courses in general sciences we find the course which was little more than a combination of the elementary parts of the special sciences offered in the high school, each section representing a logical organization of a special science. Thus we find in one outline such chapter headings as these: Matter, Constitution of Matter, Effect of Heat on Matter, Transfer of Heat,

Three States of Matter, Chemical Phenomena, Carbon, Water, Soil, Leaves, Stems, Roots, and Animals. Such courses had certain exploratory and preparatory values, but they did not represent a serious attempt to bring together the different sciences in such a way that the pupil could gain a perspective of the relation of science as a whole to the activities of life. The content was largely factual and formal, calling for a memoriter type of learning.

Another type of course found its organization and selection of content in line with the topics of a single special science—physiography, for example— and extended the content, here and there, along various by-paths into the fields of other special sciences or into environmental topics. This type of course had the advantage of having a thread of thought which tied together the different topics, but unfortunately many of the topics included discussions of unrelated materials and altogether the course failed to orient the pupil within the broad field of science and in the relation of science to life.

A third type of course that was taught in some schools during the early days of general science, and that persists in certain sections of the country to-day, was the course based upon the traditional idea that the first part of a course must be in the nature of basic facts, definitions, and so-called 'fundamental concepts' and that the second part (the second half-year) can then proceed to a consideration of topics bearing direct significance to daily life. Thus Matter, Force and Energy, Heat, Elements and Compounds, Magnetism and Electricity, and Light and Sound represent some of the early topics, followed in the latter part of the course by such topics as The Weather; Water, Heat, Air, and Light in the Home; Rocks and Soil; and The Human Body and Its Food.

While the various types of courses mentioned in the preceding paragraphs were being formulated and their content chosen in keeping with their general plans of organization, there developed in several centers another type of organization of general science which was the forerunner of most of our present courses. "Creator-made units" and "environmental topics inherently interesting to pupils" were two characterizations of this general plan of organization. In these courses the sections, units, chapters, or major topics represented aspects of the environment. Thus we find among the headings of sections of the courses such titles as these: Water, Air, Heat, Bacteria, Fuels, Clothing, Metals, Germs and Disease, Light, Sound and Music, Machines, The Universe, Animal Life, Electricity in Modern Life, Weather, and Transportation. In some outlines of courses of this type there was evidenced a truly environmental point of view in the organization and content. In others some of the larger topics, like Air, were treated in several separate chapters, e.g., in chapters on the physics of the air, the chemistry of the air, the hygiene of the air, the meteorology of the air, and so on. Evidently there was in this latter type of treatment a remnant of the special-science point of view.

The limitations of space permit us only to mention a number of other types of courses that were organized. Some were composed largely of physical-science topics; some might be designated as the 'home and community type' of organization; some were organized about the principles of the special sciences. In most cases there was evidence of a special-science point of view both in organization and in content. Even some of the investigations into the nature of the content of the textbooks published up to 1920 analyzed the books in terms of the percentage of space given to the special sciences, thus keeping before teachers the special-science point of view.

Probably the most effective influence making for greater uniformity in the content and organization of general science was the report of the Commission on the Reorganization of Science in Secondary Schools already cited. Many authors of textbooks and syllabi that appeared after the publication of this report heeded the recommendations of the report, from which we here quote the section dealing with the selection and organization of subject matter:

The subject matter of general science should be selected to a large extent from the environment. It will therefore vary greatly in different communities. The science involved in normal human activities, and especially the science involved in the reconstruction period after the war, presents many real problems which must be met more intelligently than formerly if there is to be the needed increase in effectiveness of the service which individuals and groups are expected to give. Science is universal and constant in the life of our citizens, and hence to be useful to all pupils general science must accept the science of common things as its legitimate field. The science of common use and that of the classroom should be the same. General science should use any phase of any special science which is pertinent in the citizen's interpretation of a worth-while problem.

The particular units of study should be those that truly interest the pupils. Interest not only secures productive attention but is an evidence of attention. To be substantial educationally, interest must rest upon a sense of value, an evident worthwhileness in the topics considered.

No topic should be selected which is meager in content or lacking in significant problems. The range of material which can be used is in reality limited only by the capacity, experiences, and needs of the pupils. The materials should be concrete and capable of leading to many avenues of new and untried experiences.

In *organizing* this material the topic should be the large unit to which many specific pieces of work are related. For example, a general topic such as *fire* may be selected. Many specific pieces of work will arise—one of practical value being "The Hot Air Furnace," or any other definite system of heating. The problems for solution under this topic will be varied and many, as: What causes the air to circulate? How does it circulate? How should pipe valves be arranged to cause equal circulation in all rooms of a house? To answer these questions many experiments and demonstrations must be made. Again, in the study of the local water system, determine the uses now made of water and the benefits and dangers of the system, construct models of mechanical devices used in the system for securing and delivering water and for disposal of wastes, etc. The following list of subtopics will suggest the content of the whole topic:

the common uses of water; local dangers of contamination; sources of supply in use and possibilities for extension of system; relation to public health with typhoid as an illustration; sewage, its uses and dangers.[5]

The general emphasis that the report of 1920 laid on environmental science of significance in human activities and of interest to pupils was quite generally accepted as a criterion of selection of subject matter. Similarly, the plan of organization that called for large environmental topics with subordinate problems and projects became the pattern for many textbooks and syllabi in the subject.

Following the publication of the report, there appeared several investigations of the content of general-science courses.

Webb's[6] quantitative analysis of the content of eighteen current textbooks in the field aided greatly in gaining a picture of the branches of the special sciences represented and of the major topics of each science found in the textbooks. It also aided in giving to the authors of later books and to syllabus committees an excellent check list to supplement the less extensive list obtained by Howe[7] in an earlier study of teachers' judgments as to the desirable content of general science. A study by Overn[8] of thirteen textbooks published prior to 1920 gives an additional check on the topics and subtopics treated in general-science courses of that period.

The study by Weckel[9] revealed the fundamental concepts and topics occurring in fourteen of the textbooks then in use and gave the frequency of the topics as found in the textbooks examined. Meier[10] examined quantitatively the types of exercises included in current textbooks and laboratory manuals and then subjected her list to evaluation by seventh- and eighth-grade teachers to determine the relative values of the different exercises. The results showed that teachers greatly favored the applied-science type of exercise rather than the pure-science type and that, in the twenty-five exercises having the highest rank, the

---

[5] Bureau of Educ. Bulletin, 1920, No. 26, pp. 25-26.

[6] Webb, Hanor A. *General Science Instruction in the Grades:* Part I. (Contributions to Education, No. 4) Nashville, Tennessee: George Peabody College for Teachers, 1921, pp. 1-40.

[7] Howe, C. M. "What eighty teachers think as to the aims and subject matter of general science." *General Sci. Quarterly,* 20: May, 1918, 445-458.

[8] Overn, O. E. *An Analysis of Textbooks in General Science.* (Master's thesis, University of Chicago, 1921. Digest in Curtis, Vol. I, pp. 72-73.)

[9] Weckel, Ada L. "Are principles of organization of general science evidenced in the present textbooks in the subject?" *Sch. Sci. and Math.,* 22: Jan. 1922, 44-51.

[10] Meier, Lois. "Current practices in the teaching of science in the seventh and eighth grades." *General Sci. Quarterly,* 9: Nov., 1924, 1-7.

physical sciences and the biological sciences were almost equally represented.

These studies revealed a rather surprising similarity in the major topics elaborated in the different sources, despite the fact that the subject was new in the curriculum. They showed, too, that general science was weighted heavily with the content of physical science, as indeed is the case with the majority of present general-science courses.

Following the various analyses of textbooks and manuals, another set of investigations was reported. These concerned the interests in science materials of children of junior-high-school age. The studies were projected by earlier studies of children's interests in the field of nature study and by the changing philosophy of education, which in this period, the third decade of the century, came to emphasize children's interests and children's activities as valid bases or criteria for curriculum determination. The studies by Pollock[11] and by Curtis,[12] following similar techniques, of children's interests in science as expressed in questions by the children, shed some light in determining the relative degrees of interest which children had in various environmental topics and problems. The evaluation by the Committee of these and other studies of interests is stated in Chapter II of this Yearbook. The point of view of this Committee is that such studies may furnish valuable suggestions concerning means of approach in science study, but cannot be relied upon to determine the basic content of a course in science for seventh-, eighth-, and ninth-grade pupils if it is to meet the objectives set forth in an earlier section of this chapter.

Two recent reports of studies, those by Curtis[13] and by Downing,[14] afford an excellent perspective of the present subject-matter content of general science and provide the best available up-to-date check lists of topics and principles that have received recognition in textbooks and courses of study.

---

[11] Pollock, C. A. "Children's interests as a basis of what to teach in general science." *Ohio State Univ. Educ. Research Bulletin,* III, No. 1, 1924, pp. 3-6.

[12] Curtis, F. D. *Some Values Derived from Extensive Reading of General Science.* (Contr. to Educ., No. 163) New York: Teachers College, Columbia University, 1924, pp. 27-40.

[13] Curtis, F. D. *A Synthesis and Evaluation of Subject-Matter Topics in General Science.* Boston: Ginn, 1929. 77 pp.

[14] Downing, E. R. "An analysis of textbooks in general science." *General Sci. Quarterly,* 12: May, 1928, 509-516. See also Curtis, F. D. *Second Digest of Investigations in the Teaching of Science.* Philadelphia: Blakiston's, 1931, pp. 75-79, for a list of 93 principles of science found in twenty textbooks on general science by Aislie M. Heinemann as reported by Downing.

We have traced briefly some of the stages through which science on the junior-high-school level has developed into its present form and content. It is understood, of course, that the changing points of view in the philosophy and practice of education in general, as well as the investigations referred to, were giving to the science course new directions. The demand for self-activity in our schools, the view that the child and not the subject should be the center of educational effort, the emphasis on the social values of education, the conception of education as gradual growth in the direction of habits and behaviors that make for a happy and productive life, and the growing view that subject matter is but a means to education are but a few educational postulates which had direct influence upon the selection and organization of the general-science course, as an examination of the prefaces and contents of the more recent textbooks and syllabi will show.

Principles of Selection Recommended by the Committee

On the basis of ideas gained from the study of the development of general science and in harmony with a philosophy of education acceptable to its members and developed elsewhere in this report, this Committee agrees upon certain guiding principles of selection of content for the science work of the seventh, eighth, and nine grades:

1. The content shall be chosen on the basis of its possible contribution to the objectives set forth in a preceding section of this chapter.
2. Subject matter shall be considered primarily as a means to an end and not merely as something to be remembered.
3. The course shall consist of a variety of physical and mental activities that shall lead to those knowledges, skills, interests, and attitudes essential to desirable mental and practical adjustments to the environment.
4. The content of the course shall bear direct significance to life's problems and activities.
5. The order of difficulty of the learning activities shall be such that pupils through reasonable effort may gain the satisfaction of accomplishment.
6. The learning activities shall call for experiences with the materials and forces of everyday life.
7. The learning activities shall be of such a nature that pupils may be interested in undertaking them and in carrying them to comple-

tion under the motivation and helpful guidance of a well-trained teacher.

8. The activities shall be such that they lead to the comprehension of the elementary generalizations of science that have important social implications.

9. The activities shall include abundant opportunities to apply the acquired knowledges, skills, and attitudes in life situations.

10. The activities, by their nature and order of difficulty, shall afford opportunity for the exercise of the creative abilities of youth and for the joy, romance, and adventure that discovery, invention, and self-production in science afford.

11. The activities shall be objective enough to be attainable and to make possible the determination or measurement of the attainment desired.

12. There shall be some activities that afford pupils means of judging and measuring their progress in the more specific learning activities.

13. Some activities, at least, shall be of such a nature that they may be organized into problems identical with the problems of life.

14. The activities shall call for direct, concrete experiences so far as possible, but vicarious experiences that are educative should not be neglected.

Principles of Organization Recommended by the Committee

There have been no adequate investigations dealing with the relative merits of various types of organization of the content of science for pupils of grades seven, eight, and nine. Until such investigations are made, it becomes necessary to rely upon experience and authority. The Committee recommends the following tentative principles of organization:

1. The course shall be organized into units, each of which shall be related to some significant aspect of the environment.

2. The unit shall be essentially a major problem of everyday life to which science may contribute the intelligent basis for human adjustment.

3. Each unit shall include only a few principles or generalizations of science.

4. Each unit shall be divided into subordinate problems to facilitate learning by pupils.

5. The continuity of the units shall be such that the entire course develops a sequential story of man's understanding of, and adjustment to, his whole science environment.

6. The organization, in part at least, shall be in the form of problems or projects to insure education in problem-solving, which is the nature of science.

7. There shall be relatively few units, in order to insure that pupils are brought to the understanding of the larger relationships of the facts and principles of science rather than to the mere memory of detailed facts.

8. The units shall be so organized that the conceptions of science and their social implications, once learned, shall be used in new relationships in later units.

9. The interrelationships of generalizations and their social significance shall be brought to the attention of pupils by abundant cross references and 'cross exercises.'

10. Not only shall generalizations be developed in each unit, but there shall also be abundant opportunities to apply the generalizations in the interpretation of novel problems and novel phenomena.

11. In so far as possible, the units and their study materials shall be arranged and organized in such a way that the succeeding units will call for the understanding of larger and larger relationships and conceptions, will contain progressively difficult activities, and will arrive at more and more comprehensive adjustments.

12. There shall be provided in each unit enough activities to insure accomplishment of the objectives by pupils of different interests and capacities.

13. In general, the units and the subordinate problems within each unit shall proceed in line with the scientific methods of problem-solving; that is, (*a*) from sense perceptions of materials, forces, or phenomena to the formulation of ideas, to the testing of the hypotheses, to the tentative conclusions, and to the application of the conclusions in life situations, or (*b*) from principles or generalizations to the interpretation of specific situations.

14. The distribution of time and emphasis to the various units shall be determined by the total, functional, social value of the unit, its teachability and 'learnability,' the teacher's and pupils' interest in the unit, the local significance of the unit, and its value to other units of the course.

15. The entire set of units shall be so formulated that the pupil will have revealed to him the kinds and nature of the major fields of science.

16. The laboratory work shall be included as an integral part of problem-solving and shall, therefore, have the characteristics of experience-getting work rather than of illustrative or confirmatory work.

17. Historical and biographical content shall be introduced when and where it will aid in the understanding of the concepts developed and of their social implications and in the attainment of the human adjustments sought.

18. Subject matter shall be so arranged that it will be a means to the solution of problems and not an end in itself.

19. In so far as possible, the materials and activities shall be organized around the pupil's life but shall project the pupil into the problems of adulthood.

20. The organization shall be such that it will lead to the attainment of the immediate and ultimate objectives.

IV. INTEGRATION AND ARTICULATION

Whatever the specific form of organization used, the entire plan should be integrated with the elementary science and with the special sciences of the later years of the high school, to the end that the growth of pupils in science may be gradual and natural. This integration does not require a complete reorganization of the science courses now offered on the different levels but rather a careful modification of all courses concerned.

Studies by Leker[15] and by Osburn[16] of the overlapping of present courses in general science and the special sciences of the high school indicate the need for a careful scrutiny of the courses on both levels. This scrutiny should take into consideration both the objectives of the courses and the order of difficulty of the learning products sought on the two levels.

The Committee is of the opinion that there is little justification for the view held by some teachers of the special sciences that the special sciences are sacred ground, not to be trespassed upon by the earlier

---

[15] Leker, W. R. "The articulation of general science with special sciences." *General Sci. Quarterly,* 9: March, 1925, 158-173; also *Sch. Sci. and Math.,* 35· October, 1925, 724-735.

[16] Osburn, W. J. *Overlappings and Omissions in our Courses of Study* Bloomington, Illinois: Public School Publishing Company, 1928. 167 pp.

science courses. It seems defensible to suggest that if certain content now in the special sciences is socially significant and of such order of difficulty that it is appropriate for study by pupils on the seventh-, eighth-, and ninth-grade levels, it should not be kept in the special sciences and thereby denied to a large number of boys and girls who leave school early or who do not elect the special sciences. Educational perspective and judgment coupled with objective evidence are needed to determine on what level this or that aspect of content finds its true educational place.

When general science came into the school curriculum, its value was judged to some extent upon the basis of the contributions it could make as a preparation for the special sciences. In fact, there has been advanced the idea that its true worth in a sequence of science courses should be judged by its preparatory values. Obviously such argument is to a large degree contrary to the accepted objectives of the course in general science and yet, notwithstanding, the great majority of studies—such as those by Carpenter, Hurd, Cramer and Dvorak, which are reported in Chapter IX of this Yearbook—show that pupils who have studied general science do come to the special sciences with a better background of scientific information than do those who have not studied general science.

The Committee stresses again, in this connection, the views expressed in Chapter I: first, that the science courses on this level are not to be judged primarily on the basis of their contribution to the special sciences but rather on the basis of the contributions they can make to the improvement of human adjustments in a modern environment; and second, that the science courses on this level should be an integrated three-year series of courses, built upon and comprehending the objectives attained in the science work of the elementary school. The degree to which such a curriculum in science, during the first nine years of school life, prepares pupils to live in a scientific age should be the primary measure of the success of the study. If at the same time the pupils become acquainted with the opportunities for further work in science and gain some measure of their interest in, and capacity for, this or that special science or vocation, then a secondary objective will have been attained. With this attitude toward an integrated series of science courses for the first nine grades the Committee advocates strongly that the special sciences for the later years of the high school be modified in such a way and to such a degree that they may build firmly and sensibly upon the foundations provided during the earlier years.

V. Methods of Instruction

The very nature of science and the objectives of science education in the seventh, eighth, and ninth grades prompt, at the outset of this section, the statement that mere lesson-assigning and lesson-hearing is a technique of instruction in science that the Committee highly disapproves. The present practice in some schools of limiting the science work in the seventh, eighth, and ninth grades to mere textbook study and recitation cannot be too strongly condemned as a harmful procedure. Science is essentially an experimental study of materials and phenomena and requires, therefore, learning activities that are designed to solve problems relating to concrete and objective instructional materials, whether in pure science or in its applied aspects.

The teacher of science who has carefully formulated the ultimate and immediate objectives of his course, who has chosen and organized the learning activities in harmony with acceptable criteria, and who has provided the proper instructional materials is ready to begin his work with the class. In the classroom it becomes his duty to diagnose the pupils' previous learning; to direct, to motivate, and to supervise the learning activities; to provide direct and vicarious learning experiences not obtainable from other sources; to measure the learning products; and to instill the desire for the continuance of learning. It should be understood here that the learning products to be sought are not primarily the acquisitions of information but rather modified adjustments in individual and social life.

At the outset of a new unit of work the teacher may provide the means of making an inventory of the pupils' present acquisition of the learning products which the unit is planned to give. This inventory is successful to the degree that it discovers the individual pupil's background, for only with such individual diagnosis can the teacher proceed intelligently with the work of the unit. The inventory may be a new-type test, a class discussion, a written composition, or any other form of activity that accomplishes its purpose. If the inventory is adequate and if at the same time it is a satisfying activity for the pupils, it may also both serve the purpose of arousing a deep interest in the new unit and provide an excellent review of the learning acquired in previous units.

Since the large topic or problem is the teaching unit, it is essential that the laws of learning be applied to the entire unit as well as to its subordinate parts or to the work of a single class period. It thus becomes necessary that the pupil be stimulated and orientated with respect to the new unit through some class activity designed for this purpose. Such class activity—whether a presentation by the teacher; the reading of a pertinent article, story, or section of a book by teacher or pupils; a field trip; a visit to a scientific institution or industrial plant; or a class conference—should arouse an interest in the new unit, give a general view of it, and raise those problems or points on which further learning is necessary. Above all, the activity should make clear to the pupil, upon the basis of his experiences, the significance of the new topic or problem to his everyday life and to community life.

Once stimulated and orientated in the new unit, the pupil should engage in a variety of physical and mental activities, chosen and arranged in accordance with the principles of selection and organization proposed in Section III of this chapter, to the end that through his own learning, under the supervision of the teacher, he will acquire the learning products which were set as the objectives.

The activities to be used in this stage of the unit should be of at least three kinds: (1) those designed for the purpose of gaining new abilities, new skills, new knowledges, new interests, and new attitudes, (2) those designed to give practice in the use of abilities previously gained, and (3) those designed to give the pupil means of measuring his acquisition of the learning products sought.

While most supervisors and teachers of science can readily list a great variety of activities useful in this stage of a unit, it may not be out of place to suggest here some of the activities and types of exercises which in practice have proved to be valuable:

1. Reading for various purposes, such as (a) to gain perspective, (b) to find unsolved problems, (c) to reproduce ideas, (d) to make comparisons, (e) to gain facts for the solution of problems, (f) to select major ideas, (g) to find illustrations of generalized ideas, and so forth.
2. Interpreting diagrams or analytical drawings.
3. Interpreting maps.
4. Interpreting statistical tables.
5. Interpreting graphs.
6. Making analytical drawings.
7. Drawing from description.
8. Drawing from observation.
9. Making graphs of data.

10. Making tables of data.
11. Making maps.
12. Taking notes on reading.
13. Taking notes on a talk or lecture.
14. Manipulating in laboratory experimentation.
15. Observing manipulation in demonstration.
16. Observing and interpreting natural phenomena.
17. Observing and interpreting experimental phenomena.
18. Writing reports on experimentation.
19. Organizing and writing compositions.
20. Organizing and presenting oral reports.
21. Preparing topical and statement outlines.
22. Preparing summaries.
23. Solving mathematical problems.
24. Making collections.
25. Constructing models, appliances, and so forth.
26. Repairing appliances.
27. Interpreting construction and operation of appliances.
28. Evaluating popular notions or fallacies.
29. Making local surveys (home and community).
30. Asking questions.
31. Preparing written questions to test knowledge gained.
32. Answering questions[17] (oral and written) such as those (a) involving observation, (b) involving pure memory, (c) involving analysis, (d) involving selective recall, (e) involving the making of problems and questions, (f) requiring a statement of causes or effects, (g) requiring the pupil to suggest or make applications of rules or principles in new situations, (h) requiring a decision, (i) requiring the pupil to compare two things in general, (j) requiring the pupil to give illustrations or examples, (k) requiring an evaluating recall when the basis is given, (l) requiring the pupil to state relationships, (m) requiring the pupil to compare two things on a single designated basis, (n) involving discussion, (o) requiring the pupil to explain the use or meaning of some phrase or statement in a passage, (p) requiring the pupil to summarize some unit in the text, article read, or experiment performed, (q) requiring the pupil to classify, (r) involving new methods of procedure, (s) requiring the pupil to reorganize on a new basis facts learned in one organization, (t) requiring the pupil to give a brief outline, (u) involving aim—the author's purpose in his selection or organization of material, (v) requiring the pupil to criticise some statement as to adequacy, correctness, or relevancy of a printed statement.
33. Evaluating social and civic problems on the basis of science knowledge.
34. Answering new-type examination questions.
35. Answering essay-type examination questions.

---

[17] The types of questions listed under (32) are taken from Cunningham's list. See Cunningham, Harry A. "Types of thought questions in general science textbooks and laboratory manuals." *General Sci. Quarterly*, 9: January, 1925, 91-95.

36. Keeping a science notebook.
37. Keeping a science scrapbook.
38. Helping in demonstration.
39. Taking charge of the bulletin board.
40. Taking part in science-club and assembly programs.
41. Writing the science notes for the school paper.
42. Consulting authorities (personally).
43. Taking charge of class discussion.
44. Home experimentation.

It cannot be overemphasized that the activities chosen should serve a defensible and definite purpose in the solution of a science problem or in the direction of acquiring something significant to life. There has been too much 'busy work,' too much aimless activity, and too much memory and drill of detailed facts in science classes.

The number and variety of activities within a unit should be great enough to care for individual differences in the preparation, in the capacity, and in the interests of pupils, both for the accomplishment of the minimal objectives and for voluntary, supplementary study.

As pupils proceed with the various activities, they should be made conscious of the steps in learning and conscious of the particular elements of scientific procedure involved in each kind of activity. Studies, such as those by Beauchamp[18] and by Persing,[19] reveal the value of assisting pupils to become conscious of the nature of the psychological steps involved in various learning activities in science.

The demonstration, the laboratory experiment, the field trip, the reading of the textbook and the science reference book, the examination of visual aids, and similar activities should be considered primarily as sources of experiences that provide the bases for reflected thinking in problem situations and not as ends in themselves. The Committee particularly disapproves of the view that laboratory work, individual or group, finds its chief value in confirming or fixing learnings gained from other activities.

In recent years there have appeared pupils' workbooks and tests in the field of seventh-, eighth-, and ninth-grade science. These, if properly used as means to the accomplishment of the major objectives, are valuable aids. There is in the use of these, however, the danger

---

[18] Beauchamp, W. L. *A Preliminary Experimental Study of Technique in the Mastery of Subject Matter in Elementary Physical Science.* Studies in Secondary Education, I. (Supplementary Educational Monographs, No. 24) University of Chicago, Chicago: 1923, pp. 47-87.

[19] Persing, Kimber M. "A practice study in paragraph summarizing in chemistry." *Sch. Sci. and Math.,* 24: June, 1924, 598-604.

that pupils will measure their success in the course by their perform-ance of the assimilative activities and not by their accomplishment of the larger objectives. The teacher will find it necessary to make per-fectly clear to pupils the purposes that these aids to learning are designed to serve.

The discussion of methods of instruction has, up to this point, given considerable emphasis to individualized work, especially following the inventory and orientation stages of the unit. This, the Committee be-lieves, is essential to a valid technique of instruction. It is not, how-ever, our view that these individualized activities shall constitute all of the activities during the study stage. Pupil-committee reports, group demonstrations, class discussions, class debates, and science-club activities are types of group enterprises that are encouraged as learning experiences of value in humanizing and socializing the science work.

Experiences of successful teachers in science and in other subjects and the study by Curtis[20] support the Committee in suggesting to supervisors and teachers of science at this level that they encourage in pupils the extensive reading of articles and books on science. This type of activity not only yields results in giving to students scientific information and assistance in developing scientific attitudes, as shown by the investigation of Curtis, but it also enhances the interest in the regular work of the course and may, at the same time, develop a whole-some habit which carries on into later years. It is suggested that if extensive reading is made a voluntary activity, it will yield results far beyond those obtained through assigned extensive reading. This activity, moreover, offers an excellent means of meeting individual differences.

At the end of the study stage of each subordinate topic or problem within a unit, and particularly at the end of the last problem of the unit, it becomes necessary to provide pupils with activities in which they are given the opportunity to organize and synthesize the ideas acquired through the various preceding stages of the unit. We may speak of this as the organization stage. These organizing exercises or activities may well be substituted for the summaries often found in textbooks. Teachers are encouraged to give pupils assistance in organizing their thoughts and thereby to help them reach the larger ideas that are the knowledge goals of the unit.

---

[20] Curtis, Francis D. *Some Values Derived from Extensive Reading of Gen-eral Science.* pp. 50-112.

So important is still another stage in the process of teaching and so commonly is it neglected that the Committee wishes to make especial mention of it. In the Herbartian system it was called "application." It is in this stage that pupils should be given special opportunity to apply the generalizations to the interpretation of specific life situations.

VI. MEASUREMENT OF LEARNING PRODUCTS

Reference has already been made to the self-testing exercises or activities that are in the nature of instructional tests and that should be interspersed among the learning activities of each unit. These informal tests serve particularly as guides that enable pupils and teacher to determine whether the particular objective of learning has been reached and to suggest the possible need for further study.

At the end of the unit and at the end of the course it is desirable—it is often administratively imperative—to 'take stock'; that is, to determine the degree to which pupils have attained the objectives sought in the unit or course. Obviously, the larger objectives should receive the greater recognition in formulating such tests or measures of success in the science work.

In the field of knowledges and skills the measures applied to ascertain the intellectual growth and status of the pupil should comprise more than detailed facts. The knowledges and skills to be tested include: (1) the understanding of the big ideas or generalizations, (2) the understanding of relationships of the facts and of the larger ideas, (3) the ability to develop and organize the larger ideas from given or known facts, (4) the skill to obtain essential knowledge from the experiment, the reading material, and other sources, (5) the ability to use generalizations in interpreting new situations, (6) the ability to interpret relationships of cause and effect, (7) the ability to classify, (8) the ability to control simple experimental procedures, and (9) skill in solving problematic situations by scientific thinking.

While it is difficult to measure the acquisition of the interests, attitudes, and appreciations that we set as objectives in science, this should not keep us from attempting to do so. Already much has been accomplished in measuring these desirable learning products in other fields. Curtis[21] has developed a test of scientific attitudes that offers suggestions to teachers of science. There appears to be no sound reason why

---

[21] Curtis, Francis D. *Some Values Derived from Extensive Reading in General Science*, pp. 57-72.

we cannot develop tests of interests in, attitudes toward, and appreciations of, the aspects of the environment that are so intimately related to our lives and why we should not attempt to measure the growth of pupils in these fundamental qualities.

Finally and most important of all the measurable outcomes of science on this level are the actual behaviors—the human adjustments —performed by pupils in life situations. What pupils do in that way as a result of their work in science is a more significant measure of the success of the course than is the acquisition of knowledges and skills. Unfortunately, the measures of these outcomes are difficult to create and still more difficult to apply. We do find one excellent measure in the number and quality of voluntary activities, beyond the requirements of the course, which pupils complete—the home projects they carry on, the science reading they do, the science-club activities they share, the helpfulness they exhibit in the classroom, the bulletin-board material they supply, the community activities in which they engage, the kinds of lunches they select, the care of their physical health, and so on.

VII. Materials for Instruction

The objectives of science for grades seven, eight, and nine make it highly desirable that pupils and teachers be provided with workrooms in which the pupils may engage in a variety of learning activities. Separate classrooms and laboratories are not only unnecessary but undesirable. The teaching of science in ordinary classrooms is deplored by the Committee.

A serviceable workroom for the study of science in grades seven, eight, and nine is described in Chapter XVI. This room should contain a good demonstration table; movable work tables for the pupils; adequate blackboard space; a large bulletin board; shelves of reference books; files or cases containing pamphlets, bulletins, and pictures; an aquarium; a terrarium; a plant growing bed; an exhibit case or shelf; storage space for equipment, laboratory supplies, and exhibit materials; a projection apparatus for still and motion pictures; and adequate gas, electrical, and water connections.

The Committee recommends that teachers of science and school administrators give more attention to the need for better equipped science workrooms and that school architects and administrators consult with experts in science education on matters concerning the layout and equipment of science workrooms.

The Committee further recommends that all instructional materials, such as books, pamphlets, exhibits, laboratory equipment, and laboratory supplies, be selected on the basis of the contribution they can make toward the attainment of the objectives of the science work on this grade level. The composite lists of materials offered by commercial supply houses should be carefully scrutinized to insure that the public funds are intelligently disbursed. It seems highly improbable, regardless of the care exercised in its compilation, that a list of science materials intended to meet many different school situations can adequately meet any one of them.

CHAPTER XIV
THE COURSE OF STUDY IN BIOLOGY*

By the biology course is here meant not merely that year of work at about the tenth-grade level which bears the title of biology (or botany and zoölogy), but also the elementary science of the grades below in so far as it studies life; the physiology, hygiene, and sanitation; and the advanced life science of the high school, college, and university. With the college and university courses we shall not be directly concerned, except it must be remembered that beginning biology work need not undertake to cover the field. Much that is of large significance to the technical biologist will be left out of the lower levels, to be included in the more advanced courses.

Before one can effectively plan the knowledge content of that portion of the course of study in our school system which seeks to impart knowledge of biology, three things need to be known: First, what are the important principles needed to solve the problematic situations involving biology that arise in life? Second, how much time is required to teach each of these principles so that it will function in life? Third, at what grade level can each principle best be taught without undue expenditure of time and energy on the part of pupils and teacher?

SELECTION OF CURRICULAR MATERIALS

Without discussing the several rival methods that have been in vogue for the selection of the knowledge materials for the curriculum, it will suffice to state that here we assume that if we can find out what biology one needs to know to meet life's practical and potential needs, *that* is the stuff that should constitute the course of study. Those principles most often needed should come as early as possible in the course, to insure that no pupil can escape from school without possessing this knowledge of paramount importance.

There are many problematic situations involving biology that arise in the life of the average person. Some of these are problems concerning which he must do something, as: What foods shall I eat? How can I most effectively avoid disease? What type of individual shall I

---
* For the Committee, by Elliot R. Downing.

marry? Other problems arise that one wants to solve merely to satisfy his intellectual curiosity, as: What is the meaning of this fossil taken out of the neighboring quarry? What becomes of frogs in the winter? Why does a cat avoid going out in the snow while a dog romps in it with glee?

PRINCIPLES VERSUS SPECIFIC SOLUTIONS

Theoretically one might list all such questions that arise in a given community and teach the answers to every pupil in the biology work of the schools in that particular place, but that seems an impossible task, for the specific questions are so multitudinous. But the principles of biology involved in them are relatively few. It is wiser, therefore, to give the pupils an understanding of the more important principles— important because they do help in solving these oft-recurring questions —and enough drill in applying them to typical life problems to insure skill in their use when the need may arise in their lives.

There is investigational evidence which indicates that there is little or no correlation between mere ability to state a principle in science and skill in its application to the solution of problematic situations.[1] Only as pupils are given abundant drill in the use of the principle is such skill imparted. Yet most of our present tests in science, in the little demand they make for a knowledge of principles—they are largely factual—too often call for mere ability to state the principle and not for skill in its application to life problems.

To give pupils a mastery of the more important principles of biology gives some assurance that they will still be able to meet situations that arise when they go, as many will, into quite different communities from the particular ones in which they attended school. It assures the ability to meet the problems that will arise in their maturity when the particular problems to be settled will probably have changed greatly from those we have to face now-a-days. Specific problems are local in place and in time; principles are well-nigh universal. Moreover, the teaching of principles is the essential step in developing in the pupil a clear understanding of the major generalizations.

On the whole, it seems wise to state the knowledge content of the curriculum in terms of the important principles of biology to be mas-

---

[1] Schafer, Benjamin F. *The Relation between Knowledge of the Principles in the Laws of Physics and the Ability to Make Applications.* Master's thesis, School of Education, University of Chicago, 1925. (Unpublished)

tered. A course in biology is much more likely to put emphasis on fundamental principles than are courses in botany and zoölogy. In these latter, attention is too often focused on the material to be studied and the course is outlined in terms of the time to be spent on the fern plant, the corn plant, or on Ameba, Grantia, the frog, etc.

DETERMINATION OF IMPORTANT PRINCIPLES

How can we go about it to determine what are the most important principles on which we depend for the solution of the biological problems that most frequently arise in the lives of average individuals? It would evidently be very helpful if trained investigators could follow around in their daily tasks the farmer, doctor, housewife, carpenter, teacher, and other workers, for several years in the life of each, and note what problems involving biology they meet and what principle (or principles) is to be used for the solution of each. Such a method involves practical difficulties aside from the objection that it makes inadequate provision for improvement, since it is based upon an analysis of conditions as they now exist; therefore, the studies that have been made have commonly sought the desired information in a less direct way.

If one should read the articles touching on biology in many years' issues of the *Literary Digest* and list the principles needed to read them understandingly, he would know some of the biology needed by doctors, teachers, lawyers, and ministers, who are the chief subscribers to this journal. Or if one should find from librarians what ten or twenty books of a biological character are most commonly read and should then analyze these books in a similar fashion, he would get additional evidence. Or let one read and analyze the government bulletins by various departments concerned with matters biological, such as the Farmers Bulletins, those of the Bureau of Plant Industry, the Bureau of Animal Industry, the Bureau of Fisheries. These bulletins are issued to meet the practical needs of persons engaged in biological occupations and should indicate principles needed in real situations.

Several such studies have been made and others are in progress.[2]

---

[2] The following are published or are available in university libraries:

Ambrose, Luther L. *A Classification of Scientific Materials in a Widely Read Weekly (The Literary Digest).* Master's thesis: University of Chicago, 1927. (Unpublished)

Bobbitt, Franklin, and Others. *Curriculum Investigations.* Supplementary Educational Monographs, No. 31: University of Chicago, 1926.

Coon, Beulah I. *Suggestions for Content and Methods for Courses in Science*

Some of the latter, though incomplete, are far enough along to furnish valuable evidence. The pooled results of these several investigations afford a list of the biological principles that function most frequently in the solution of the problems of everyday life. The principles are listed here in the order of importance indicated in available objective evidence. Those statements are brought together which are intimately related as subordinate parts of one main principle, even when in the results of the several studies they have been separated. The order of importance has then been calculated as the average of the several parts.

Additional investigations may change this list somewhat or alter the order of relative importance, but here at least is a selection of the knowledge content of the biological curriculum based on objective evidence of the life needs of the average person.

A LIST OF THE PRINCIPLES[3]

I. Energy cannot be created or destroyed, but merely transformed from one form to another.

   a. That energy required by the living organism to carry on its activities is generated by the oxidation of its substance, so liberating stored up chemical energy.

   b. The oxidized substance is replaced by rebuilding it out of the foods taken.

   c. Since living material (protoplasm) is protein in character, containing nitrogen, a certain proportion of protein foods is essential.

   d. Substances used as foods should not contain any deleterious compounds. Stimulants and narcotics cause excessive irritability of the nerve cells that regulate vital processes and hence are likely to derange such processes in ways unfavorable to the survival of the organism.

   e. In the process of oxidation in the organism certain waste products are formed that, if retained, induce fatigue. To facilitate their removal and allow for recuperation, sleep and good ventilation are essential.

Related to the Home. Federal Board for Vocational Education: Washington, D. C. Misc. 837. Rev. 1926.

   Finlay, C. W., and Caldwell, Otis W. *Biology in the Public Press.* Lincoln School of Teachers College, Columbia University, 1923. See Curtis, F. D., *Investigations in the Teaching of Science*, I, 259-264.

   Lee, Ata L. *The Minimum Science Principles for the Required Subject Matter in Vocational Home Economics in Kentucky.* Master's thesis: University of Kentucky, 1929.

   Weber, Lynda M. *Scientific Principles Underlying Legislation Concerning Biological Matters.* Master's thesis; University of Chicago, 1929.

   [3] This list illustrates an application to the field of biology of the point of view presented in Chapter IV.

II. The ultimate source of the energy of all living things is sunlight.

    a. Green plants combine such absorbed simple substances as carbon dioxide, water, and nitrates to make sugars, starches, oils, proteins, and other materials. The energy for this process is furnished by the sunlight acting through the chlorophyll.

III. Micro-organisms are the immediate cause of some diseases.

    a. The transfer of micro-organisms from infected to non-infected individuals is prevented by (1) destroying them, (2) preventing the infection of carriers, (3) disinfection or destruction of carriers, (4) retarding the multiplication of infecting organisms through conditions inimical to their life, (5) establishment of immunity in individuals subject to infection.

    b. Microbes differ in their resistance to adverse conditions. Certain of them escape such conditions by forming highly resistant spores which survive them.

IV. All organisms must be adjusted to the environmental factors in order to survive in the struggle for existence.

    a. Since other organisms constitute an important part of the environment of every living thing, there is a complex web of life and an interdependence of organisms, producing a balance of nature that man is prone to upset and that he is forced to restore by artificial means.

    b. Man must protect those plants and animals that he has pampered by his care under domestication (1) by cutting off the food supply of their natural enemies and competitors, (2) by preventing the reproduction of natural enemies and competitors, and (3) by direct destruction of these organisms.

V. All life comes from previously existing life and reproduces its own kind.

    a. The new organism in the higher forms of life usually starts as a fertilized egg.

    b. Unit characters are usually inherited as such and are determined by genes carried in the chromosomes.

    c. Corresponding maternal and paternal genes go to different daughter cells in the reduction division, so that characters associated in one parent often separate and combine with those from the other parent in the offspring.

    d. In some cases a character is determined not by a single gene but by a combination of two or more genes, in which case the character is not inherited as a unit; the factors are inherited.

    e. Genes that lie in the same chromosome move together in the reduction division, so that characters which they determine may be linked in inheritance.

    f. Some apparent exceptions to these principles are due to crossing over. The greater the distance between any two genes in one chromosome, the more often they will separate if the chromosome breaks and part of it adheres to another chromosome.

VI. Animals and plants are not distributed uniformly or at random over the surface of the earth, but are found in definite zones and in local societies.

    a. These zones are separated on the large scale by such more or less impassable barriers as oceans, mountains, deserts, and broad and deep rivers.

    b. Locally, societies are separated more commonly by variations in the moisture content of the soil, its chemical composition, by differences of light intensity and the distribution of food materials.

VII. Food, oxygen, certain optimal conditions of temperature, moisture, and light are essential to the life of most living things.

    a. Frequently undesirable organisms, such as disease germs and insect pests, may be destroyed by denying them one or more of these essential factors.

VIII. The cell is the structural and physiological unit in all organisms.

IX. The more complex organisms have been derived by natural processes from simpler ones, these in turn from still simpler, and so on back to the first living forms.

These principles may be regarded, then, as a series of more immediate or specific objectives under the major objective, knowledge. Instructional units may well be formulated that will afford such a mastery of one principle or of a group of closely related principles as will insure their use in solving life's problems when the need shall arise.

SUBORDINATE UNDERSTANDINGS: EXPERIENCES AS IMMEDIATE OBJECTIVES

But in order to acquire an understanding of one of these principles, the pupil needs a background which must in turn be acquired through sensory experiences. Either such experiences which the pupil has already had must be recalled and organized for the purpose or the pupil must be given the needed experiences at the time he is working to master the principle.

To illustrate, consider Principle I. The teacher must analyze the learning process to see what elements constitute the needed background. Has the pupil had a sufficient number of experiences that make clear to him that light is energy, capable of doing work, that sound is energy, that electricity and heat are energy? Has he gathered from these experiences a definite idea as to what energy is? Has the pupil experienced the transformation of one sort of energy into another sort? Has his experience been sufficiently quantitative in character so that he at least can understand how the scientist goes about it to learn that, when energy is changed from one sort to another, there is no loss—that all the mechanical energy, for instance, does reappear as electricity, heat or friction, or in some other form or forms, in exactly equivalent amount? Has he seen the activities of a sufficient number of organisms, especially of plants, to know that all are at work, even dormant seeds; that, so long as a thing is alive, it is doing things that demand energy?

Has he had experience with oxygen so that he knows what it is like? Has he seen the process of oxidation in the form of rapid oxidation or combustion and as slow oxidation illustrated in such a process as rusting? Has he had sensory evidence of the energy released thereby?

Each principle must be carefully studied in that way to see what are the percepts which contribute to the simple concepts, which in turn constitute the background essential to its understanding. And the curriculum must make provision for the experiences that will clarify such concepts. These experiences suggest the more specific objectives of instruction. The learning from experiences is the thing to be achieved by a particular lesson or part of a lesson. Many such experiences can be given in the lower levels of the school as things worth while in themselves and at the same time desirable as a basis for the later mastery of a principle of science.

How Many Principles?

Downing has reported a study[4] made to determine how long it takes at the tenth-grade level to give pupils in the average high school such a familiarity with, and skill in the use of, certain typical principles of biology as will enable them to apply these principles successfully to the solution of problems likely to arise in life. The results indicate that such a principle as that of photosynthesis requires from three to four weeks, while an understanding of merely the simpler laws of heredity requires from six to eight weeks. In view of these findings it is evident that we cannot hope to develop a thorough understanding of more than six or eight such principles in the year's work of the high school, and not even that number if there are to be included also units to develop desirable scientific attitudes and units to give skill in scientific thinking. In the opinion of the Committee these latter two

---

[4] Downing, Elliot R. (Chairman). "An investigation." *North Central Association Quarterly*, March, 1931.

outcomes are major goals of science teaching quite as important as the knowledge goal.

PRINCIPLES IN CURRENT TEXTS IN BIOLOGY

An available study[5] indicates that the commonly used secondary-school textbooks in biology devote as little as a fourth and none of them as much as a half of their space to an elucidation of principles and that the remainder of the space deals with factual material *that does not have any bearing even on the mastery of principles*. This Committee condemns the practice of teaching unrelated facts and recommends the arrangement of instructional material so that facts presented are clearly seen as contributory to the understanding of principles and generalizations.

GRADE PLACEMENT

Few, if any, experimental studies have been made to determine at what grade levels knowledge of the various biological principles, subordinate concepts, and percepts may most readily be imparted. True, various courses of study have tried them at sundry levels, but not with any adequate measures of success or failure. It might be assumed that the various elements of biological instruction have gravitated, through repeated trial and error, to about their proper place in the grades and upper schools; but that assumption seems contrary to the meager facts available. Venturesome teachers who have moved certain units of instruction commonly dealt with in high-school biology —like photosynthesis, for instance—down to the fifth- or sixth-grade level report a mastery which they deemed satisfactory for that level. At present the same biological topic may appear in different courses anywhere from fourth-grade or fifth-grade science to advanced courses in high-school botany or zoölogy.

We are still more at sea, if that be possible, as to the appropriate grade level at which to undertake to establish the desirable scientific attitudes and to impart skill in the use of the various elements and safeguards of scientific thinking.

At present, then, we have only fragments of the knowledge we need upon which to base a wise selection and placement of the materials

---

[5] Hackett, Glenn L. *An Analysis, in Terms of Generalizations, of Ten Biologies Used in High Schools.* Master's thesis: School of Education, University of Chicago, 1924. (Unpublished)

for the course of study in biology. But since we are faced in the schools with the necessity of giving a course in the subject, the course must be outlined, even though it be tentative in character and subject to change as later investigations shall show need.

Since other chapters of this volume deal with the organization of the science courses for Grades I to VI and Grades VII to IX, there are listed here merely those principles which might well be used on these levels and those elements of knowledge and experience which are needed as the basis for an understanding of the principles. The background of material needed for the comprehension of type principles to be mastered in the high school is listed under each, with the expectation that some of it will be accomplished in the elementary grades and the junior high school. In any particular course of study it should be indicated for what portion of this each grade teacher and teacher of general science is responsible, so that the biology teacher may know what foundations are already laid and may not duplicate instruction that has been accomplished.

The Biology Course

The course in biology in the schools, stated in terms of its outcomes, will consist of (1) such an understanding of most, possibly all, of the principles listed earlier in this chapter that the pupil will in all probability apply them to the solution of such problems of a biological character as will arise in his life; (2) an appreciation of some of the scientific attitudes exemplified in the work of such great biologists as Vesalius, Malpighi, Pasteur, and others, and a sense of the lawfulness of nature and of every man's obligation to obey such laws and other similar emotionalized standards; and (3) a reasonable degree of skill in the use of the scientific method of thinking on matters biological, so that the pupil will not go astray in his attempt to think through to a successful issue the biological problems with which he will certainly be faced.

It may reasonably be assumed that the work in Grades I to IX will have given pupils a broad knowledge of the principles of adaptation and of the germ theory of disease and the ability to apply these principles in practical situations.

The principles and generalizations we have been discussing are eminently desirable objects of instruction in biology. We may now consider what subordinate understandings must be developed to enable the pupil to comprehend these major principles, gain some appreciation of associated scientific attitudes, and acquire some skill in the use of the elements of scientific thinking. What are the instructional elements that will become the subject for each successive lesson? Several illustrations are here given.

Adaptation: an Instructional Unit

Every organism must in the main be adjusted to the factors of its environment, else it will of necessity die out in the keen struggle for existence. Similarly, every organ must be adjusted to its particular function so that it can perform successfully the particular thing it has to do.

What are the factors of the environment?

I. The physical environment. (1) Presence of oxygen and its concentration, (2) moisture, (3) an optimal temperature, (4) light, either directly or indirectly, (5) pressure, atmosphere and water, (6) character of the soil, which largely affects its water content and also determines the concentration of certain chemical substances, some of which may be essential, others injurious, (7) character of the atmosphere, (8) currents both of air and water, etc.

II. The biological environment.
   a. Inter-relations of individuals of the same species.
   (1) Sex relations, (2) colonial relations.
   b. Inter-relations of individuals of different species.
   (1) Dependence of animals on plants, (2) food relations, (3) parasites, (4) saprophytes, (5) epiphytes, (6) symbiosis, (7) insects and pollination.

It is probably not necessary to cover in its entirety this topic as just outlined. The pupils should have had or be given contacts with material that will make clear by actual experience that lack of moisture, of oxygen, or extremes of temperature kill living things. They should see some cases of parasitism and the consequent degeneration, of symbiosis, and other interdependencies, so that they will realize for themselves some of these complex relations of the organism to its environment.

Their experiences will be used to develop a realization that an organism must either (1) become adapted to its environment, (2) adapt the environment to its needs, as birds do when they build nests or as beavers do when they build dams, (3) migrate to a more congenial environment, or (4) die out.

Then abundant problems must be introduced to give drill in the application of this principle of adaptation to problems encountered in everyday life. A fisherman after brook trout casts in rapid streams. These fish are exceedingly active, needing abundant oxygen to develop the energy they expend; so they seek the well-oxygenated waters. The bass fisherman may cast his minnow near the surface of the lake in early morning and late evening with good hope of success, but in the middle of the day he lets his bait down into deep water because the organisms on which minnows feed are repelled by intense light and sink to lower levels in the brilliant light of midday. So the bass must also go down to get their food.

The pupil needs to realize that he, himself, is an organism and that the law of adaptation applies to him. His success is proportional to his skill in adjusting himself to his environment or in changing his environment to suit his needs. Barring such adjustment, his only recourse is migration.

Similarly, the pupil must study at first hand several cases of the adaptation of organs to their particular functions and be given many opportunities to apply the principles to phenomena that arouse his curiosity. A study of the structure of the legs of the honey bee to see how the parts are adapted to collecting pollen is an example of the sort of work needed. Let him go into the details of the adjustments in his own blood to its functions and he will perhaps begin to realize the complexity of his own body and will tend to be more careful of it.

The Germ Theory of Disease: an Instructional Unit

Some diseases are caused by very tiny living things that get into the organism and multiply to enormous numbers, killing the host, either by eating some vital organ or by generating poisons that stop essential processes.

To the average pupil this world of the microscopic is an unknown territory. He must see, best by means of the projection microscope, samples of the single-celled creatures actively moving about, feeding, reproducing. Such forms as Paramecium, Euglena, Stentor, or similar ones may be used for the demonstration. He must see bacteria. The rod-shaped forms or the large Spirilla that occur in a hay infusion shortly after it has been started are readily demonstrated.

He needs to make cultures of some of the bacteria and molds to see that each sort develops a characteristic colony, that these reproduce their own kind when a fresh sterile plate is inoculated with a few of the individuals. He must have experiences that will show him that the dust of the air is carrying such micro-organisms which grow and multiply when they meet with favorable conditions, that these micro-organisms are found on the fingers, teeth, on the feet of such insects as the fly, often in water. In a word, he must realize by his own experiences, not merely be told, how nearly omnipresent are these micro-organisms. He should see such germs killed by heat, by germicides, but should learn that they often survive mere drying.

The teacher whose many experiences have gradually built up the background needed to appreciate the germ theory of disease often does not realize how slowly it has accumulated, how completely it is lacking in the pupils. Words whose significance is perfectly clear to the teacher are meaningless to the pupil. The pupil may glibly use them but it is so much 'parrot talk.'

Again, abundant drill is to be given in applying the principle to problematic situations that arise in life. Why wash the hands before meals? Why clean the teeth? Why should we use covered garbage cans? Why do we have isolation hospitals for smallpox and diphtheria? Let the pupils graph the statistics of the effect of the use of antitoxin on the annual death rate from diphtheria, of the use of vaccination on the smallpox death rate. What do these graphs show?

Ecological Relations: an Instructional Unit

Plants and animals are not distributed hit or miss over the surface of the earth, but are confined to certain areas. The determining factors are such things as moisture content of the soil, light intensity, rate of evaporation, soil acidity, location of food materials, etc. Similarly, the world over, organisms are arranged in definite zones, limited by such barriers to migration as oceans, mountain chains, deserts, and competing organisms.

The study might well begin with the distribution of plants in the school yard. The margins of the playground support very hardy plants that can stand the tramping, the intense light, the dry, closely packed soil. A different lot of plants may be found among the shrubs close to the buildings. Compare the forms found growing on the north side of the building, where they are shaded much of the time, with those on the south side. Information relating to these points is found in general treatises[6] and in the bulletins issued by state departments of agriculture and by the United States Department of Agriculture.

Then compare the trees, shrubs, and annual flowering plants of nearby contrasting areas, a weed lot exposed to the glare of the sun, the flood plain of a stream, the margin of a pond, the deep oak or maple woods where the shade is noticeably intense. With appropriate directions pupils can do this work individually if the class as a whole cannot be taken on such field trips.

Let pupils keep record of the succession of plants that appear on one particular area or of the animals that appear in a pond, so that they will realize the distribution of organisms in time. Early maturing types appear, reach a climax of abundance, and die out, to be replaced by others that last only a few days or weeks, when they in turn are succeeded by a new lot.

The world-wide distribution may have to be studied largely from pictures and maps. Old numbers of the *National Geographic Magazine*, encyclopedias, and textbooks will yield pictures of the tropical jungles, desert zones, prairies, deciduous forest areas, the conifer zone, tundras, arctic wastes, etc. The life zones of the United States are mapped in bulletins of the U. S. Biological Survey and in Chapman's *Handbook of Birds of Eastern North America.*[7]

As a result of such studies pupil will have clarified the meaning of terms like species, genera, plant or animal societies, ecological succession, barriers to migration, limiting conditions of soil moisture, of light intensity, etc.

Again, problems must be introduced to drill pupils on the application of these principles of distribution. Where are figs grown in the United States? Why not in Illinois? Are they native or introduced? How was the cottony-cushion scale successfully combatted in the groves of California? Why did Englishmen have to introduce water cress, their favorite salad plant, into

---

[6] Georgia, Ada E. *A Manual of Weeds*. Macmillan: New York, 1914. 593 pp.
[7] Chapman, Frank M. *Handbook of Birds of Eastern North America*. Appleton: New York, 1914.

Australia? Why is mahogany such an expensive wood? What crops are characteristic of the prairie states, and why?

Space will not permit an analysis of each unit to determine the subordinate understandings. Enough has been given to show how each principle must be studied to see what elements are needed to make up the background for its comprehension, and that the development of these elements becomes the specific object of those experiences that must be introduced in successive lessons. The principles are made significant by actual experiences so that the words by which the principles are formulated become meaningful.

ATTITUDES

Teaching material organized into textbook form for the purpose of establishing acceptable desires, ideals, and attitudes is largely wanting, although there are some available books and articles[s] that contribute to meeting this need. Perhaps the teacher will himself be so imbued with contagious enthusiasm that he can impart some of it to his pupils by talks which he gives. Possibly such supplementary reading as DuKruif's *Microbe Hunters* or his *Hunger Fighters* might be used and the books discussed in the class after pupils have read them. Certain it is that the establishment of ideals, the development of desires, of ambitions, of attitudes of mind is an important function of the teacher, for without such motivating outcomes the knowledge imparted remains inert. The material for units of this type is to be found abundantly in such books as are mentioned above, in the biographies of great biologists, in the histories of biology, like Locy's *Biology and Its Makers*. Its use in current texts, however, is exceedingly meager. It must be left to the occasional teacher who is impressed with the importance of establishing such driving emotions to devise units or parts of units for these purposes with samples like those that have been suggested as aids.

SKILL IN THINKING

Skill in scientific thinking is to be developed, as is any other skill, (1) by becoming aware of the elements involved in it, (2) by learning in advance what errors one is most likely to make in the use of the elements, and (3) by practice in problem-solving.

---

[s] See, for example, Downing, Elliot R. "The added years." *School Sci. and Math.*, 28: 1928, 813-828; also his *Science in the Service of Health*. Longmans: New York, 1931.

In this discussion it will be convenient to recognize two types of problems: (1) those which are primarily inductive, or problems of discovery; and (2) those which are primarily deductive, or problems which are solved by applying known scientific principles. In the process of solving a problem it is recognized that it may take the form, at one time, of an inductive and, at another time, the form of a deductive problem. For the sake of clarity these two types are considered separately.

The Inductive Method

The elements and safeguards of the inductive method may be outlined as follows:

Elements	*Safeguards*
Purposeful observation	a. Must be accurate
	b. Must be extensive
	c. Must be done under a variety of conditions
Analysis-synthesis	d. The essential elements in a problematic situation must be picked out
	e. Dissimilarities as well as similarities must be regarded. Danger of analogy
	f. Exceptions are to be given special attention. Selective interpretation
Selective recall	g. A wide range of experience necessary
Hypotheses	h. All possible ones must be considered (fertility of suggestion)
Verification by inference and experiment	i. Inference must be tested experimentally
Reasoning by:	j. Only one variable permitted
1. method of agreement	k. Data must be cogently arranged
2. method of difference	l. Judgment must be passed on the adequacy of the data
3. method of residues	
4. method of concomitant variation	m. Judgment must be passed on the pertinency of data
5. joint method of agreement and difference	
Judgment	n. Must be unprejudiced
	o. Must be impersonal
	p. Must be suspended if data are inadequate

Robert Koch was interested in trying to discover the cause of tuberculosis. Whenever he could have access to the bodies of people who died of this disease in the hospitals, he carefully dissected such bodies to see whether he could find any peculiarities in them. He did discover that in the lungs and often in other tissues there were little nodules, or tubercles. He made such examinations not once but many times, because he realized that his observations had to be extensive to be of value.

He crushed these nodules and examined the material under his microscope. He discovered that they invariably contained multitudes of tiny rod-shaped bacteria. These bacteria are very tiny, and it is hard to make sure that you are seeing the identical one in repeated examinations of such nodules. But Koch knew that he must make certain, for observations to be of value must be accurate. After many trials and many failures he found the particular dye that would stain this species of bacterium in a way to distinguish it from others.

He examined the bodies of people who had died from other diseases than tuberculosis and did not find in them the tubercles which he did find in the people who died of tuberculosis. The presence or absence of the tubercle bacillus seemed to him to be the essential element in this problematic situation. And so he seemed to have enough facts to warrant an hypothesis that this particular bacterium was the cause of this particular disease.

But how could he test his hypothesis experimentally? After many trials he succeeded in growing colonies of these bacteria in culture media in his laboratory. He could plant a bit of the tubercle in the culture medium kept from contact with the dust of the air; then, when this had grown millions of the germs, he could transplant a bit of this colony to another culture tube, and so proceed until he had a culture free from any of the original tissue of the tubercle. When he now injected such material into a guinea pig, he found the animal developed tuberculosis. He repeated this experiment time after time. These experiments that he used to test his hypothesis gave him plain evidence that his hypothesis was correct. And so he reasoned on the basis of all these facts to his judgment; namely, that this particular bacterium is the cause of tuberculosis. This example will show how some of these elements and safeguards have functioned in a specific instance.[9]

The Deductive Method

The same elements and safeguards are used in the deductive process, but in a somewhat different order. In all cases one must sense a problematic situation and define it clearly, before undertaking the solution of the problem.

In a book that I am reading there occurs the statement that fishermen on the banks of Newfoundland make a much heavier haul of fish in years when there are many sunny days than in those when the sky is overcast

[9] Downing, Elliot R. "The elements and safeguards of scientific thinking." *Scientific Mo.*, 26: 1928, 231-243.

much of the time. That challenges my curiosity and I wonder why. The problem is already clearly defined. Evidently the pertinent item in this problematic situation is the presence or absence of sunshine. I hold this in the focus of attention to see whether I can recall some general fact or principle that may apply to the solution of the problem. Light suggests seeing and I guess that perhaps the fish can see the bait better in sunny weather. Then I recall that some fish may depend more upon smell than sight in locating food. So I reject this hypothesis regarding the correct generalization to apply. I try again. Cloudy days suggest storms. Possibly the fishermen cannot fish as continuously in cloudy years. Then I think that these hardy men whose living is dependent on plying their trade are probably not much deterred by disagreeable weather. That guess at a solution is rejected. Sunlight now suggests photosynthesis. In sunshiny years the water plants along the shore will grow vigorously. The small animals that feed on them will be more numerous. The fish that feed upon these small forms will grow to larger size and so yield a heavier catch to the fishermen. That seems plausible and I accept it as the probable explanation.

One must be aware of a problem and define it clearly. Then he proceeds to the solution in this deductive manner by analysis of the complete situation to pick out the essential elements. These are held in the focus of attention as one endeavors to recall first one, then another, principle that may serve to explain the situation. When one appears promising, it is tested by other facts one can recall or secure by experiment. If the facts do not confirm the first guess, another hypothesis is tested. So one continues until all the facts available can be used as a basis on which to reason to a more or less correct judgment in regard to the solution of the problem. In much of our thinking to solve problems we use first one, then another, type of procedure; inductive and deductive methods often follow each other in rapid succession.

Conscious Skill Desirable

Mere practice in solving problems is inadequate for the rapid development of skill in scientific thinking unless pupils are at the same time made conscious of the elements and safeguards that are involved. Unfortunately not much material organized with this end in view is now available in textbook form. The teacher who would accomplish this major goal must be in large part responsible for furnishing the material for its achievement. That means effort, but certainly if any teacher is to assume responsibility for imparting skill in the use of the scientific method, one might expect it to be the science teacher.

There is experimental evidence which indicates that children think quite as well as do older persons, provided that the problems deal with concrete materials rather than abstractions.[10] Further, it has been shown that the rate and accuracy of thinking may be improved in pupils by making them aware of the elements of the process and drilling them in their use.[11]

Thought Units

Space forbids the detailed outline of the sort of units desirable to accomplish this major goal, improvement in thinking. There can only be given some suggestions regarding the use of some materials and the method of procedure.

The teacher must first present, either by his own talks or by assigned reading, the elements and safeguards of good reflective thinking, with enough examples to make the matter clear to pupils both for the inductive and deductive method. Dewey's *How We Think* (Part II)[12] will be read by pupils of high-school age; so also will the article by Downing previously mentioned.[13] Jastrow's *Effective Thinking*[14] is recommended for the teacher and Darrow's *Thinkers and Doers*[15] for the pupils. Let pupils be on the lookout for good examples of scientific thinking in the textbook they are using. Instruction should be given in setting up controlled experiments and in evaluating controls of various sorts. Also the pupils should be made acquainted with the list of scientific attitudes determined by Curtis.[16]

After having had considerable contact with examples of good reflective thinking, they might collect magazine advertisements that do violence to the elements and safeguards. Many of them are biological in character. There are the advertisements of dog foods, profitable fur-farming, insecticides, tooth paste, yeast as a medicine, health beverages, breakfast foods, etc. Is there any assurance in the

---

[10] Freeman, Frank N. *The Psychology of the Common Branches.* Houghton Mifflin: Boston, 1916.
[11] Johnson, Elsie P. *Teaching Pupils the Consciousness of a Technique for Thinking.* Master's thesis: University of Chicago, 1924. (Unpublished)
Beauchamp, W. L. *An Analytical Study of Attainment of Scientific Learning Product in Elementary Science.* Doctorate dissertation: University of Chicago, 1930. (Unpublished)
[12] Dewey, John. *How We Think.* Heath: Boston, 1910.
[13] See footnote 8.
[14] Jastrow, Joseph. *Effective Thinking.* Simon and Schuster, New York, 1931.
[15] Darrow, Floyd. *Thinkers and Doers.* Silver, Burdett, 1925.
[16] This list is printed in Chapter IV.

advertisement that the facts stated have been accumulated by accurate, extensive observations made under a variety of conditions? Is there any evidence that the statements made have been experimentally verified? Are they capable of such verification? Do the conclusions reached on the basis of the so-called facts seem to you impartial and unprejudiced? Might the facts be accounted for in some other way? In other words, have all possible hypotheses been considered? Is the reasoning of the advertisement by analogy or by one of the legitimate types?

A study of such materials should help to develop in pupils so critical an attitude that they will examine thought material presented to influence their action to see whether it does observe the safeguards of good thinking and use the elements in proper ways.

Organization into Teaching Units

It is desirable to organize the work of biology in definite teaching units. By a unit is meant a relatively small mass of learning material, so selected and organized as (1) to clarify a principle and afford abundant drill in is application to such problems as arise in life, (2) to contribute to the attainment of scientific attitudes, and (3) to give abundant practice in the use of the elements and safeguards of scientific thinking.

The success of a given unit can be assured only when the ends to be achieved by its use are clear to the teacher, when their achievement is tested, and when the pupils are conscious of their accomplishment.

THE HIGH-SCHOOL COURSE

In considering the construction of the course or courses in high-school biology, it is interesting to recapitulate briefly some of the significant changes which have taken place in the purpose and presentation of this subject, as indicated by the investigation of Finley.[17] In the earlier biological courses, which were botany, zoölogy, and physiology, major emphasis was placed upon anatomy, morphology, and classification of plants and animals. "Coupled with this emphasis upon anatomical structure and its attendant classification was a religious aim"—to bring the pupil "to a better understanding of God

---

[17] Finley, Charles W. *Biology in Secondary Schools and the Training of Biology Teachers.* Teachers College, Columbia University, Contributions to Education, No. 199: New York, 1926. For summary, see Curtis, *Second Digest of Investigations in the Teaching of Science,* 134-141.

through a study of His works as shown in living things." Mental discipline was a major objective, and as an odd anomaly in a course purported to be scientific, physiology became the instrument of propaganda against alcohol and narcotics. Significant changes from these earlier positions are summarized by Finley:

> Accompanying the reduction of time and emphasis on anatomy and classification in biological instruction has been a like reduction of time and emphasis on individual laboratory work. The *practical, ecological, economic, human welfare* aspects of biology do not lend themselves so well to laboratory work as did the anatomical, morphological, and microscopical work of former times. . . . Time has eradicated or reduced to negligible consideration [the attempts to lead] the pupil to realization of Deity through a study of works of nature. . . . The aim of biology teaching in our secondary schools has changed from 'biology for the sake of biology' to 'biology in relation to human welfare.'

This Committee supports the thesis that the materials of the biology courses should be organized definitely in such a way as to contribute to an understanding of biological principles, to the end that this training may contribute to a reification of major generalizations and their accompanying scientific attitudes. Fortunately the choice of subject matter of high-school biology has not been standardized and crystallized in the manner in which standardization of course content exists in physics and chemistry; there is opportunity for freedom in the selection of elements and materials with which to effect the accomplishment of the major goals indicated in the thesis just stated.

Some guidance to the selection of course content has been supplied through extensive researches of several investigators, conspicuously Downing, Finley and Caldwell, Harap, Hill, Hunter, Persing, Ruch and Cossman, and others.[18] Suggestions of practical value to the teacher in meeting the day-to-day problems of classroom and laboratory instruction are found in a number of research investigations briefly reported in Chapters VI and VII.

The Committee recognizes that there are a number of ways in which the materials of the high-school biology course may be so organized as to contribute to the major aims of the course and the major goals of science teaching. It is not yet possible from the results of research now available to state with authority or even with much conviction which plan or plans of organization are most certain to contribute maximally to the attainment of these goals. A departure from conven-

---

[18] For brief summaries of these investigations, see Chapter VIII.

tional methods is always valuable and stimulating. In the paragraphs which follow, therefore, an attempt has been made to indicate one method of organizing the materials of the biology course to secure to the pupil a mastery of principles and therefore an attainment of the major goals of the subject. This method is presented not because it is believed by this Committee to be necessarily superior to all other plans of organization which may be used or plans in accordance with which materials already organized as courses may be revised; it is presented as an attack upon the problem which has been proved in actual classroom use to be successful, and as therefore of suggestive value to the writer of a textbook or of a syllabus in high-school biology.

The sequence of units may be left to the judgment of the teacher. For those who desire such a recommendation it is suggested the principles listed earlier in this chapter be taken in the following order: IV, VII, VI, III, VIII (not in too great detail), I, II, then the unit on scientific thinking and the unit to establish an appreciation of what science has cost in human effort or some other similar important scientific attitude, followed by V, VI, and IX.

A Typical Unit

The following unit outline is suggested as a sample of the way in which such units may be organized.

Better Plants and Animals

Challenging Introduction. Tell the dramatic story of how Burbank produced the Shasta daisy or how, by selective breeding, a wheat plant was produced that would stand the early frosts and high winds of the Canadian northwest, or how the egg-a-day hen has been developed.

Preliminary Experiences and Understandings. Study the flower and its parts, especially the essential organs. Give pupils experiences in cross-pollinating such plants as garden peas and nasturtiums. Let them watch the development of frogs' or toads' eggs, silk-moth eggs, potato-beetle eggs, or other similar ones. Possibly all of this has been done in the grades. If so, merely recall these experiences.

Presentation. (This outline serves as a basis for the pupils' study, which the teacher supervises.)

I. What is the nature of fertilization?

The following or similar readings are suggested for study:

Atwood. *Civic and Economic Biology*, pp. 220-205, 220-225.

Downing. *Elementary Eugenics*, Chaps. IV-VI.

Shull. *Principles of Animal Biology*, pp. 174-180.

The teacher will demonstrate with experiments or prepared exhibits the breeding of fruit flies, garden peas, or similar materials to enable pupils to answer the questions below.

II. What is meant by an hereditary character?

When tall and short pea plants are crossed, are their offspring tall, short, or intermediate?

If a pea plant bearing smooth green seeds is crossed with one bearing wrinkled yellow seeds, do these characters remain together in the offspring or do they separate and recombine?

What is a dominant character? What is a recessive character?

In what proportion would tall and short pea plants appear in the third generation?

What is the law for the proportion of the several (how many?) kinds of individuals of the third generation in the case of the plants with smooth green seeds and those with yellow wrinkled seeds?

Complete these statements (after the readings):

Characters are..............as such; they...........blend, as a rule.
Characters united in the parents...........and...........in all possible combinations of the offspring.
In the F-1 generation only the...........characters appear.

What is meant by partial dominance as found in black, white, and 'blue' Andulasian chickens? Red, white, and pink four-o'clocks?

The following readings are suggested for study:
Atwood. *Civic and Economic Biology*, pp. 309-340.
Shull. *Principles of Animal Biology*, Chap. XI.
Woodruff. *Foundations of Biology*, pp. 272-305.

III. How are these laws of inheritance explained by the phenomena of reduction division? (It is assumed that a unit on the cell has preceded this unit on inheritance and that pupils are familiar with the equation division.)

What happens in reduction division that is in marked contrast to equation division?

When does reduction division occur in most animals? In plants?

How do these reduction phenomena clarify the inheritance of characters as such? The separation of characters in one parent and combination in the offspring, with those of the other parent?

The following readings are suggested for study:
Caldwell, Skinner, Tietz. *Biological Foundations of Education*, pp. 235-245.
Downing. *Elementary Eugenics*, Chap. V.
Haupt. *Fundamentals of Biology*, Chap. XIII.

IV. Use these or similar problems as practice material to apply the principles learned to problematic situations.

1. Let us suppose that in a cross between a squash plant producing yellow fruit and one producing white fruit, all the offspring produce white fruit. If two of these hybrid plants were to be crossed, what would be the expected character of their offspring?
2. A rough-coated male guinea pig is mated with three females. The first is also rough-coated and the young are all rough-coated. The second is also rough-coated, but there are both rough-coated and smooth-coated offspring. The third is smooth-coated and the young are both smooth and rough. What are the genotypes of all four guinea pigs? (Rough is dominant.)
3. A cross is made between a jimson weed with spiny seed pods and one with smooth pods. When the plants grown from the seed so produced are mature, they are crossed with plants like the spineless parent. The resulting seed, when planted, gives plants with spiny pods and plants with smooth pods in equal numbers. Are spiny pods dominant or recessive?
4. When a tall pea plant bearing yellow seeds is crossed with a short plant with yellow seeds (tall and yellow are dominant), the offspring are in the proportion of three tall plants with yellow seeds, three short plants with yellow seeds, one tall with green seeds, one short with green seeds. What are the genotypes of the parents?

CHAPTER XV

INSTRUCTION IN PHYSICAL SCIENCE IN THE SECONDARY SCHOOLS*

PRESENT OFFERINGS IN THE PHYSICAL SCIENCES

Data for the school year 1927-28, taken from the *Biennial Survey of Education,* 1926-28, of the Bureau of Education, show that the following physical sciences are offered by high schools in the United States: physics, chemistry, physical geography, geology, and astronomy. These are listed here in the frequency of offering in high schools. Schools offering physics numbered 7,346; those offering astronomy numbered but 39. General geography and electricity are also listed, geography being offered by 4,063 and electricity by 229 schools. There is some doubt concerning the classification of these last two subjects as physical sciences. The physical geography listed undoubtedly belongs in the group of natural sciences. General geography is as often listed with the social subjects. The fact that it is offered in approximately as many schools as chemistry may be noted here as indicating trends in present offerings. The course in electricity is very likely an applied science or vocational course, although the data quoted do not show this.

The positions of the natural sciences offered are changed if the order is based upon the number of pupils enrolled in each subject instead of upon the frequency of offering. Based upon pupil enrollment the order is as follows: chemistry, physics, physical geography, geology, astronomy, and meteorology (offered in one school in North Dakota).

The relative positions of physics and chemistry are interesting when compared on these two bases; 7,346 schools offer physics and 4,783 schools offer chemistry. When compared on the basis of pupils enrolled, chemistry leads by 204,694 pupils to 198,402. On percentage of pupils enrolled there is little difference, 6.9 percent of all high school pupils are enrolled in physics and 7.1 percent in chemistry. Both physics and chemistry are much more popular with boys than with girls; physics is preponderantly a boy's subject; the proportion

---

* For the Committee, by Ralph K. Watkins.

of boys to girls in physics classes is almost two to one and in chemistry approximately three to two.

Trends in Enrollment and Offerings

Percentages of enrollments at various periods may serve to indicate trends. Percentages of the total number of high-school pupils enrolled in natural sciences for the four years of high school (9th to 12th grades, inclusive) during the last two decades show a decided falling off as follows: in 1910, 82; in 1915, 65; in 1922, 64; and in 1928, 61. Note that this falling off has not been nearly so rapid in the later intervals.

In the physical sciences, decreases from 1910 to 1928 have been as follows: in physics from 14.6 to 6.9 percent, in physical geography from 19 to 3 percent. Chemistry has stood approximately still in this same period with percentages of 6.89 to 7.10.

Certain interpretations of these figures are possible. Physics and chemistry are by far the most frequently taught physical sciences. Teaching in other physical sciences, other than the 3 percent in physical geography, is practically negligible. Physical geography is disappearing at a fairly rapid rate. Since far more schools offer physics and yet the enrollment in chemistry is slightly greater, it seems apparent that chemistry is chiefly offered in the larger high schools and physics in a greater number of small schools. Enrollments in chemistry are practically at a standstill. Physics enrollments are still declining somewhat.

The general decrease in percentages of enrollments in all the natural sciences, including the physical sciences, may be a wholesale indictment of the selection and organization of subject matter and the methods of teaching in the field. When contrasted with the widespread uses of science and the popular interest manifested by the general population outside of school, this indictment seems justified. But there is at least one extenuating circumstance. During the period of enormous expansion of high schools and the apparent decrease of interest of high-school pupils in science instruction there has been a considerable widening of the range of offerings in subjects included in the high-school program of studies. A part of the apparent decrease in interest in science may be due to increased opportunity in such fields as vocational and commercial subjects, music, art, modern languages, and so on. Just where the type of instruction offered in science begins to have its effect and where the wider range of opportunity in modern curricula ceases its effect cannot be determined from statistics of enrollment.

The data available apply to the offerings in the three years of senior high school or the four-year high school. Approximately three-fourths of the high schools of the country are still four-year-high schools. No data seem readily available concerning recent offerings of special physical sciences at the junior-high-school level.

Data similar to those taken from the *Biennial Survey* are available for the twenty states of the North Central Association in the *North Central Association Quarterly* for June, 1930. Although these data are two years later than those in the *Biennial Survey*, there is shown no marked change in the status of the physical sciences. This report apparently shows a swing back to the four-year high school and a check in the reorganization of three-year junior and senior high schools.

The present program of instruction in physical sciences, as such, would seem to be limited to the upper years of four-year high schools and three-year senior high schools and largely limited to the subjects of physics and chemistry. Courses offered in these subjects are either not increasing or gradually decreasing in proportion.

In What Grades Offered

Courses in physics and chemistry in the senior high school are most frequently offered in grades eleven and twelve. In a large number of schools pupils from either of these grades are enrolled in either course. In some smaller schools physics and chemistry alternate, so that every pupil has the opportunity to take both courses. In schools offering both physics and chemistry there is a tendency to offer physics in the eleventh year and chemistry in the twelfth year, although it could not be said that this is the prevailing practice.

Courses Required or Elective

Rarely do schools specify either physics or chemistry as required. Many schools require "one unit of a laboratory science" for graduation. Some specify "two units of laboratory sciences." A few specify "one unit of physical science," but do not indicate which physical science. Most college-entrance requirements include one to two units of "laboratory science." In small schools the effect of this is to make the narrow range of science offerings a requirement for at least some pupils. For example, in a small school offering only physics the requirement of one unit of laboratory science for graduation is in effect the requirement of physics. In some places general science may be accepted as the one unit of laboratory science and in others it may not. In schools offering biology this course is generally acceptable.

Few high schools offer any other course in physics than the general introductory one-unit course. A few large high schools offer a special course in electricity. This is most often included in a definitely vocational curriculum.

Many large city high schools offer special chemistry courses in addition to the general introductory course. These other courses include, most often, some type of applied chemistry or qualitative analysis. These special courses are often associated with some local industrial situation.

Objectives of Instruction in the Physical Sciences

Anything like adequate scientific studies of tenable objectives for senior-high-school physical sciences have not been made. These subjects have been decidedly dominated by college-preparatory ideas. Two general ideas have governed the thinking of teachers of both physics and chemistry in the past. These ideas are the mastery of the subject matter of the field as such and the disciplinary value of the subject expressed in terms of training in scientific method. The typical reaction of the teachers of physics to the problem of what might be accomplished with boys and girls in the course as it is offered in the high school seems to be, "the purpose of teaching physics is to teach physics—what more?"

Objectives in Physics

In 1929 A. W. Hurd, as Chairman of the Subcommittee on Physics of the Commission on Unit Courses and Curricula of the North Central Association,[1] reported to that body the results of an investigation concerning current aims, functions, values, and purposes of physics teaching. Hurd gathered 162 statements from 68 authorities concerning the teaching of physics in high schools. These were summarized as follows:

> Physics (a) reveals and interprets physical life, giving breadth, perspective, and balanced appreciations; (b) develops a rational individual, able to use certain specific knowledge, skills, interests, abilities, or habits

---

[1] *North Central Association Quarterly*, 3: March, 1929, and 4: September, 1929.

in better solving the everyday problems of life; (c) develops social and vocational efficiency; (d) prepares students for college entrance; and (e) teaches the laws and principles of physics.

This is the most comprehensive summary of current aims of instruction in high-school physics available to date. Its usefulness lies in the fact that it gives a picture of existing thought in the field. There is little of direct help to be derived in the attempt at modernizing the course of instruction in the subject. The first three statements are so vague as to be almost entirely meaningless. They might just as well be stated for a wide variety of courses offered by contemporary high schools, while the second and third might just as well be stated for any high-school course or for the whole high school as an institution. The fourth and fifth are merely restatements of the traditional attitude concerning the teaching of physics, referred to at the beginning of this section, that has existed in the thinking of academic teachers for the past hundred years. None of them is of particular use in pointing a way to better adaptation of the subject matter and instruction in the field of physics to the needs of pupils growing up in a modern world.

The Subcommittee on Physics of the Commission on Unit Courses and Curricula of the North Central Association, in its original report on objectives for the course, followed the pattern laid down by the larger Committee on Standards for Reorganization of Secondary-School Curricula. This general pattern included an adherence to a modification of the *Cardinal Principles of Secondary Education.* "The Committee has set up four major or ultimate objectives of education as follows: health, leisure time, social, and vocational." A pattern of "immediate objectives" to serve as a means of analyzing the more general ones was also set up. These were: "acquiring fruitful knowledge; development of attitudes, interests, motives, ideals, and appreciations; development of definite mental techniques in imagination, memory, judgment, and reasoning; acquiring right habits and useful skills."

The work of the Subcommittee on Physics first took the form of applying this general pattern to the selection of specific material from the field of physics. Their outline is only one illustration of the application of this pattern to the field. It was emphatically stated that the outline was to be considered only as an illustration of the application of a technique and not as a final judgment concerning objectives in the field of secondary-school physics.

The general pattern laid down by the Committee on Standards may be characterized as consisting of large institutional aims that are to be applied to the whole of secondary education as a social institution. Such statements may be useful as a guiding philosophy that might indicate the general usefulness of a whole field in the carrying out of the functions of secondary education, but their usefulness in determining specific values contributed by such a subject as that of physics may be doubted. Serious question may be raised concerning the practical meaningfulness of the labels "vocational," "vocational-exploratory," "avocational," and the like, attached to the illustrative units set up by the subcommittee. This does not mean that the units selected by the Subcommittee on Physics are not worth while, but that the general formula outlined by the Committee on Standards may have little significance in the selection of material from the field of physics.

The formula for determining immediate objectives would seem to be more directly useful. If applied to each of the units of instruction selected, it would serve the purpose of assisting in the selection from available materials those which might be most useful in securing desired effects upon the high-school pupils concerned. The workers in the field of physics have been especially in need of some stimulus which would center attention upon the needs of the learner rather than upon the mere structure of the subject matter involved in the instruction. Note that the formula is again a blanket formula that may be applied to specific units of instruction within a particular field. From the details of the illustrative units set up by the Subcommittee on Physics, it is evident that that committee profited by the point of view and the analysis suggested by this formula of immediate objectives. The committee did not, as might have been anticipated, list the particular outcomes to be expected in each unit as indicated by a close application of this formula. The direct relation between such habits, attitudes, and fruitful knowledge as might be attained by instruction in a selected unit and the details of subject matter and learning activities selected is, therefore, not made clear.

Another recent study[2] has attempted to analyze the larger institutional aims of secondary education, such as health, applying fundamental processes, etc., into the specific objectives that might apply to the field of physics and to use these specific objectives as criteria for

---

[2] Williams, Jessie. *Study Outlines in Physics, Construction and Evaluation,* (Unpublished Ph.D. Dissertation). New York: Teachers College, Columbia University, 1931.

selecting subject matter from the several divisions of the traditional physics course.

The chief merit in the type of analysis made in this study lies in the fact that it emphasizes values from the study of physics for their contribution to the understanding of vital human problems.

An older attempt to adapt the physics course to the more immediate needs of high-school pupils is to be found in the report of the Subcommittee of the Central Association of Science and Mathematics Teachers.[3] The aims stated by this report are not clearly distinguished from methods of work and topical statements of subject matter. The report, however, has had considerable influence in shifting emphasis from the subject matter of physics as such to the values of the subject matter for pupils themselves.

Objectives in terms of the relatively few major concepts from the field of physics that have contributed most to man's thinking and way of living, in terms of those attitudes that may be best developed by work in elementary physics, and in terms of those modes of thinking and methods of attack upon problems training for which may be best developed in physics, remain yet to be scientificially determined. Some work has been done in the attempt to get at major generalizations in the field of science, and some studies have been made to show the principles of science common to elementary courses in science. These are discussed in connection with the development of the curricular materials for senior-high-school physical sciences.

POSITION OF THE YEARBOOK COMMITTEE CONCERNING OBJECTIVES FOR PHYSICS IN THE SENIOR HIGH SCHOOL

In setting up a guiding philosophy this Committee has taken the position that objectives for science teaching through the grades and high school should be stated in terms of the major ideas, concepts, and principles that control the understanding of scientific facts and their application in the world; in terms of training in the kinds of scientific thinking that may be produced within such fields, and in terms of certain attitudes that may guide conduct in the use of science materials and serve as guides in scientific thinking.

---

[3] Vestal, C. L., *et al.* "Report of the Subcommittee of the Central Association of Science and Mathematics Teachers on the Content of High-School Physics." *Sch. Sci. and Math.*, March, 1921, 274-279.

The first of these does not indicate that the Committee believes in the formulation of objectives in terms of subject matter as such rather than in terms of the effects of subject matter upon the learners. The emphasis should be placed upon the *understanding* and *ability to use* which is developed within the pupil. The Committee does believe, however, that the key to such understandings and abilities to use scientific facts and principles is dependent upon an adequate determination of the essential basic concepts of science.

Work in the analysis of the major controlling concepts necessary for understanding facts and applications in the fields of physics and chemistry has been insufficient to make it possible to set up accurately determined objectives for these fields of high-school science. Not enough is known about the training of pupils in the types of problem-solving utilized in these fields or about the extent of application of such methods of problem-solving to be at all sure concerning the validity of this type of objectives.

The lists of major generalizations suggested by this Committee in an earlier section of this report[4] illustrate the type of material needed to set up a program of objectives consistent with the point of view of the Committee. Examples applying more specifically to high-school physics are given herewith.

Objectives for High-School Physics That Illustrate the Point of View of the Yearbook Committee

I. Pupils in high-school physics courses should develop *better understandings of*, and *abilities to use*, those fundamental concepts and major generalizations of physics that will enable them better to interpret natural phenomena, common applications of physical principles, and industrial applications of the principles of physics.

A. *Illustrations of Such Major Generalizations from Physics*[5]

1. The sun is the chief source of energy for the earth.
2. Matter and energy cannot be created or destroyed, but may be changed from one form to another.

----

[4] See Chapter IV. Also the lists of principles suggested in a summary of studies by Downing, in Curtis, F. D., *Second Digest of Investigations in the Teaching of Science.* Philadelphia: Blakiston's, 1921, pp. 211-214.

[5] These statements are taken from the larger list submitted by the Committee in Chapter IV and are those which are believed to contribute most to the further development of pupils who have reached the level of senior-high-school physics. They are by no means all the essential ideas for which understanding should be built up, but only samples.

3. Units of time are defined by the earth's movements in relation to the sun.
4. Distances in space seem incredibly great when compared to distances on earth.
5. Chemical and physical changes are manifestations of energy changes.
6. Sound is caused by waves which are produced by a vibrating substance and which can affect the auditory nerve of the ear.
7. Gravitation is the attractive force which influences or governs the movements of bodies.
8. Machines are devices for accomplishing useful transformations of energy.
9. Any machine, no matter how complicated, may be analyzed into a few simple types.
10. All matter is probably electrical in structure.
11. The kinetic energy of the molecules determines the physical states of matter.
12. The gravitational attraction between the earth and a mass of unconfined gas or liquid causes the pressure of that gas or liquid.
13. Liquid or gas pressure is exerted equally in all directions.
14. Chemical changes are accompanied by energy changes.
15. A change in the rate of motion, or direction of motion of an object requires the application of an external force.
16. Radiant energy travels in straight lines through media of uniform density.
17. Electricity is a form of energy that results from disturbing the position or the regular paths of electrons.

B. *Illustrations of Applications in Which Such Major Generalizations Should Be Developed*

1. Water and gas supply systems
2. Heating and ventilating systems
3. Refrigeration and refrigeration systems
4. The electric lamp and electric lighting systems
5. The electric motor and generator
6. The camera and the human eye
7. Musical instruments
8. Heat engines
9. Simple and complex machines
10. The automobile
11. The telephone
12. Radio receiving sets

II. Pupils in high-school physics classes should learn to use the processes of reflective thinking and problem-solving which are best adapted to the solution of problems within the field of physics. This is to be interpreted as "training in scientific methods" in so far as such methods are used in the field of physics and can be produced within the limits of one year's work within this field at the senior-high-school level.

No investigative evidence has come into the hands of the Committee concerning the exact nature of the type of training in scientific method which may be produced in high-school physics. Neither has any analytical or experimental work been undertaken by the Committee upon this point. Possible illustrations are as follows:

1. Forming habits of using only objective data for the proof of solutions to problems in physics
2. Learning to tabulate data or record observations of objective phenomena involved in problems of physics
3. Forming habits of translating data of physical phenomena into mathematical form
4. Learning to formulate generalizations or conclusions based upon recorded and objectively determined physical data

III. Pupils in senior-high-school physics classes should develop those attitudes towards the facts and principles of physics and towards the methods of investigation employed in the field which will serve as guides in their use of physics materials and methods of problem-solving.

1. Man's conceptions of truth change. Things which seem to be scientifically true within the field of physics to-day may not seem to be true to-morrow.
2. An individual's education in physics cannot be completed. He must learn how to continue his own education and training in the field.
3. Open-mindedness concerning theories and hypotheses in the field of physics is highly desirable.
4. Effects have physical causes. Causes produce physical effects.
5. Form conclusions only upon the basis of sufficient objective evidence.
6. Research in the field of physics should be supported.

THE CONTENT OF HIGH-SCHOOL PHYSICS COURSES

Typical Content

The general pattern of content of the high-school physics course is familiar to any one who is at all acquainted with physics texts. A casual examination of the table of contents of any high-school physics textbook published more than ten years ago or of most of those of later date will serve as an illustration of this characteristic content. The general outline has been topical. The development suggests memoriter mastery of many details briefly developed and explained. A host of critics of the teaching of high-school physics have for twenty years laid the apparent decrease of interest in physics on the part of high-school pupils, as evidenced by falling percentages of enrollment, to the selection and organization of the content of the course.

Criticisms of This Content

The first of the modern attempts at change in content which seems to have been at all far-reaching in its effects is to be found in the recommendations of the Vestal Report.[6] Apparently the list of basic topics recommended would indicate no change at all over the accepted pattern, unless it be in a reduction in number. Changes are to be found, however, in *some* of the details of the basic topics, as for example this beginning of the outline from the topic 'mechanics of solids.'

Mechanics of Solids

1. Levers: scissors; crowbar; jack handles; human arm; balances; teeter-board; wheelbarrow; . . .
2. Wheel and axle; bicycle; auger; brace and bit; grindstone; sewing-machine drive; . . .
3. Gears: automobile gear shift; differential gear; clock gears; gears in electric meter; gas meter; water meter; worm gear, as in some auto trucks.

The report shows evidence of an attempt to meet the problem set up by the Vestal Committee, "to outline a syllabus for the high-school physics course from the point of view of life situations."

The study of content of the high-school physics course made by J. M. Hughes,[7] six years after the report of the Vestal Committee, shows a striking similarity among the textbooks analyzed—70 of 73 topics are common to all three of the most frequently used texts. That the selection of the material for textbooks is a decided factor in determining what is actually taught is shown by the same investigation. Hughes found that practically none of the text material was omitted by the teachers who replied to his questionnaire. In the same year Peters[8] in Missouri, found 81 percent of the high-school teachers using two popular high-school texts in physics; the other 19 percent were scattered among five texts. Of the 50 percent using the more popular text, 96.5 percent were following the organization of the large divisions of the text throughout. Ninety percent of all of the teachers replying were using the organization of the adopted text. The six major topics and their sequence, as found by Peters, were: mechanics, heat, mag-

---

[6] *Loc. cit.* Footnote 3.

[7] Hughes, J. M. "A study of the content of the course in high-school physics," *Sch. Sci. and Math.*, June, 1926, 619-623.

[8] Peters, C. J. "An evaluation of a reorganization of the present core of subject matter in high-school physics," *Sch. Sci. and Math.*, Feb., 1927, 172 ff.

netism, electricity, sound, light. No evidence of organization based upon major generalizations of science is given in these studies.

A recent attempt at a break from the traditional pattern of organization is to be found in the work of A. W. Hurd[9] for the North Central Association. This is an attempt to select subject matter by using the formula of the North Central Association objectives quoted earlier. The result has been an organization of the physics material into units, using various applications as types to carry the physics information desired. Hurd has carried these units experimentally into selected high schools and measured results obtained by their use by means of a battery of objective tests. He found that the application of these units of instruction in physics did produce measurable results.

Hurd's eighteen units[10] would seem to put into practice the avowed but unattained purpose of the Vestal Committee, but what the ultimate effect of this material upon the established pattern of physics courses will be it is difficult now to predict.

Downing[11] has summarized the results of a group of investigations in which attempts have been made by analysis of objective materials, such as farm journals, trade journals, and the activities of housewives, to determine the most useful principles of physics. In this list are found thirty-two of the more important principles of physics. There is no attempt to make a course outline. There is an attempt to determine the basic principles underlying the high-school physics course. Such a body of principles needs to be organized about certain other, much larger, controlling concepts in order to give a course continuity and integration. To make such principles teachable they must be worked back into settings of application and phenomena within the range of pupil's experiences.

Suggestions of the Yearbook Committee concerning Content for Physics in the Senior High School

The Committee has attempted to group principles of science into larger generalizations in the list submitted in Chapter IV. Those generalizations selected for their appropriateness for the high-school physics course are listed under the first section of the objectives for the high-school physics course.

---

[9] *Loc. cit.*, Footnote 1; also *North Central Association Quarterly*, March, 1931.
[10] Hurd, A. W. *Work Test Book in Physics.* New York: Macmillan, 1930.
[11] Curtis, F. D. *Second Digest of Investigations*, pp. 211-214.

It is the opinion of this Committee that the underlying major generalizations necessary for the understanding of phenomena and applications of the field of physics should be used as criteria for the selection of the content of the course in high-school physics. Those generalizations we have listed are suggestive and considered as worthy of use as tentative criteria for this purpose. The integration of the physics course can be greatly improved if a very few large concepts be accepted as the basic organizing themes running through all the instructional units. For the high-school course it is suggested that the concept, *the indestructibility of matter and energy,* and the concept, *all physical phenomena are based upon energy transformations,* be accepted as tentative organizing themes. The acceptance of such basic concepts as the central themes of organization for the high-school physics course would avoid the traditional compartmentalization of physics into short, separate, unrelated sections, almost short courses in themselves, without meaningful interrelations. Each division of the new course could be integrated through its contribution to enlarged understanding of the basic concepts.

Specific content for the high-school course is to be chosen for its contribution to the major objectives listed in the preceding section and organized in terms of its contribution to the enlargement of the major organizing concepts. Those particular experiences are to be selected for inclusion in the course that are of greatest importance in the lives of the pupils and that at the same time contribute to the development of the basic concepts. For example, consider a high school in a rural setting.

Here a farm lighting plant might be selected as a familiar and useful application of principles of physics worthy of study. This would be treated as a complicated device for the conversion of stored energy into forms useful in daily life. The gasoline engine would be treated as a device for converting the stored energy of the gasoline into heat, and the heat into mechanical energy for turning the electric generator. The generator would be treated as a device for converting the mechanical energy into electrical energy. The storage cells would be treated as devices for converting electrical energy into chemical energy and chemical energy into electrical energy. Various household and farm machines would be treated as machines for converting the electrical energy taken from the power plant or the storage cells into useful forms of energy. The electric lamp would be considered as a means of converting electricity into heat and light, two other forms of energy; the electric iron as a means of converting electrical energy into heat.

Friction in the machines, necessity for lubrication, and the heat developed in moving parts of machines could be used as a means of building up the notion that energy is not lost or destroyed, but merely changed into other forms, some of which are not directly useful for the human purpose for which the machine is built. It would be possible to trace the energy stored in the gasoline back to the crude oil, the crude oil to prehistoric primitive organisms, and the stored chemical energy of these organisms to the radiant energy of the sun. Pupils might eventually see that radiant energy given off from the electric lamp in the living room on a particular winter evening came from radiant energy released from the sun ages ago.

Through such study pupils might be enabled to enlarge their understandings of such generalizations as the following:

1. The sun is the chief source of energy for the earth.
2. Energy may be derived from matter.
3. Energy may be stored in chemical substances.
4. Energy is not destroyed.
5. Machines serve the purpose of changing energy into its different forms.
6. All matter is probably electrical in nature.
7. Chemical changes are accompanied by energy changes.
8. The 'loss' of energy in machines is only apparent. These losses may be accounted for by energy transformations which are not parts of the useful output of the machines.
9. Electricity, heat, and light are forms of energy.
10. Complicated machines may be reduced to a relatively few simple types of machines.

In urban situations a similar treatment might be made of the local electric power supply. Certain extensions of the foregoing generalizations would be possible with power supplied from coal and steam plants or water power and through the increased ramifications of power supplies to modern transportation and industry.

OBJECTIVES OF INSTRUCTION IN CHEMISTRY

In 1925 Powers[12] compiled the aims of chemistry-teaching gathered "from many sources." As Powers remarks, the list "is probably sufficiently comprehensive to include all the possible objectives which have been defined for this subject in the educational literature." The list follows:

---

[12] Powers, S. R. "Objectives of high-school chemistry," *Sch. Sci. and Math.*, 25: 1925, 882-883.

Cf. also Lyons, F. W., *The Educational Value of Chemistry*, University of Pennsylvania, 1925; and Cornog, Jacob, and Colbert, J. C., "A quantitative analysis of aims in teaching high-school chemistry," *Sch. Sci. and Math.*, February, 1924, 168-173.

Objectives of Chemistry
(An eleventh- or twelfth-grade subject)

a. To give pupils a broad genuine appreciation of what the development of chemistry means in modern social, industrial, and national life.

b. To satisfy the natural interests in the things and forces of nature with which men are surrounded and with which they must deal; to give information which is interesting, purely for its own sake.

c. To provide opportunity for the student to become acquainted with the application of chemistry to industry for the purpose of educational and vocational guidance and possibly to furnish a beginning of vocational training.

d. To develop such broad concepts and natural laws as the ultimate composition and indestructibility of matter, nature of chemical composition, interrelation of chemical elements, etc., to the end that science and reality may function in place of superstition and uncertainty in explaining natural phenomena.

e. To contribute such specific ideals, habits, and concepts as those of accuracy, achievement, persistency, open-mindedness, honesty, cause and effect, which are essential to the study of science.

f. To develop system, order, neatness, and possibly other attributes, to the end that they will function in the ordinary affairs of life.

g. To afford in some measure an opportunity to show the importance of scientific research and to stimulate the spirit of investigation and invention on the part of the student.

h. To give to children full opportunity to indulge in the playful manipulation of chemical material, in order that they may explore the world of reality as widely and as deeply as possible.

i. To provide opportunity for acquaintance with such applications of chemistry in public utilities, in order that the student may more adequately fulfil the duties of citizenship.

j. To provide opportunity for acquaintance with such applications of chemistry as contribute to the maintenance of health of the individual and the community.

k. To provide opportunity for acquaintance with the elementary laws of nature which aid in understanding those citizenship problems which arise in connection with such topics as utilization of waste products, elimination of smoke, pure foods, etc.

l. To make pupils able to read more intelligently and with greater interest, articles on chemistry in magazines and in scientific books of a popular character.

m. To give such training as will result in increasing respect for the work of recognized experts.

This compilation gives a comprehensive picture of the opinions concerning the objectives of chemistry-teaching in the secondary schools, from which certain trends may be gathered. There is a definite trend towards the expression of objectives for teaching chemistry in terms of the effect to be produced in pupils rather than in terms of the subject itself; note the form of expression in objectives *a, b, c, g, h, i, j, k,* and *l*. Notions of the broad disciplinary value of chemistry still hold; note the expression of objectives *e* and *f*. Some objectives are so broad and general as to be practically meaningless, at least as applied to instruction in high-school chemistry; note aims *b, e, f,* and *g*. There are apparently rather too many objectives to be well accomplished by one year's work in any subject. Some basis must be found for limiting the objectives expressed for a single course to those things which may be reasonably accomplished within the given time.

Report of Committee of the American Chemical Society

In 1924 the report of the Committee on Chemical Education of the American Chemical Society on a "Standard Minimum Course in High-School Chemistry" was published.[13] The revised list of objectives for this course as published in the *Journal of Chemical Education* was said to have been modified to meet 30,000 criticisms and suggestions of chemistry teachers from the country at large. Unfortunately the technique used in taking account of these criticisms of the original objectives was not reported. It is probably fair to assume that the objectives represent the pooled opinions of members of the committee and that the 30,000 criticisms were effective only indirectly through the thinking of members of the committee as they perused them.

The objectives set up by this Committee on Chemical Education do not differ materially from those included in the list quoted above. Some of them show evidence of centering the course about the needs of the learner; others center definitely in subject matter. Five of the eleven statements are not really objectives at all, but suggestions for organization and teaching. Other objectives indicate a continuing remnant of belief in the general disciplinary value of the subject which seems out of line with modern psychological experimentation. Preparation for the college course that follows looms large as one of the major objectives.

This report of the Committee on Chemical Education has had considerable influence; in many schools its outline forms the basis for instruction in chemistry.

---

[13] *Jour. of Chemical Educ.*, 1: 1924, 87 ff.

Report of North Central Association Committee

The Committee on Standards for Use in the Reorganization of Secondary School Curricula for the North Central Association of Colleges and Secondary Schools also appointed a Subcommittee on Chemistry. In its report[14] the general pattern and the formula of immediate objectives are identical with those used by the subcommittee on physics previously quoted. No objectives especially adapted to instruction in chemistry are set up. The patterns of the general committee are used to select sample units of subject matter for instruction. No suggestion is made of a standard body of subject matter; presumably any chemistry teacher is free to make his own sampling with the same general formulae. No attention is paid to the essential concepts or principles necessary for understanding any or all of the facts and principles in the field of chemistry. Many of the selections are as yet nebulous, so that the average teacher of high-school chemistry is not likely to find satisfactory guidance in them.

POSITION OF THE YEARBOOK COMMITTEE CONCERNING OBJECTIVES FOR CHEMISTRY IN THE HIGH SCHOOL

As in the field of high-school physics, so in the field of high-school chemistry, comparatively little progress has been made in the formulation of objectives in terms of the controlling concepts or major ideas necessary to understand the facts in chemistry, in terms of the attempt to train in the kind of scientific methods used in solving chemistry problems, or in terms of desirable attitudes that may be built up in such a course in high-school science. The point of view of this Committee is that objectives for high-school chemistry will need to be stated in such terms before adequate progress can be made.

Objectives for High-School Chemistry That Illustrate the Point of View of the Yearbook Committee

I. Pupils in high-school chemistry courses should develop better *understandings* of those fundamental concepts, major ideas, laws or principles of chemistry that will enable them *better to interpret* natural phenomena, common applications of chemical principles, and industrial applications and uses of the principles of chemistry.

---

[14] See preliminary report in *North Central Assoc. Quarterly*, March, 1927, and later report, *ibid.*, March, 1931.

A. *Illustrations of Such Major Ideas or Principles from Chemistry*[15]

1. The sun is the chief source of energy for the earth.
2. Matter and energy cannot be created or destroyed, but may be changed from one form to another.
3. Chemical and physical changes are manifestations of energy changes.
4. There are less than one hundred chemical elements.
5. Every substance is one of the following: (a) a chemical element, (b) a chemical compound, (c) a physical mixture.
6. The properties of the different elements depend upon the number and arrangement of the electrons and of the protons contained in their atoms.
7. All matter is probably electrical in structure.
8. The kinetic energy of the molecules determines the physical states of matter.
9. Chemical changes are accompanied by energy changes.
10. Electricity is a form of energy that results from disturbing the position of the regular paths of electrons.
11. In a chemical change a quantitative relationship exists between the amounts of substances reacting and the amounts of the substances that are the products of the reaction.[16]

B. *Illustrations of Applications in Which Understandings of Such Major Ideas Should Be Developed*

1. Household chemicals, such as common salt
2. Petroleum products
3. Foodstuffs
4. Fertilizers
5. Solutions, including colloids
6. Acids and bases
7. Fuels
8. Paper
9. Photography
10. Dyes
11. Metallurgy

II. Pupils in high-school chemistry classes should learn to use the processes of reflective thinking, problem-solving, and techniques of study that are best adapted to the solution of problems within the field of chemistry, especially those which most often present themselves in daily life.

---

[15] These illustrative statements of important generalizations suitable for the course in high-school chemistry are selected from those presented in Chapter IV. This list of eleven statements is, of course, not exhaustive.

[16] For an extensive study of principles and concepts from the field of chemistry see Sites, John Theodore, *Chemical Principles, Concepts, and Technical Terms Used in Science Magazines,* in Curtis, F. D., *Second Digest of Investigations,* pp. 269-276.

Suggestive illustrations are:

1. Developing skills in reading and interpreting chemical formulae.
2. Learning to use and interpret symbolic diagrams of organic chemistry.
3. Learning to interpret symbolic diagrams of atomic structure.
4. Forming habits of using objective data as the basis of proof for the solution of problems of chemistry.
5. Learning to record and tabulate chemical data.
6. Learning to formulate conclusions based upon objective data within the field of chemistry.
7. Learning to translate data of chemical experiments into mathematical form.

III. Pupils in senior-high-school classes in chemistry should develop those attitudes towards the facts and principles of chemistry and towards the methods of investigation employed in the field that will serve as guides in their use of chemical facts and principles and methods of problem-solving. Illustrations of such attitudes are:

1. Man's conception of truth changes. Things which seem to be true within the field of chemistry to-day may not be accepted as true to-morrow.
2. Pupils in chemistry classes must learn how to continue their own training and education within the field of chemistry.
3. Chemistry may be made of enormous service to human beings.
4. The forces of chemistry may be enormously destructive. These forces should be turned to constructive rather than destructive uses.
5. Research in the field of chemistry is worthy of support; it is worth more than it costs.
6. The claims of the promoters of many chemical compounds, mixtures, and nostrums should be investigated by the objective methods of attack of the trained chemist.
7. Much advertising of chemical materials is unreliable and should be checked by scientific methods.

The Content of the High-School Chemistry Course

The syllabi of the College Entrance Examination Board and of the New York Regents have been among the more powerful agencies operating to standardize the course in high-school chemistry. The requirements for college entrance, as interpreted by college authorities, have determined the content of these syllabi. Textbooks have been written to meet the demands of these syllabi.

Studies of Koos, Powers, and Cornog and Colbert

In order to determine the extent of overlapping of high-school and of college chemistry Koos[17] analyzed texts commonly used in the high

---

[17] Koos, Leonard V. *The Junior College.* (Research Publications of the University of Minnesota, 1924.) Chap. 33.

school and others commonly used in freshman college classes. Compared on the basis of percentage of total space in each given to identical topics, the texts were found strikingly similar, and there were no topics peculiar to either level. The college texts merely treat more fully the topics treated in the high-school texts. The similarity of laboratory manuals is revealed by the fact that 99.07 percent of all the lines in two college manuals are devoted to experiments contained in one or more of the high-school manuals, and that 95.21 percent of the lines in three high-school manuals are devoted to experiments contained in one or the other of two college manuals. The unescapable conclusion is that the student who has studied chemistry in the high school repeats practically the whole of his high-school work when he studies chemistry in college.

An early study bearing upon the content of the high-school chemistry course is that of Powers.[18] The findings have to do primarily with the extent to which items of the Powers' Chemistry Test were mastered by high-school pupils. They indicate lack of uniformity in learning and lack of mastery of such things as comprehension of the meanings of the laws and theories stated by famous chemists, definitions of chemical terminology, a knowledge of the chemical composition of substances, knowledge of the use of common chemical substances, mathematical computations used in chemistry, writing names of chemical substances from formulae or formulae from names, writing oxidation and reduction equations.

Cornog and Colbert,[19] in an analysis of five widely used textbooks in chemistry in 1924, found in them the following average percentages of types of materials:

Descriptive content 55.8
Content on useful applications. 25.2
Content concerning chemical theory. 13.1
Content on equations and problems. 5.9

In the same study are tabulations of similar content as determined from teachers' stress, New York State Regents Examinations, high-school questions, and Entrance Board questions. These latter show 32 to 42 percent of descriptive matter and approximately the same emphasis upon useful applications as the textbooks. The reduction in

---

[18] Powers, S. R. *A Diagnostic Study of the Subject Matter of High-School Chemistry.* (Teachers Coll. Contrib. to Educ. No. 149, 1924.)

[19] Cornog, Jacob, and Colbert, J. C. "A quantitative analysis of aims in teaching high-school chemistry," *Sch. Sci. and Math.*, 24: February, 1924, 168-173.

emphasis upon descriptive matter as shown from these other sources is compensated for in the emphasis of 20 to 30 percent upon equations and problems in these other sources.

These courses are largely descriptive. There is little evidence of conscious attempt on the part of their makers to base them upon the larger controlling concepts or of attempts to set up problem situations that might train in scientific thinking within the field of chemistry.

Report of Committee of the American Chemical Society

An outline of content which has had considerable influence upon the high-school chemistry course as it now exists is to be found in the report of the Committee on Chemical Education of the American Chemical Society.[20] The "Standard Minimum Course" is largely descriptive. There is little evidence of intent to organize this course about major controlling concepts or ideas. Indeed, the topic, The Electronic Structure of Matter, is placed in the "Additional Topics" in the third category of topics of minor importance, "not to be required for college entrance but to be added if time permits," and left to the discretion of the individual high-school teacher. Here are placed also such topics as The Periodic Table, the Hydrogen Equivalent, and Radio-Active Metals. From the point of view of the Committee preparing this Yearbook such a major idea as that of the electronic structure of matter is basic to any proper understanding of all the phases of modern chemistry, and the high-school chemistry course should be so organized that high-school pupils, as far as their maturity will permit, should grasp its significance and use it in the interpretation of most chemical phenomena.

A wealth of illustrative material concerning everyday uses of chemistry is suggested by the Committee on Chemical Education. This should undoubtedly prove of value in stimulating interest in the course and in further establishing its value. Unfortunately, nearly all of this material is placed in the second and third categories, outside the limits of the "Minimum Standard Course," and marked "not to be required for college entrance." It is to be feared that the typical high-school teacher of chemistry, in attempting to follow the suggestions of the outlined course, will confine the work largely to the minimum core required for college entrance.

---

[20] *Loc. cit.*, Footnote 13, pp. 88-92.

However, we are informed that a revision of this outline is now in progress in which special attention is being paid to the points just mentioned. This promises well for the greater usefulness of the outline.

Report of the Committee of the Central Association of Science and Mathematics

In 1920 the Committee on Reorganization of High-School Chemistry of the Central Association of Science and Mathematics attempted "to formulate (in accordance with the aims and objectives stated in Unit I) the content in terms of concepts rather than materials."[21] This proposal is, of course, in essential agreement with the point of view expressed by the present Yearbook Committee. The material reported consisted of expressions of opinions of forty-two high-school teachers of chemistry. No statements of controlling concepts are made; these must be read into the terms used in the report, and in many cases the exact concept that was in the minds of the committee members and teachers is in doubt. Sections I, II, and V of the report would indicate a consideration of important major ideas or concepts; the other sections, with the exception of III, are purely topical. In general this report indicates a topical descriptive course similar to that recommended by the American Chemical Society.

Report of the Committee of the North Central Association

The Subcommittee on Chemistry of the North Central Association has recently produced a definite set of units suggestive of content for the high-school chemistry course. In the report[22] appears this list of fourteen recommended units:

1. Chemical changes in everyday life.
2. Elements, the simplest form of matter.
3. The ten elements necessary to life.
4. Some simple compounds of the essential elements.
5. How simple compounds combine to form others.
6. Some other useful and interesting elements.
7. The relation of chemistry to human health.
8. Uses of chemistry in the home.
9. Applications of chemistry in our daily life.
10. How chemistry is applied in industries.
11. How chemistry contributes to the welfare of society.

---

[21] Osborne, R. W., (Chairman). "Report of the Committee on Reorganization of High-School Chemistry," *Sch. Sci. and Math.,* 20: 1920, 240-242.
[22] *North Central Association Quarterly,* March, 1931.

12. The chemistry of plant and animal life.
13. The relation of chemistry to the progress of civilization.
14. Generalizations and the solution of problems.

The recommendations of this report indicate emphasis upon the human uses of chemistry rather than a mere topical treatment of subject matter, but it seems to fall short of the integration which might be achieved by a consideration of the larger generalizations of the science as a basis for organization. The work done upon the details of this course has been insufficient to predict its ultimate usefulness.

SUGGESTIONS OF THE YEARBOOK COMMITTEE CONCERNING CONTENT FOR CHEMISTRY IN THE HIGH SCHOOL

The list of generalizations which best meets the point of view of the Committee of this Society is that quoted in connection with the statement of objectives for high-school chemistry in a preceding section of this chapter. These statements attempt to set up these ideas in terms of controlling concepts rather than in topics. No attempt is made to set these in a teaching order or in the form of units to be taught. It is recommended, however, that such controlling concepts be used as centers of organization about which to build teaching units in chemistry. These teaching units will need to be expressed in terms of topics or problems set in terms of familiar applications and uses within the experience of pupils.

Generalizations such as the following are suggested as possible organizing themes to be used in building up the high-school chemistry course:

I. When a chemical change takes place, the substances that are involved are changed in such a way that they no longer behave as they did before this reaction occurred.

II. In a chemical change, a quantitative relation exists between the amounts of the substances reacting and the amounts of the substances that are products of the reaction.

An Illustrative Outline of Chemistry Organization Determined by a Major Generalization as an Organizing Theme

There are many simple experiences that may be used in the laboratory and classroom to develop interpretations that, when associated, accomplish an understanding of the first major generalization suggested above. The following material is presented to show what might be used for this purpose.[23]

A. *Burning Magnesium in Air or in Oxygen*

Some of the learning elements which may come out of this experience are:

1. A compound, magnesium oxide, is formed by the union of the two elements, oxygen and magnesium.
2. Magnesium oxide differs in chemical properties both from magnesium and from oxygen.
3. This chemical change involves the combination of unit particles of magnesium with unit particles of oxygen, forming particles of magnesium oxide.

Some experiences similar to the burning of magnesium are: burning sulphur, carbon, hydrogen, iron, phosphorus in oxygen, heating zinc with sulphur, and heating iron with sulphur.

The student may associate the ideas learned into the generalizations:

1. When elements combine with each other, a substance is formed that resembles neither of the elements but has a peculiar characteristic behavior.
2. Chemical changes may involve combinations of unit particles of elements into unit particles of compounds.

B. *Heating Mercuric Oxide*

Some of the learning elements which may come out of this experience are:

1. A compound, mercuric oxide, may be decomposed into the elements mercury and oxygen.
2. Mercury and oxygen differ in chemical properties from mercuric oxide.
3. This chemical change involves the decomposition of unit particles of mercuric oxide into unit particles of oxygen and unit particles of mercury.

The electrolysis of water is a simple reaction which may be used to develop similar ideas. The student may associate these and come to the following generalizations:

1. The products formed by decomposing a substance differ in mode of behavior from each other and from the substance decomposed.
2. Chemical changes may involve decomposition of unit particles of compounds into simpler particles.

These generalizations are associated with those made after studying many more chemical changes and the generalization—*when a chemical change takes place, the substances that are involved are changed in such a way that they no longer behave as they did before this reaction occurred*—will be developed. The chemist who has spent his life studying chemical changes will have the fullest appreciation, but students of elementary chemistry may also reach some appreciation of this complex concept.

---

[23] The Committee is indebted to Miss Ruth M. Johnson, of the Newton High School, New York City, for assistance in preparing the outline from which this illustration is taken.

The student may come to an understanding of the major generalization— *in a chemical change, a quantitative relation exists between the amounts of the substances reacting and the amounts of the substances that are products of the reaction*—by associating the ideas learned in his study of:

1. Experiments on combining gas volumes.
2. Gay-Lussac's Law, a generalization concerning the behavior of gases.
3. Avogadro's hypothesis as an explanation of Gay-Lussac's Law.
4. The application of Avogadro's hypothesis to the determination of molecular and atomic weights.
5. Molecular weights as they are used in the calculation of formulae.
6. Formulae, as exact statements of the composition of substances.
7. Chemical equations, as statements of the quantities of the substances taking part in a chemical change.

From the demonstration experiment in which hydrogen and oxygen are run into a eudiometer over mercury and exploded the student may learn that "two volumes of hydrogen unite with one volume of oxygen to form two volumes of steam when the gases are all measured at the same temperature and pressure."

He may also learn that

1. One volume of hydrogen combines with one volume of chlorine, forming two volumes of hydrogen chloride.
2. Two volumes of carbon monoxide combine with one volume of oxygen, forming two volumes of carbon dioxide.
3. Three volumes of hydrogen combine with one volume of nitrogen, in the presence of a suitable catalyst, forming two volumes of ammonia.

CONTENT FOR THE ATTAINMENT OF A WIDER RANGE OF OBJECTIVES WITH REFERENCE ESPECIALLY TO SCIENTIFIC METHODS AND ATTITUDES

Specimens of content submitted in this report have had to do almost wholly with content that might be useful in the attainment of the first category of objectives recommended by the Yearbook Committee. There remains the problem of the selection and organization of content in physics and chemistry that might furnish specific training in the types of scientific method or scientific thinking needed in these fields, and similar selection and organization of content that might be useful in producing desirable scientific attitudes. These problems are almost entirely virgin territory for the educational experimenter. At best, this Committee can but call attention to these problems and urge their consideration by those interested in the scientific approach to improved science instruction. Until these problems are attacked by the techniques of modern experimental education, such objectives as the development of training in scientific methods and the building of scientific attitudes will continue to be will-o'-the-wisp catch words to enchant unscientific science teachers. Instead of using these as means to befuddle issues in teachers' gatherings and decorate the reports of committees, a frank facing of present ignorance and a definite program of attack is needed.

Learning Activities and Teaching Procedures in the Physical Sciences in the Senior High School

A modern point of view with reference to teaching procedures would indicate that the older notion of teacher-applied methods is an outworn conception of the teaching process. A modern concept of teaching would imply that the effective part of a teaching process is to be found in the activities of the pupils that are included in the process. Modern literature of teaching stresses, therefore, the learning activities of pupils rather than those processes which the teacher, as such, might seek to apply to pupils. The teacher's method or procedure is important only in so far as it is effective in guiding pupil activities that will attain the desired ends of instruction. This is the point of view from which we are here to discuss the teaching of high-school physical sciences and the experimental evidence concerning such teaching.

There is a such a wealth of experimental material on learning activities in high-school science teaching, especially of physics and chemistry, that no attempt will be made to summarize all of the studies,[24] but to present the material that illustrates recent trends in learning and teaching procedures in physics and chemistry.

This summarization[25] is based largely upon reports published in *School Science and Mathematics* from January, 1927, to date, and in *General Science Quarterly* and *Science Education* from November, 1926, to date. To these have been added some reports of large-scale investigations completed during this period or now in progress. Not all the studies of teaching procedures in high-school physics and chem-

---

[24] For additional summaries the reader is referred to the summaries of studies for the whole field of science in Chapters VI, VII, VIII, and IX. Other summaries of earlier investigations are to be found in F. D. Curtis' *Investigations in the Teaching of Science*, in E. R. Downing's *Teaching Science in the Schools*, and in the *Sixth Yearbook of the Department of Superintendence of the N.E.A.*, "The Development of the High-School Curriculum."

[25] For a similar summarization see: Watkins, R. K., "Trends and investigations in teaching procedures for high-school sciences and some possible values." *Proc. Nat. Educ. Assoc.*, 1930, 534-542.

istry made during this period have been covered, but only enough of them to give a representative picture of what is going on.

Twelve Significant Trends

The material gathered has been grouped according to a number of significant trends, of which twelve have been selected for this section of the Committee's report. These are as follows:

1. A critical review and analysis of the investigations already reported of teaching procedures.
2. An attempt at refinement, better description and definition of science demonstrations as teaching devices.
3. An attempt at redefinition, better limitation and description of laboratory instruction, with attempts at evaluation of laboratory instruction as a means of producing certain definite outcomes in pupils.
4. A marked swing toward a unit organization of subject matter and instructional techniques in all high-school sciences.
5. A critical review of existing science tests, accompanied by attempts to select and build tests to meet particular instructional needs.
6. A movement for the diagnosis of pupil difficulties in the learning of science materials.
7. A frank facing of the laboratory-instruction issue upon the basis of available apparatus and equipment now found in high schools.
8. A revival of interest in simple, homely, and home-made laboratory and demonstration apparatus.
9. A beginning of experimental investigation upon the value of visual aids, especially of moving pictures, to instruction.
10. A continued development of the use of extensive reading for general instruction in science.
11. A continued interest in the possibilities of science clubs.
12. A general and spreading interest in the use of free and inexpensive supplementary material drawn into the school from outside commercial sources.

Comments on these twelve trends are next in order.

The First Trend. The first noticeable tendency in the present period is the attempt to take stock of recent investigations in science teaching, consolidate the findings, and thus form a base for future research. This has been accompanied by constructive criticisms of the limitation and definition of problems, of the research techniques employed, and the questioning of interpretations and conclusions drawn from studies. Summaries of this kind have been published by Curtis, Croxton, Downing, Klopp, Riedel, and Watkins.[26]

---

[26] See references in first group of the bibliography at the end of this chapter.

The Second Trend. Numerous experiments comparing the relative merits of lecture-demonstration and individual laboratory instruction have been carried on by different experimenters in different parts of the country. The results of this work are summarized in Chapter VII in this Yearbook.

The Third Trend. It is very probable that experimenters have not yet been able to measure the more valuable outcomes of laboratory instruction, as a number of critics have pointed out. If there are valuable outcomes, the added expense needed to secure them may be justified, but just how valuable the laboratory experience as a whole may be, we do not yet know. At least we do not know how valuable this experience could be made in terms of as yet unmeasured outcomes.

Certainly, in their evaluation of laboratory instruction experimenters have not paused to describe in full detail the kind of laboratory instruction being considered, although any critical evaluation of laboratory instruction ought to consider the nature of the laboratory work and the kind of outcomes it is assumed to produce.

Just what is laboratory instruction expected to accomplish? Here are six or seven possibilities that may be suggested as general purposes for laboratory instruction in high-school science:

1. The development of simple laboratory techniques, such as weighing, glass bending, microscopic manipulation, etc.
2. Proving and establishing for the pupil himself principles which have long since been well established and generally accepted.
3. Using the laboratory as an instrument for object, or 'thing,' teaching, according to the historical concepts of Pestalozzi, Comenius, and Basedow.
4. Using the laboratory for the purpose of developing better understanding and interpretations of the principles of science, as a means of better illustration.
5. To produce training in scientific method.
6. As a means of possible training in the experimental solution of the pupil's own problems.
7. The use of the laboratory as a workshop for the study of science problems which arise in the science class or in the life of the pupils.

Consider for a moment the pros and cons of these purposes of laboratory instruction. It is doubtful if the majority of science teachers are conscious of any of them as they carry on the work in their laboratories from day to day. It is doubtful if any of them are being adequately reached to-day in most high-school science laboratories.

If the simpler types of laboratory techniques to be used in later high-school or college science courses are to be the major aims of laboratory instruction, then it would seem feasible to have much simpler laboratories, much simpler apparatus, and less time-consuming schedules. More direct drill could be given in the processes of handling and manipulating materials and somewhat less upon scientific data and proof. Tests would need to be constructed to measure such techniques in order to determine the results of the work. Horton[27] carried on just this type of investigation in high-school chemistry and demonstrated that certain laboratory techniques useful in chemistry can be established by laboratory procedures. Suggestive experiments by Beauchamp and Webb,[28] and by Webb[28] indicate further possibilities in this direction.

Suppose the major purpose of the high-school laboratory is that of proving principles to the pupil's own satisfaction—objectification and illustration: it would seem that a skilled demonstrator and illustrator, the science teacher, with satisfactory apparatus and diagrammatic aids, could then do better than a very inexperienced illustrator, with very poor apparatus and little or no skill, could do for himself. This is what the series of earlier experiments upon the relative merits of lecture-demonstration and individual laboratory instruction seem to prove.

Present-day psychology would seem to indicate that there are *scientific methods* rather than *a scientific method*. The position could readily be defended that in all probability training in scientific methods is to be attained by the whole complex of the pupil's science training rather than by that part of it represented by the school laboratory in one of the high-school physical sciences. A case might also be made out for the assertion that any training in scientific method is impossible by the type of laboratory instruction prevalent in physics and chemistry in many of our schools.

There remain of the proposed purposes, the possible use of the school laboratory as a means of training high-school pupils in the experimental solution of their own science problems within the fields of physics and chemistry, and the use of the laboratory as a workshop for solving the problems which develop in classes in these subjects. This would seem to be the most promising of the possibilities for laboratory instruction at the high-school level. It is the very essence of the original reason for the existence of every laboratory, from that of the alchemist seeking to transmute base metals into gold to that of

---

[27] See reference in third group of the bibliography.
[28] See reference in fifth group of the bibliography.

the modern investigator seeking to split the atom or even that of the lad in a corner of the basement trying to determine the effect of a new type of radio coil. In high schools this type of laboratory is illustrated by a few of the more advanced general-science laboratories, but very rarely by a senior-high-school physics or chemistry laboratory. Just what the product of such laboratories in physics or chemistry would be in terms of outcomes for pupils is yet a matter of conjecture.[29]

In laboratories of this latter pattern trite illustrations of proofs of accepted theories and principles merely as laboratory busy work would be barred; such illustration would be left largely to teacher demonstration (available experimental evidence would bear out this practice). Supplies would include much raw material. Some apparatus would be of the home-made, pupil-constructed type. Little apparatus of the delicate and expensive kind would be provided, except that needed for the teacher's demonstration work. Much use would be made of the apparatus in common use in the commercial world outside the school. The household gas and electric meters would find a place; so would such things as real telephones, radios, fire extinguishers, and cameras. Use would be made of materials available in the community and in the homes of pupils.

In such a laboratory the pupils would be concerned, in the main, with questions concerning the applications of principles rather than with the reëstablishment of well-known laws and principles. These established principles and facts would be accepted by them upon the basis of customary authorities and the proofs set forth and illustrated by the text, lecture-demonstration, motion picture, everyday observation, and so on. Problems of application which are acute in every community, in every group, and for every individual would be brought into the classroom, library, and laboratory for solution. Such applications exist by the thousand for every established fact or principle. Curriculum-makers need to gather some of these and organize them as possibilities about the more important concepts and major ideas of physics and chemistry as suggestive patterns for possible laboratory instruction in these subjects.

Would the laboratory described be worth while? Who knows? Such laboratories would need to be set up in schools. Their possible outcomes for pupils could then be postulated and tests devised to

---

[29] The contribution from laboratory work to the development of ability to solve problems is discussed in Chap. V.

verify or disprove them. Long-term experimental studies would need to be carried out to be sure that the results were consistent and not merely a chance product of a local teaching situation.

The recent summaries of earlier experimental attacks on the relative merits of teaching procedures in science have emphasized the need for further investigations. Certain limitations or criteria to be met stand out clearly as a result of these criticisms: (1) Procedures to be investigated must be clearly described in detail. What is laboratory instruction? How are lecture demonstrations done? (2) Investigations need to be repeated in the same way, with similar controls, and with the same tests. (3) Investigations must be repeated under normal public-school conditions. (4) Smaller areas need to be selected for investigation. (5) Simpler investigational procedures for producing definite types of results in pupils need to be built up and experimentally evaluated.[30]

Out of the attacks upon the older type of laboratory instruction there have developed attempts at improvement in demonstration and a new interest in demonstration. This new interest is evidenced by people who are concerned with the training of teachers, by the teachers themselves, and by the manufacturers and designers of apparatus. Work on the improvement of demonstrations has been described by Black, Colwell and Holmes, Duff, Haut, Jared, and Klopsteg.[31] Progress has been made in both physics and chemistry, but almost no work has been done in the experimental evaluation of demonstration techniques for producing particular outcomes. Here lies an open field for new experimentation. The criteria for judging demonstrations suggested by Duff and the possible instructional uses for demonstrations listed by Jared offer points of departure.

Although little progress has been made in the experimental evaluation of accurately described demonstration techniques, some progress has been made in the attempt to determine the outcomes of laboratory instruction and the relative merits of certain smaller laboratory techniques. For the first type, the work of Dyer, Horton, and Knox is outstanding.[32] Utterback and Walters[32] have also contributed to this movement, although their studies lack in one case careful description and in the other adequate measurement.

---

[30] For critical discussion of research in this field, see Curtis, F. D. *Second Digest*, Pt. I.

[31] See references in the second group of the bibliography.

[32] See references in the third group of the attached bibliography.

The net results to date of this third trend would seem, in general terms, to be these: (1) It is possible to set up laboratory teaching procedures that give promise of producing certain outcomes in pupils. In some cases the laboratory produces these outcomes better than a demonstration technique. Whether these outcomes are worth producing might sometimes be questioned. Further work of this kind must depend upon further refinement of measurement devices. (2) Gradually we shall learn the relative merits of the smaller techniques which make up the complex of the thing which we have called laboratory instruction.

The Fourth Trend. Unit organization as the basis for planning instruction is apparently here. How far this movement has reached into the actual practice of the rank and file of science teachers, it is extremely difficult to determine. Curriculum-makers, professional educators, trainers of teachers, curriculum committees and textbook writers seem to have adopted this basis of organization. Those who have been interested in physics teaching have done considerable recent work upon this problem; less has been done in the field of high-school chemistry. Decided progress has been shown by the work of Hurd, Hughes and Hurd, Muthersbaugh, and Peters.[33] The North Central Association is definitely committed to unit organization in its curriculum-construction program. The work of Downing with the high-school biology course and that of Hurd with the high-school physics course are excellent illustrations. Hurd's work in the experimental trial of new units in high-school physics, with measured results in terms of progress of pupils, is to be especially marked.

It would seem that, given the time to retrain a portion of teachers now in service and to train the coming generation of science teachers, large-unit organization will become practically universal.

The Fifth Trend. There is a considerable body of literature dealing with science tests. Some of it is concerned with critical review and evaluation of existing material; *e.g.*, Cunningham, Haskell and Hudelson, and Lohr[34] have done work of this type. With this, there is a growing consciousness of the need for selecting tests for particular service uses. Other studies[34] have had to do with test forms and the technicalities of test construction. The studies of Beauchamp and Webb and of Webb[34] in the measurement of laboratory resourceful-

---

[33] See references in the fourth group of the bibliography.
[34] See references in the fifth group of the bibliography.

ness suggest a new line of departure in the field of scientific testing. Unit tests in physics and chemistry have been constructed and are now available to teachers of these subjects.[35]

The Sixth Trend. A few recent studies have been concerned with difficulties inherent in the nature of high-school sciences or with the diagnosis of pupil difficulties or their remedying. Recent workers in this field are Bedell, Cramer, Lohr, and Stewart.[36] These studies, in general, have been in general science, physics, and chemistry. Cramer has shown that pupils having had general science are more successful in later special sciences than pupils who had not had general science.

The Seventh Trend. One group of investigations that do not bear directly upon instructional procedures is included here because of its implications, which set definite limits upon the instructional procedures that may be undertaken by teachers actually at work in the field. This group of studies is concerned with the equipment available for work in high-school science courses. The studies include those of Jensen and Glenn, and of Watkins and Harty.[37] Watkins and Harty found less than half of their schools in Northeast Missouri without water and gas facilities for teaching physics, although these were first-class schools and their physics instruction was fully accredited.

The Eighth Trend. With this gloomy picture of available equipment it is not strange that there is some interest in simple and home-made apparatus. Nevertheless, it is doubtful whether teachers should be encouraged to spend time in the manufacture of crude apparatus. Though there is almost no serious research in this field, the work of Haupt, Obourn, and Underhill is worthy of note.[38] Haupt's collection and annotation of home-made physics apparatus from the files of *School Science and Mathematics* is the most helpful of the recent studies in this field.

The Ninth Trend. Probably the most extensive recent contribution to the available procedures in science teaching has been made by workers who have been concerned with the value of visual aids, especially of motion pictures, in science instruction. The work in this field

[35] Glenn-Obourn, *Instructional Tests in Physics.* Glenn-Welton, *Instructional Tests in Chemistry.* Peters-Watkins, *Objective Tests in High-School Physics.*

[36] See references in the sixth group of the bibliography.

[37] See references in the seventh group of the bibliography.

[38] See references in the eighth group of the bibliography.

extends from the large scale development of teaching films done by the Eastman Kodak Company through the extensive learning studies of Freeman and Wood to the evaluation of particular films for special teaching as by Wood and Watkins. Contributions in this field include those of Brown, Finegan, Freeman, Freeman and Wood, Wood and Watkins, and Wilbur.[39]

Practically all of these investigations show positive results in favor of visual aids. Tests of motion pictures have been favorable to their use. In some studies instruction by means of motion pictures produced results as good as those secured by other means of instruction. Brown found strip film superior to motion pictures for some types of biological illustration. There is still difficulty in obtaining films that have high instructional value without too much advertising material and too many superficial entertainment features. Expense is another factor that limits decidedly the use of films and of most other visual equipment. No investigators have recommended the substitution of motion-picture instruction for other means of teaching. Microprojection would seem to have decided possibilities in the field of high-school chemistry, although it has not as yet been experimentally evaluated. Most teachers have not made even a good beginning in canvassing the possibilities of the visual aids to teaching that are now on the market.

The Tenth Trend. Encouragement of extensive reading in the field of natural science is noticeable.[40] H. A. Webb is continuing his annual review of new science books suitable for high-school libraries. Gere and others have contributed reports upon the values of reading in chemistry. Hildebrand has reported upon a similar program for high-school science in general, but almost no research has been done in this field since the pioneer investigation of F. D. Curtis in the field of general science. Caldwell, Slosson, and Kellog have compiled a list of recent science books for lay readers for the Women's Division of the National Civic Federation that should be in the hands of every science teacher and on the bulletin board in every science classroom.

The Eleventh Trend. Science clubs continue to flourish. No major evaluations of their products seem to have been done since the work of Morris Meister in the field of general science. Webb has collected a large body of practical data upon current practices in the management

---

[39] See references in the ninth group of the bibliography.
[40] See the tenth group in the bibliography.

of these clubs, and Miller has gathered outlines for their guidance.[41] These collections should be of major value to the teacher who administers a science club in connection with his program of science teaching.

The Twelfth Trend. Teachers, as well as other folks, have always been interested in getting something for nothing. For a long time many teachers have used advertising pamphlets, models, and charts as supplementary teaching aids. Several persons have prepared lists to guide teachers in securing and using such material. The best of these lists are those of Dunbar, Roller, and Woodring.[42] To date there seem to be no experimental data to prove the values of such material or to distinguish between the merits of different kinds of it.

In conclusion some final general impressions of the present status may not be out of place. For the modern teacher of science there seems to be little excuse for drifting along with the monotonous daily grind, doing what has always been done. These twelve trends in science instruction should offer a possibility of a well-rounded armamentarium for instruction in high-school physics and chemistry. Some of the suggestions for improved instruction have been well enough proved to offer little danger of malpractice. On the other hand, since, after weeks of reading, there are gleaned only a handful of really experimentally evaluated procedures, it would seem that we are only entering the era of making our work more scientific and that what remains to be done offers a clamorous challenge to every individual interested in the teaching of high-school physical science.

A Classified Bibliography of Illustrative Studies and Reports
1. Review and Analysis of Earlier Investigations

Curtis, F. D. "Some reactions regarding the published investigations in the teaching of science." *Sch. Sci. and Math.*, 27: 1927, 634-641, 710-720. Also in *Second Digest of Investigations in the Teaching of Science.* Blakiston's: Philadelphia, 1931, 3-24.

Croxton, W. C. "Shall laboratory work in the public schools be curtailed? —a reply to a criticism." *Sch. Sci. and Math.*, 29: 1929, 730-733.

Downing, E. R. "Individual laboratory work vs. teacher demonstration." *Gen. Sci. Quarterly*, 11: January, 1927, 96-99.

Downing, E. R. "Shall laboratory work in the schools be curtailed?" *Sch. Sci. and Math.*, 29: 1929, 411-413.

---

[41] See the eleventh group in the bibliography.
[42] See the twelfth group in the bibliography.

KLOPP, W. J. "Laboratory vs. demonstration." *Gen. Sci. Quarterly,* 13: January, 1929, 98-100.

RIEDEL, F. A. "Relative effectiveness of demonstration and laboratory methods in science." *Sch. Sci. and Math.,* 27: 1927, 512-519, 620-631.

RIEDEL, F. A. "Present status of the controversy, demonstration vs. laboratory." *Gen. Sci. Quarterly,* 11: May, 1927, 246-254.

WATKINS, R. K. "What price laboratory science instruction in the high school." *Gen. Sci. Quarterly,* 13: January, 1929, 70-78.

2. Improvement of Demonstrations

BLACK, N. H. "Better demonstrations in physics." *Sch. Sci. and Math.,* 30: 1930, 366-373.

COLWELL, R. C., and HOLMES, M. C. "Demonstrations in electricity." *Sch. Sci. and Math.,* 28: 1928, 835-837.

DUFF, A. W. "Demonstration experiments, desirable qualities in." *Sch. Sci. and Math.,* 28: 1928, 857.

HAUT, A. "Oxidation-reduction demonstrations." *Sch. Sci. and Math.,* 30: 1930, 361-365.

JARED, R. R. "What constitutes efficient demonstration work in general chemistry." *Sch. Sci. and Math.,* 28: 1928, 43-49.

KLOPSTEG, P. E. "A lecture demonstration of new apparatus." *Sch. Sci. and Math.,* 30: 1930, 546-570.

3. Redefinition and Evaluation of Laboratory Instruction

FRANKLIN, G. T. "Chemistry experiment as the basis for a study of fundamentals." *Sch. Sci. and Math.,* 30: 1930, 415-419.

DYER, J. H. *An Analysis of Certain Outcomes in the Teaching of Physics in Public High Schools.* University of Pennsylvania: Philadelphia, 1927.

HORTON, R. E. *Measurable Outcomes of Individual Laboratory Work in High-School Chemistry.* Teachers College: New York, 1928. (Teachers College Contributions to Education, No. 303)

KNOX, W. W. "The demonstration method vs. the laboratory method of teaching high-school chemistry." *Sch. Review,* May, 1927, 376-386.

UTTERBACK, C. P. "A laboratory method in physics." *Sch. Sci. and Math.,* 28: 1928, 634-636.

WALTER, C. H. "The individual laboratory method of teaching when no printed directions are used." *Sch. Sci. and Math.,* 30: 1930, 429-432.

4. Unit Organization of Science Instruction

HURD, A. W. "Present inadequacies and suggested remedies in the teaching of physics." *Sch. Sci. and Math.,* 30: 1930, 539-546.

MUTHERSBAUGH, G. C. "Objectives of a proposed course of study in physics for senior high school." *Sch. Sci. and Math.,* 29: 1929, 943-954.

North Central Association Quarterly, March, 1931, 453-460, 471-483, 494-507.

PETERS, C. J. "An evaluation of a reorganization of the present core of subject matter in high-school physics." *Sch. Sci. and Math.,* 27: 1927, 172-182.

5. Tendencies in Science Tests

BEAUCHAMP, R. O., and WEBB, H. A. "Resourcefulness, an unmeasured ability." *Sch. Sci. and Math.*, 27: 1927, 457-465.

CUNNINGHAM, H. A. "Character and value of existing tests for pupils and teachers of general science." *Gen. Sci. Quarterly*, 13: January, 1929, 61-70.

CURTIS, F. D., and WOODS, G. G. "A modified form of the multiple response test." *Jour. of Educ. Research*, 18: 1928, 211-219.

GORDON, H. C. "Some new-type test forms in high-school physics." *Sch. Sci. and Math.*, 27: 1927, 721-733.

HASKELL, M. E., and HUDELSON, E. "What test should I use?" *Sch. Sci. and Math.*, 29: 1929, 841-848.

HURD, A. W. "Achievements of students in physics." *Sci. Educ.*, 14: January, 1930, 437-447.

LOHR, V. C. "A comparison of some tests given in high-school physics." *Sch. Sci. and Math.*, 27: 1927, 74-85.

McCLUSKY, H. Y., and CURTIS, F. D. "A modified form of the true-false test." *Sch. Sci. and Math.*, 27: 1927, 362-366.

WEBB, H. A. "Variety, the spice of testing." *Gen. Sci. Quarterly*, 13: January, 1929, 93-98.

6. Diagnosis of Pupil Difficulties

BEDELL, R. C. "A method of diagnosis and remedial treatment in general science." *Sci. Educ.*, 13: May, 1929, 260-266.

CRAMER, W. F. "A study of some achievements of pupils in special sciences— general science vs. non-general science groups." *Sci. Educ.*, 14: March, 1930, 505-517.

LOHR, V. C. "Some factors of success in physics." *Sch. Sci. and Math.*, 28: 1928, 389-398.

STEWART, A. R. "A study of difficulties in chemistry." *Sch. Sci. and Math.*, 28: 1928, 838-848.

7. Limitations of Teaching Due to Limited Equipment

JENSEN, J. H., and GLENN, E. R. "An investigation of types of classrooms for chemistry and other sciences in small high schools." *Jour. of Chemical Educ.*, 6: April, 1929, 634-664.

WATKINS, R. K. "Equipment for teaching physics in Northeast Missouri high schools." *Sci. Educ.*, 13: May, 1929, 199-211.

8. Use of Simple and Home-Made Apparatus

HAUPT, G. W. "An annotated bibliography of contributions to *School Science and Mathematics* describing ingenious and homemade physics apparatus." *Sch. Sci. and Math.*, 29: 1929, 763-769.

HYDE, G. H. "Homemade apparatus for the physics class." *Sci. Educ.*, 15: March, 1931, 159-174.

OBOURN, E. S. "The effective use of practical equipment in a physics course." *Sch. Sci. and Math.*, 28: 1928, 275-280.

UNDERHILL, G. E. "Homemade apparatus." *Gen. Sci. Quarterly*, 13: March, 1929, 147-153.

9. Investigation of the Values of Visual Aids to Instruction

BROWN, H. E. "Motion pictures or film slides?" *Sch. Sci. Math.*, 28: 1928, 517-526.

FINEGAN, T. E. "An experiment in the development of classroom films." *Gen. Sci. Quarterly*, 12: January, 1928, 391-406.

FREEMAN, F. N., et al. *Visual Education.* University of Chicago Press: Chicago, 1924.

FREEMAN, F. N., and WOOD, BEN. *Motion Pictures in the Classroom.* Houghton Mifflin: Boston, 1929.

MILLER, L. P. "The contribution of slides and films to science teaching." *Gen. Sci. Quarterly*, 11: November, 1926, 13-17.

WATKINS, R. K. "The learning value of some moving pictures in the teaching of high-school physics and general science." *The Educational Screen*, 10: May, 1931, 135-137, 156-157.

WILBUR, H. "An experiment in the use of visual methods of instruction." *Gen. Sci. Quarterly*, 12: March, 1928, 480-484.

10. Use of Extensive Reading in Science Teaching

CURTIS, F. D. *Some Values Derived from Extensive Reading of General Science.* Teachers College: New York, 1924. (Teachers College Contributions to Education, No. 163)

GERE, M. C., GUNTHER, J. U., and HENDRICKS, C. B. "The high-school chemistry library." *Sch. Sci. and Math.*, 29: 1929, 859-863.

HILDEBRAND, L. E. "Outside reading in science in secondary schools." *Sch. Sci. and Math.*, 28: 1928, 61-63.

WEBB, H. A. *The High-School Science Library.* H. A. Webb: Nashville, 1928, 1929, 1930, 1931.

11. Science Clubs

DUNBAR, R. E. "Chemistry for fun." *Sci. Educ.*, 14: March, 1930, 547-548.

MILLER, D. W. "Suggested programs for science clubs." *Sci. Educ.*, 14: November, 1929, 331-334.

WEBB, H. A. "Some first-hand information concerning science clubs." *Sch. Sci. and Math.*, 29: 1929, 273-276.

12. Use of Supplementary Materials

DUNBAR, R. E. "Sources of free material for science instruction." *Gen. Sci. Quarterly*, 12: May, 1928, 551-559.

ROLLER, D. E. *Sources of Free Material for Use in the Teaching of Natural Science.* University of Oklahoma: Norman, 1925.

WOODRING, MAXIE, et al. *Enriched Teaching of Science in the High School.* Bureau of Publications, Teachers College: New York, 1928.

CHAPTER XVI
SCIENCE ROOMS AND THEIR EQUIPMENT[1]

The present program of science teaching in elementary and secondary schools is conducted in a specialized group of rooms equipped with a specialized set of materials. This feature of the science teaching is particularly significant. There are few if any other curricula in which so much attention is given to the physical environment in which effective teaching and learning can proceed. In the work of the science teacher a large amount of time and energy is devoted to procuring, devising, organizing, caring for, and manipulating materials. The pupil, too, approaches the work in science with a mental set in which the terms, *experiment, laboratory,* and *apparatus* are important elements. In these respects the teaching of science presents problems that are unique. The solutions of these problems, as embodied in existing practices with regard to laboratories and their equipment, are the result, to some extent, of analysis, research, and testing; to a much larger degree, however, they are the result of tradition, fortuitous factors, and extraneous influences.

It is important that we examine our procedures with, and attitudes toward, equipment problems. The mounting cost of school budgets tends to draw attention to the sciences. Although school systems differ widely in their generosity to science departments, it is nevertheless true practically everywhere that science is more costly than other subjects in floor space per pupil, in furniture, equipment, time, and teaching load. The justification for these expenditures must come from accepted educational philosophy, sound administrative policy, and the psychology of learning. If the most effective learning experiences in the field of science cannot be brought to the pupil except by way of laboratory situations, then each science room, each piece of furniture, and each piece of equipment must be evaluated in terms of the learning situation which it makes possible. Furthermore, every learning situation thus created must be viewed in the light of the objectives of

---

[1] The Committee acknowledges the valuable aid of Dr. Morris Meister, New York Teacher Training College, College of the City of New York, who has contributed most of the material of this chapter. Thanks are also due to Professor Lillian Hethershaw, Drake University, for her contribution cited specifically in the course of the chapter.

science teaching, of the aims of education to which the study of science contributes, and of the results secured in learning by the pupils.

A Brief Outline of Present Practices

The growth of science during the nineteenth century and during the last three decades has quite naturally called attention to laboratory procedures and the experimental approach to problems in natural science. When, therefore, the sciences were accepted in the curriculum of studies, it seemed proper to provide laboratories in which pupils might learn science. The great popularizers of natural philosophy had, during the nineteenth century, developed a demonstration technique which was very attractive to the beginner and to the uninformed. This, too, was incorporated into the science teacher's approach, so that science teaching tended to proceed along the lines of demonstration and individual laboratory work.

When laboratory work and demonstrations began to develop in a substantial way (about 1875), the colleges were in control of the objectives, content, and method of high-school teaching. In the sciences this domination resulted in a formalization of laboratory exercises and in a standardization of equipment. Faculty psychology and an unquestioning belief in the transfer of training developed a type of laboratory work and demonstration exercise which persists to an appreciable extent even to-day. Since about 1910, college influence upon high schools has been waning. Also, new points of view in educational philosophy and new knowledge of the learning process have given different meanings to laboratory experiences. The phenomenal growth of high-school population brought curricular problems to the forefront, and for a while there was much diversity and some confusion in the science studies. Many different science subjects were offered, each attempting presumably to develop its own special rooms and equipment.

The situation to-day is simplified, to the extent at least that four subjects dominate the science curriculum and that these subjects are offered in a sequence which is being accepted by a large majority of school systems. Thus, special science rooms and equipment are provided to care for general science in the seventh, eighth, and ninth grades, biology in the ninth or tenth grade, or in both, physics or chemistry in the eleventh grade, and physics or chemistry in the twelfth grade. The equipment problem for the course in science of the first six grades has as yet been given very little attention. Aside from an occasional 'Nature Room' or 'Science Museum,' the usual practice is to adapt the ordinary classroom for work of this type. Just as little attention has been given to the laboratory and equipment problems of teacher-training institutions, either from the point of view of preparing the elementary-school teacher or of training the prospective teacher of science. However, several attacks upon this problem are in progress.

A cursory examination of special science room facilities in modern school systems shows a number of different kinds of rooms.

1. The Science Classroom

Sometimes called the 'recitation room,' the science classroom serves all the purposes of the ordinary classroom. Its dimensions are usually about 24' x 28', and it has seating accommodations for about 30 pupils. At one end is a demonstration table, about 6' to 8' long, equipped with gas, hot and cold water, and electricity. In the large high schools the electrical service is controlled from a central switchboard, and provision is made for 110 volt D.C., 110 volt A.C., and battery current at varying voltages. The electrical provision, as well as the type of additional furniture, depends largely upon whether the classroom is used for general science, biology, chemistry, or physics. The pupils sit either in tablet armchairs or at small tables. One can also find in this type of room an apparatus case, bookshelves, a teacher's desk, a bulletin board, and blackboard space. Frequently, the classroom also contains a notebook cabinet and an electrical outlet for a projection lantern. The heating and lighting are cared for in the ordinarily accepted manner; the plumbing for the demonstration table is made to withstand the attacks of acids and other corrosive materials.

2. The Laboratory[2]

a. *General Science.* It is not a common practice to provide a laboratory exclusively for general science. Usually the classroom and laboratory are combined as outlined in (3) below.

---

[2] Powers, S. R., and Manzer, J. G. "Equipment for elementary and high-school science rooms." *American School and University,* American School Publishing Company: New York, 1931. Fourth Edition, p. 441.
(This article includes drawings showing arrangement of laboratories for science in the elementary school, in the junior high school, and for senior-high-school biology. Furnishings and equipment are given in detail.)
See also Donovan, J. J., and Others. *School Architecture,* Macmillan: New York, 1921. Chap. XIX.

b. Biology. Here, too, a common procedure is to design a room for both recitation and laboratory. However, many schools provide a special biology laboratory. Important features in such a room are the following:

Small demonstration table
About six pupil tables, each accommodating four persons
Microscope case
Supply case
Blackboard and bulletin space
Two sinks
Window shelves for growing plants
Notebook case
Aquarium and terrarium table
Projection facilities

The dimensions of this room vary considerably. The usual size to accommodate thirty pupils doing individual work is 28′ x 40′.

c. Physics.[3] In size and in pupil accommodation the physics laboratory resembles the chemistry laboratory. In furnishings one may note the difference in the style of pupil table and the absence of fume hoods. The essential items of furniture are the following:

Teacher's demonstration table
Pupil tables, each accommodating four persons
Cross-beams over pupil tables, supported by rods which fit into flush
    plates set into the table tops
Supply case
Notebook case
Wall table
Blackboard and bulletin space

d. Chemistry. The specialized work which is carried on in a room of this type makes it more difficult to combine recitation and laboratory work in one room. Thus, chemical laboratories are more frequently found as one-purpose rooms.

According to Mattern,[4] a room 22′ x 36′ can accommodate thirty-two pupils for individual work. The essential furnishings to be found in laboratories of this type are the following:

Teacher's demonstration table
Four pupil tables, each accommodating eight (or eight tables each ac-
    commodating four)

---

[3] Donovan, *op. cit.*, Chap. XVIII.
[4] *Laboratory Construction and Equipment* (National Research Council Committee Report). The Chemical Foundation, Inc.: New York, 1930. Chap. XIII.

About eight wall fume hoods
Notebook case
Supply case
Reagent shelves
Wall table
Blackboard and bulletin space.

All table tops are either of soapstone or of wood treated so as to make it acid-resisting. The problem of plumbing is especially important. The drainage from sinks, troughs, and collecting traps is usually not discharged directly into the sanitary drainage system. Soapstone, chemical stoneware, or silicon cast iron is the material employed in the plumbing systems for chemical laboratories.

3. Combination Classroom and Laboratory

A study by Packer[5] indicated that seven years ago in eight large city high schools, the biology laboratories were used 56 percent of the time, the chemistry laboratories 41 percent of the time, and the physics laboratories 29 percent of the time. Partly for the sake of economy and partly from the point of view of certain educational advantages, there is a growing tendency to combine classroom and laboratory.

In general, two distinct types of combination rooms have developed.

a. The Additive Type. Here, a room one and one-half times as large as the usual classroom is fitted up so as to provide armchairs or tables for about thirty pupils at one end of the room and laboratory tables at the other end. In this arrangement there is room, usually, for only twenty laboratory positions. The plumbing and furnishings are adapted from those ordinarily found in classrooms and laboratories.

b. The Functional Type. Here, the pupil tables are built and arranged so as to enable a class to recite, watch teacher demonstrations, or do individual work, as the occasion may demand. The pupil's position is fixed at all times; all facilities are provided him within arm's reach.

---

[5] Packer, P. C. *Housing of High-School Programs.* Bureau of Publications, Teachers College, Columbia University: New York, 1924. (This contribution, No. 159, is out of print.)

In a careful study of science teaching in small high schools Jensen and Glenn present data and recommendations concerning different types of laboratory arrangement and equipment. Their report is a practical contribution to problems of equipment, especially the problems that arise in the small high school.

Two developments of this type are worthy of mention: the "Lincoln Science Table"[6] and the "New York City Public School Pupil Table for General Science and Biology Rooms."[7]

Rooms of this type are usually about 24′ x 40′ and can accommodate from twenty-eight to thirty-two pupils. Considerable economy in cost of plumbing installation is one merit of this arrangement.

The following list is typical of the important items of furniture which may be found in the combination type of room:

> Teacher's demonstration table
> Instrument board
> Pupil tables to accommodate about 32 pupils and equipped with gas and electricity
> Storage case
> Supply case
> Exhibit case
> Large laboratory table
> Sinks for pupils
> Work bench
> Aquarium rack
> Vivarium
> Notebook case
> Book case
> Projection outlets
> Display fixture

Figure 1 shows essentially how these items are arranged in the scheme adopted for New York City High Schools.[8]

4.   The Science Lecture Room

In some of the larger high schools a science lecture room is provided to serve one or more of the sciences. This room may accommodate as many as two hundred fifty pupils and is equipped for demonstration and projection.

5.   The Storeroom and Preparation Room

One common practice is to plan a group of science rooms around a central storeroom. In very large schools where several storerooms are

---

[6] Glenn, Earl R.; Finley, Charles W.; and Caldwell, Otis W. *A Description of the Science Laboratories of the Lincoln School of Teachers College.* Lincoln School of Teachers College: New York, 1925.

[7] Board of Education, New York City, Department of Buildings. "Blue Print Plans of General Science and Biology Laboratories."

[8] See also Powers and Manzer, *op. cit.*

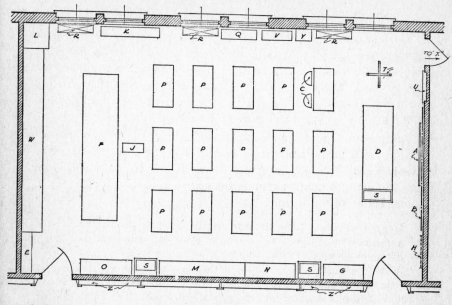

A. Screen
B. Blackboard
C. Pupil chair
D. Demonstration Table
E. Book Case
F. Laboratory Table
G. Supply Case
H. Bulletin Board
J. Projection Table

K. Work Bench
L. Teacher's Locker
M. Pupil Locker Cabinet
N. Exhibit Case
O. Apparatus Case
P. Pupil Table
Q. Aquarium Rack
R. Radiator
S. Sink

T. Display Fixture
U. Switchboard
V. Vivarium
W. Wall Table or
    Clothing Lockers
X. Preparation Room
Y. Notebook Case
Z. Corridor Display Cases

FIGURE I.—PLAN AND ARRANGEMENT OF A COMBINATION CLASSROOM AND LABORATORY
(General Science or Biology)

available, a less centralized arrangement is possible. Often, the storeroom is combined with or adjoins the preparation room. Though the practice varies widely, the average area devoted to preparation and storerooms is about 20 percent of the total laboratory space.

6. The Museum Room

This room is sometimes made available in very large schools. Ordinarily, a corner of another room is set aside for exhibits and displays. Many schools recently built and many now in process of building include a room of classroom size or larger set aside to serve as a school museum under the supervision of the science department.

7. A Science Workroom for the Elementary School

In some school systems laboratory experiences for the course in elementary science and nature study are provided by means of a science workroom. Uusually, a spare classroom or office is utilized for this purpose. The School Nature League of New York City and the American Museum of Natural History have done much to develop a technique for organizing and caring for rooms of this type.

An interesting and significant development of this type of science room is found in the Elementary Science Workroom in the Woodrow Wilson School, Newton, Iowa (see Figure II), where the room is designed to care for pupils pursuing the course in elementary science in Grades III to VI.[9]

This science room affords places to keep live animals (toads, frogs, snakes, and pets), growing plants, collections, a place for individual and group activities, and a demonstration table for experiments.

Where the windows face the south there are four flower boxes, two on each side of the radiator. They are level with the window sills; so whatever is in the boxes gets sunshine for several hours each day. Two of the window boxes are used as a vivarium and a terrarium. Under the window boxes are cages for keeping pets. Each cage has a window which lets in sunshine.

The aquarium is kept on a small table at the level of the window sill.

The demonstration table is equipped with a sink, hot and cold water, and gas, for experiments either by pupils or teacher.

A bulletin board is placed on each side of the swinging blackboard; a third bulletin board is near the rear of the room on the north wall.

The filing cabinet, conveniently located for the teacher, contains collections of pictures and clippings on each of the units in each of the grades.

The alcove on the north side of the room is a place for individuals or groups of pupils to carry on activities and projects. On the north wall is a sink and acid-proof shelf. Below the shelf are cupboards. On both the east and west walls of this alcove are exhibit cases in which are kept reference books and both permanent and temporary collections.

The store room in the northeast corner is light and spacious, with a window and shelves for keeping materials and apparatus. On the east wall are lockers for pupils. The space could be better utilized by having museum cases and bookcases across the back of the room.

Tables and chairs are used. The tables are loose, so that they may be moved about the room, according to the activities in which the pupils are engaged.

---

[9] The diagram and description of this science workroom have been contributed by Professor Lillian Hethershaw, of Drake University, who planned the room.

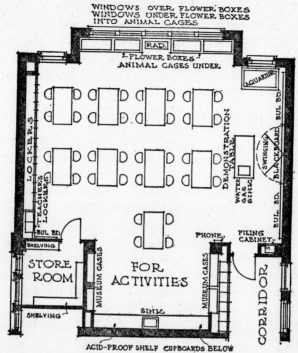

ELEMENTARY SCIENCE DEPT.
WOODROW WILSON SCHOOL
NEWTON IOWA
PROUDFOOT RAWSON SOUERS & THOMAS
ARCHITECTS DES MOINES IOWA

FIGURE II.—PLAN AND ARRANGEMENT OF AN ELEMENTARY-SCHOOL SCIENCE WORK-
ROOM AT NEWTON, IOWA

8. The Dark Room

A dark room has other uses than that of photography. Certain exercises in physics, chemistry, biology, and general science can be carried on most effectively in a room of this type. The common practice is to provide one dark room for the use of all science departments. The usual size is about 8′ x 10′.

9. The Growing Room

Used chiefly in conjunction with the courses in biology and general science, the growing room provides effective experience with living plants and animals. It is usually built around a window and is equipped with a radiator and running hot and cold water. Glass panels permit the class to inspect at a distance, and an entrance door allows for close examination and experimentation, as well as for the tending of plants, aquaria, and vivaria. The size of such rooms varies widely and depends upon the size of the school.

10.   The Chemical Balance Room

This type of room is to be found in certain large schools. Its function is to give pupils some experience with instruments of precision and to make possible advanced projects by students with special interests.

11.   The Science Library and Office

There is a noticeable tendency among the larger school systems to provide a special room for teachers and pupils. Here, the teacher confers with students about their work and about their projects. In the room may be found a science library, a rack of magazines, a library table, a teacher's desk and a large bulletin board for notices, clippings, term outlines, and drawings. In some instances, this office-library is partitioned so as to form a small private office for the head of the department.

12.   The Science Club Room

In a few of the larger school systems a small room is provided for the use of the various science clubs. The camera club, the radio club, and similar organizations are permitted to hold their meetings there. The room is equipped with gas, water, electricity, tables, and several lockers for the storage of materials.

13.   The Present Equipment of These Various Science Rooms

The elaborate catalogs of apparatus companies are eloquent expressions of the extent to which equipment is being provided for the teaching of science. Of course, instances of dire lack of materials may be found in many parts of the country, but many other instances may be found of lavishly equipped science departments.

In general, the course of study determines the type of equipment, while the ability and initiative of the teacher determine the amount of it and how it is used. There is no lack of suggestive lists of materials for various types of courses. Even the untrained and inexperienced teacher can procure with little difficulty an apparatus list that fits his needs.[10]

Many Problems Await Solution

In the preceding section, the attempt was made to describe briefly existing practices in the matter of planning and equipping science rooms. A great amount of careful thinking lies back of the situation as it exists to-day. The practical experiences of thousands of trained science teachers are incorporated in the laboratory procedures employed in our schools. Nevertheless, little effort has been made to measure objectively the specific outcomes of these practices. The use of materials in science teaching is still an art rather than a science. Despite the studies which are reported in Chapter VII of this volume, it can fairly be said that most of our problems still await a first attack upon them.

Dissatisfaction with conditions as they exist arises out of changes in educational theory. It is perhaps unfortunate that in a dynamic age physical structures, and to some extent equipment, have a longer life span than do ideas and ideals. Thus, progressive teachers are constantly faced with problems of adaptation and compromise in the matter of science rooms and their furnishings.

Nine Principles Basic to the Solution of These Problems

Most of the problems of adjustment result from a desire on the part of the teacher to comply with certain basic principles of science education. A brief statement of nine of these principles may serve to delineate the immediate needs for investigation and study in the field under discussion.

1. *A science room is a place where the pupil may receive educative experiences which add meanings to, and give better understandings of, those generalizations in science that contribute to enrichment of life.* The emphasis in this principle is on the word *experiences.* The science room, whether classroom or laboratory, is here defined as a means to an end, rather than an end in itself. No aping of the workshop of the research worker or of the platform of the public lecturer

---

[10] An excellent summary of essential equipment for the sciences may be found in Monahan, A. C. *Laboratory Layout for the High-School Sciences.* Bulletin, 1927, No. 22, Department of the Interior, Bureau of Education: Washington, D. C. See also *The American School and University, for 1929-1930,* American School Publishing Corporation: New York, pp. 343 ff.

can satisfy the interpretation here given. There is also the implication that the *experiences* are to serve a purpose. They must contribute specifically to definite objectives. Hence, a second guiding principle:

2. *Science room experiences are justified by, and take their origin from, the science curriculum, course of study, and learning experiences to be expected of pupils.* Practice based on this principle will avoid a course in physics or chemistry which is organized around facilities that chance to be available. An interesting experiment or demonstration must have more to recommend it than that it is entertaining. Rooms, equipment, demonstrations, exercises, and experiments must be so developed and organized as to contribute to specific objectives and to further the sequence of science study adopted for the particular group of students.

3. *A piece of equipment or apparatus is to be evaluated in terms of the educative experience or experiences which it makes possible.* It is undoubtedly true that no necessary correlation exists between the cost of equipment and its educative value. Cheap apparatus, pupil-made projects, and homemade materials are frequently more valuable than materials purchased from supply companies. The literature of science education is filled with suggestions and descriptions of such simple materials and homemade apparatus. Nevertheless, it is important to stress *experience* as a criterion for evaluating equipment. This experience may indicate the need for expending funds in certain directions, or it may in other cases indicate the unwisdom of devising new and sometimes more elaborate ways of performing exercises that will require only homemade materials. Too often teachers of ability and experience devote a major portion of their energies to the creation of laboratory and demonstration apparatus that has the sole merit of utilizing cheap materials. The plaudits which this activity attracts are often disproportionate when viewed in terms of the educative experience which the new apparatus provides. A costly piece of equipment is justified if its contribution in terms of pupil experience is great and if it releases the teacher's energies in the right directions.

4. *A science room is also a place where the experience of problem-solving is possible.* The secondary-school science laboratory is not primarily a place for research. This view of the laboratory harks back to the origin of laboratories among research workers in pure and applied science. Floor plans, furniture, and equipment are too often modeled after those maintained by industrial concerns or by uni-

versities for advanced work. Nevertheless, all types of science rooms should make possible "the putting of questions to nature." The effect of this guiding principle is not so much a matter of radical change in design and equipment as it is in attitude toward the use and organization of facilities. Proper consideration of this principle results in greater provision for individual differences and special abilities. The experience of "forcing nature to answer a question" is educative in a high degree. On the junior-high-school level such activity furnishes the element of exploration of pupil interests and capacities; at all levels its contributes factors of enrichment. A corollary of this thesis is that problem-solving requires some degree of skill in manipulating science materials and instruments of measurement.

5. *The plan and design of a science room must provide elements of flexibility.* There is no one best science classroom or laboratory. Local conditions, the character and size of school population, the curriculum, the sequence of studies, courses of study, and funds available —all operate as determiners of best practice. Buildings have a way of outliving teachers and courses of study. An inflexible room is often a handicap to future generations. It is difficult, of course, to project too far into the future. It is always possible, however, to avoid over-elaborate floorplans, furniture, and equipment. Except for very large school systems, one-purpose rooms might well be avoided. Any factor which prohibits the use of room space to a point approaching maximum capacity should be carefully scrutinized.

6. *The design of both classrooms and laboratories should provide facilities for effective teacher demonstrations.* The work of many investigators has called attention to the value and specific outcomes of demonstration teaching. Demonstration experiences are essential to many types of learning in science. It is fair to say that many of our traditional laboratory exercises on the individual basis can be more effectively presented as teacher or pupil demonstrations. In planning science rooms, therefore, considerable attention must be given to this activity. The size, position, and equipment of the demonstration table are matters of importance. Visibility, illumination, accessories, proper display, convenience, time-saving and labor-saving devices, and the avoidance of waste motion are all factors which must be properly considered.

7. *Certain science rooms should provide facilities for individual laboratory work.* The work of Horton[11] and others has been particularly valuable in pointing to definite desirable outcomes which may be expected from individual laboratory work. Manipulative skills, resourcefulness, and facility in problem-solving can come most effectively from a teaching procedure which enables pupils to experience individually. The need in this respect is for a room in which at least three types of activity can proceed:

(a) A group of exercises designed to provide familiarity with science equipment and to develop some degree of skill in manipulation. Such exercises may be required of all pupils, in which case multiple sets of equipment are necessary.

(b) A group of exercises from which pupils may select in accordance with special needs and interests. Here, single, or at most duplicate, sets of materials are adequate.

(c) A group of exercises originating in problems formulated by pupil or teacher. These problems may be original or may be modeled after some basic research or discovery. The laboratory should be planned so as to make possible such pursuit of knowledge by the individual pupil.

8. *Science rooms should provide certain facilities for objectification by means other than the use of concrete materials.* This guiding principle calls attention to such items of equipment as the blackboard, bulletin board, display fixtures, charts, and especially the class of materials included in the term *visual instruction.* Glass slides, homemade slides, film-slides, micro-slides, opaque projection, motion pictures, and the 'talkies,' all have a valuable place in science teaching. They can provide experiences as real to the pupil as are many of the demonstrations and laboratory exercises. Often they surpass the latter in variety, clarity, and pertinency. When properly used, they supplement other experiences, fill in gaps, and tie together ideas which belong together. Occasionally a screen experience may well supplant a somewhat fragmentary demonstration or laboratory experience.

From the point of view of equipment and design of science rooms, this principle raises questions with respect to such items as number and location of electrical outlets, window shades, types of screens, types of projectors, facilities for chart and picture display and storage,

---

[11] See Chapter VII.

slide and filmslide libraries, motion-picture film libraries, equipment for sound pictures, micro-projectors and micro-slides, and industrial exhibits. In this connection, too, must be mentioned the increasing use of radio equipment as means for bringing certain educative experiences into the classroom.[12]

Many school systems, struggling with inadequate budgets for science equipment, can reach a partial solution of their problems through a judicial selection of available materials of the sorts here indicated.

9. *The planning of science rooms and their equipment should be a coöperative project, in which the architect, the engineer, the educational supervisor, and the science teacher each play a proper part.* Each of the individuals mentioned can contribute to the ultimate success of science rooms. Too often the experience and knowledge of one or more of them are ignored. It is certainly true that those who must use a building and its rooms are the ones to exercise final judgment on essential details. It is also true that usually there is more than one way of obtaining a desired result. Experience indicates that great savings in costs as well as increased efficiency in use can result from coöperative planning. Among the important questions that early in planning require mutual understanding on the part of those who should participate in the construction and equipping of science rooms are: (a) How large shall science rooms be? (b) How many pupils shall they accommodate? (c) How shall the science rooms be grouped? (d) On what floor of the building shall science rooms be located?

Next Steps and Needed Research for the Solution of the Problems

In view of the guiding principles just set forth certain specific needs present themselves for attention. It is the opinion of this Committee that a concentrated attack upon these problems by research workers in science education can go far in liberating equipment practices from tradition and from outworn educational philosophies. Even partial solutions to the ten problems that follow would make the planning and equipping of laboratories a science rather than an art.

1. *A study to determine the available 'apparatus experiences' for the teaching and learning of each of the important generalizations in science.* Much of this material is easily available, but it is diffused in

---

[12] Blom, E. C. *Radio and Electric Power Supply Equipment for Schools.* Bureau of Publications, Teachers College, Columbia University: New York, 1930.

many textbooks and manuals, in magazine literature, and in the class-room practices of teachers of science. There is great need for a single source book to which teachers of science can refer and in which they can find helpful details concerning possible apparatus experiences for each important topic of the courses in science. Such a book will be a large one and perhaps a costly one. Also, it must be the result of coöperative effort. Its contributions to the teaching of science will be exceedingly valuable and will persist for a long time.

A study of available apparatus experiences, such as is contemplated here, must attempt to classify experiences on at least four bases: (a) those suitable for the demonstration table, (b) those suitable for individual laboratory work, (c) those possible with materials ordinarily described as 'homemade,' and (d) those possible with materials ordinarily purchased.

The selection of topics or generalizations for this study must be in accordance with accepted curricula and courses of study. The problem here involved is not very simple, yet it is very much more feasible now than it has been during the past few years. Each of the four basic courses of the science sequence, beginning with the seventh grade, is slowly but surely crystallizing into a group of widely accepted generalizations.

2. *A study to determine which of several available apparatus experiences is most effective in the teaching and learning of given science facts or principles.* There will be as many studies required as there are important generalizations in the various science subjects. The task can be simplified by first developing a measuring technique, which can then be applied by many workers in different fields.

3. *An analytical study to determine the specific educative experiences possible with each of one hundred commonly purchased pieces of science teaching equipment.* The number set for this study is of course arbitrary. It may be necessary also to distinguish between pieces of equipment according to price range. A ready source of data for assistance in an attack upon this problem is the companies that advertise and sell science equipment to schools.

4. *A study to determine the types of science problems that pupils can solve through the use of science-room facilities and equipment.* There is great need for knowledge of this kind. In the course of every science lesson, the pupil raises questions. How shall they be answered? Many can be answered categorically by the teacher. Some are suited

for supplementary reading by the pupil. Others are excellent for stimulating class discussion. Certain inquiries, however, yield the greatest educational return when the pupil is turned loose as an investigator. Such problem-solving may utilize either the demonstration equipment or the laboratory facilities or both. At the present time a major handicap in the planning of science rooms is that we do not know the kind of problems in science that pupils can successfully solve by means of self-devised experiments.

5. *A study to determine the relative value of different demonstration techniques.* This is made necessary by the increasing emphasis upon teacher and pupil demonstrations. An evaluation such as is here contemplated can serve, not only to establish an effective demonstration technique, but also to suggest desirable changes in the design and accessories of the demonstration table, in the storage and organization of materials in the classroom, and in the seating and lighting arrangements.

6. *An analytical study of laboratory arrangements and the functions of laboratory furniture.* In developing the seventh of the guiding principles in the preceding section certain desiderata were outlined. If each of three types of exercises are to be possible, then all arrangements and furniture should contribute to the success of these activities. At the present time we do not know specifically the nature of the activities which given room arrangements are to serve. This is true of the combination type of room as well as of the one-purpose laboratory. With regard to cabinets and other furniture, a study similar to the third one just listed can do much to stimulate proper planning of science-room equipment.

7. *An investigation to determine the frequency of change in basic design and equipment of given science rooms as compared with the frequency of change in the curriculum which those rooms are meant to serve.* Data of this kind will do much to insure an element of flexibility in rooms and their furnishings. It is difficult for an individual entrusted with the responsibility of designing science rooms to see his problems in proper perspective. Immediate needs loom large and tend to overshadow probable lines of growth and change.

8. *A study to determine the available screen experiences for the teaching and learning of the important generalizations in science.* Much has already been done to provide source books to which the teacher of science may go for specific information concerning illus-

trative materials.[13] However, this field is developing so rapidly that a single compendium of information, brought up to date periodically, can be of great help. Furthermore, an organization of materials of this type around the important topics of the science curriculum can make screen experiences more effective.

9. *A study to determine which of several available screen experiences is most effective in the teaching and learning of given science facts or principles.* This study and the one preceding it parallel proposed Studies 1 and 2. As has been indicated before, the methods and materials of visual instruction give much promise as supplements and perhaps as occasional substitutes for apparatus experiences. Studies reported in Chapter VI indicate some of the values of certain screen experiences. If certain cautions are to be exercised in the use of visual materials, the studies here suggested will go far in determining procedures. The same criteria for evaluating a piece of apparatus or a demonstration experiment should be applied in evaluating a chart, a set of slides, a motion-picture film, or a 'talkie.'

10. *A series of studies based on the questions set forth in Guiding Principle 9.* Some of these studies are purely educational; others involve problems in architecture, engineering, and administration. The growth of school-building programs makes this sort of information more necessary than ever before.

SCIENCE ROOMS AND EQUIPMENT IN TEACHER-TRAINING INSTITUTIONS

For the most part a discussion of this special problem must include all that has been said heretofore concerning laboratories and equipment for elementary and secondary science instruction; the same principles must guide practice, and the same needs for further study are present. The important additional problems which arise are the result of differences in the curriculum of science studies.

Teacher-training institutions are attempting to develop several types of courses in science. The recommendations of this Committee

---

[13] Woodring, Oakes, and Brown. *Enriched Teaching of Science in the High School.* Bureau of Publications, Teachers College, Columbia University: New York, 1928.

Brown and Bird. *Motion Pictures and Lantern Slides for Elementary Visual Education.* Bureau of Publications, Teachers College, Columbia University: New York, 1931.

Journal of Chemical Education, February, March, and April, 1931.

that relate to the education of teachers in the field of science are given in Chapter XVII.

Little has been done to develop scientifically a group of rooms and equipment to care for the various needs of teachers in training. In many of the teacher-training buildings erected in recent years, the standards and specifications for secondary schools are adopted almost *in toto*. Where in-service training is conducted in universities, the college and research course laboratories and lecture rooms are employed throughout. Indeed, it is not uncommon to find that in this respect no special problems exist in the minds of those in charge of in-service training.

The Specialized Science Room at the New York Training School for Teachers

With a view toward defining the special equipment needs of teacher-training institutions, one attempt to solve some of the problems is here described somewhat fully. For the past six years the New York Training School for Teachers (now the New York Teacher Training College) has been operating a specialized science room for prospective elementary-school teachers, for prospective science teachers, and for the in-service training of science teachers. An account of it follows:

KINDS OF COURSES CARED FOR IN THE ROOM

1. An orientation course, called "Science Foundations in Education." This is a required course for all freshmen, comes three times a week, and includes demonstrations, recitations, and laboratory work.
2. A special course in "Visual Instruction," in which students have an opportunity to manipulate and experiment with a wide variety of projection equipment.
3. A professionalized course in general science for prospective teachers and teachers of general science.
4. An advanced course in physics for prospective teachers of science.
5. A laboratory course in the construction, manipulation, and care of general-science teaching equipment.

KINDS OF ACTIVITIES FOR WHICH THE ROOM PROVIDES FACILITIES

1. Lecture demonstrations and class discussions.
2. Individual laboratory exercises, uniform for all students.
3. Individual laboratory exercises in which 15 students or 15 groups of students are each performing a different exercise.
4. Individual laboratory exercises on the problem-solving basis.

5. Individual laboratory exercises based upon the manipulation of a variety of projection apparatus.

6. The construction of science-teaching apparatus.

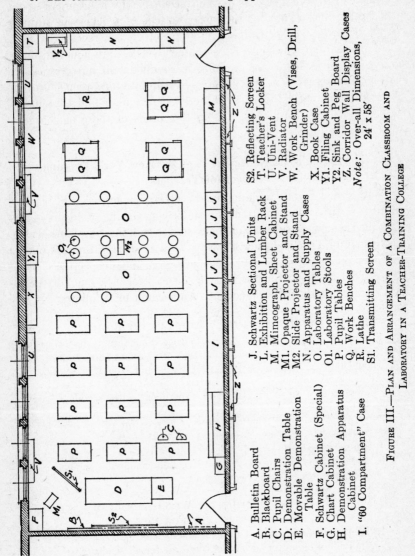

A. Bulletin Board
B. Blackboard
C. Pupil Chairs
D. Demonstration Table
E. Movable Demonstration Table
F. Schwartz Cabinet (Special)
G. Chart Cabinet
H. Demonstration Apparatus Cabinet
I. "60 Compartment" Case

J. Schwartz Sectional Units
L. Exhibition and Lumber Rack
M. Mimeograph Sheet Cabinet
M1. Opaque Projector and Stand
M2. Slide Projector and Stand
N. Apparatus and Supply Cases
O. Laboratory Tables
O1. Laboratory Stools
P. Pupil Tables
Q. Work Benches
R. Lathe
S1. Transmitting Screen

S2. Reflecting Screen
T. Teacher's Locker
U. Uni-Vent
V. Radiator
W. Work Bench (Vises, Drill, Grinder)
X. Book Case
Y1. Filing Cabinet
Y2. Sink and Peg Board
Z. Corridor Wall Display Cases
Note: Over-all Dimensions, 24' x 58'

FIGURE III.—PLAN AND ARRANGEMENT OF A COMBINATION CLASSROOM AND LABORATORY IN A TEACHER-TRAINING COLLEGE

DESCRIPTION OF THE ROOM

Figure III shows the floor plan and arrangement of furniture. In area it occupies the space ordinarily devoted to two classrooms. It combines classroom and laboratory features and has seating accommodations for as many as thirty-six students during recitations and for thirty students at various types of laboratory work.

All work is professionalized, in the sense that all storage of equipment and organization of materials are accomplished within the room proper. The demonstration table has as an adjunct the demonstration apparatus case, so equipped that the instructor or the student demonstrator can procure and assemble materials before the class. All materials are filed away in a series of vertical filing cabinets (Schwartz sectional system) and are accessible to instructor and to student at all times. One of the sectional units is supplied with all the necessary equipment for demonstrating the key exercises required by the general-science course of study in effect.

A small movable demonstration table is provided for student practice in setting up demonstrations. The table is movable, as are all the student tables and chairs, in order that small groups with a practice teacher may attempt certain teaching assignments. The movable demonstration table is not provided with gas or with water. It can be connected, however, with a source of current supply. The main demonstration table is equipped with gas, cold and hot water, 110-volt D.C., 110-volt A.C., battery current of varying voltages, ring-stand sockets, and a horizontal supporting beam. Gas and different kinds of electric current are conveyed to several outlets at each of the large laboratory tables. A special sink for students is located at one end of the room.

The "60-Compartment Case"

This item of furniture is a piece of standard equipment containing sixty lockers. Each locker is equipped with all the necessary materials for performing a basic experiment or for gaining an important manipulative experience. In addition to the materials, the locker contains a set of directions, or "work guide," and frequently one or two reference books for supplementary reading.

This compartment case functions most successfully in individual laboratory work. When a student selects or is assigned an exercise, he consults an index which directs him to a particular locker. He removes all materials and books and proceeds to a definite place in the room where he carries out all observations, manipulations, experiments, and reference work. When finished, he returns all materials to the proper locker and writes up his notes.

Some of the lockers serve also as temporary places for the storage of original experiments devised by students and for the storage of incompleted projects.

Apparatus Supply Case

An apparatus supply case at one end of the room contains the small necessaries for constructing and assembling demonstration and other apparatus. The case contains many small drawers, labeled and numbered. Such items as corks, stoppers, glass tubing, pinch clamps, test tubes, watch glasses, L's, T's, matches, wire gauze, clamps, ringstand rings, Bunsen burner, rubber tubing, etc., are all to be found in the apparatus supply case. Students are expected to get out what they need and to return all materials properly after use.

Exhibition Rack

Space is provided for the exhibition of student-made apparatus on a series of open shelves. The latter lend themselves to various types of display and of collections. Occasionally, this space is devoted to an exhibit of science scrapbooks, magazines, etc.

Projection Equipment

As indicated in Figure II, a reflecting and a transmitting screen are furnished, in order to give students experience with both types of projection. An opaque projector, a film-slide projector, a micro-projector, a slide projector, and a motion-picture projector for 16-mm. films are housed in the compartment case. It is possible to have students operating all projectors simultaneously in different parts of the room. The laboratory work in connection with the course in visual instruction requires as many as fifteen groups of students working simultaneously. Each group is assigned to a different exercise. When more than two screens are required, sheets of Upson board are set up temporarily as screens. The projectors are, of course, operated at closer range than would be the case in actual class procedure.

The Workshop

About one-third of the floor space is devoted to workshop facilities. These consist of six woodwork benches (each carrying two vises), a lathe, a long workbench carrying metal vises, a drill, and a grinder, and a case of common wood-working tools.

The prime purpose of this equipment is to give students some training in the use of tools and materials. The skills and knowledges required are those that relate to the construction of science-teaching equipment. Experience indicates that this feature is attractive to students and makes an important contribution to the training of science teachers.

Corridor Display Cases

Along the outside wall of the room, in the corridor, are attached about fifteen cases for the display of notebooks, diagrams, clippings, exhibits, and apparatus. Each case is 3' x 3' by 10" deep and is supported at eye level. The inside is backed with cork for receiving thumb tacks, and the outside has a glass door. The cases serve many purposes, not the least of which is to furnish publicity for the science department. It is important to note that the cases are sufficiently deep to permit of housing actual apparatus arranged as static demonstrations of basic science facts and principles.

The plan and equipment of this room at the New York Teacher Training College evolved from purely local needs. Many changes might easily be introduced so as to make the room more adequate for different types of work. For example, some of the workbenches might be removed so as to provide room for such items as an aquarium rack, a vivarium, and a soil table. Also, a wall table might be built over the radiators. The essential factors, however, that make for effectiveness in design are the following:

(a) Combining classroom with laboratory.
(b) Professionalization of equipment, furniture, storage, and organization
(c) Flexibility of use
(d) Provision for problem-solving and for workshop
(e) Student experience made the underlying basis for all arrangements and furnishings

CHAPTER XVII
SCIENCE TEACHING ON THE COLLEGE LEVEL*

HISTORICAL BACKGROUND

Contrary to what is generally supposed and what the casual reader might be led to believe from the literature on the subject, science courses in colleges and universities have probably passed the peak of growth in enrollment. It is not meant to imply that such enrollments are not increasing in actual numbers of students but that the percentage of the total number of students enrolled in higher institutions of learning who are taking courses in natural science is not increasing and probably has not been doing so since shortly after the opening of the present century. This was shown in a report by N. M. Grier in 1926.[1]

Thirty-seven colleges and universities, representing all sections of the country and all types and sizes of institutions, were included. In this report Grier showed that from 1912 to 1922, relative enrollments in botany, zoölogy, physiology, hygiene, astronomy, geology, and geological physics had declined at the majority of institutions studied; that the enrollment in general chemistry, general physics, and general biology had increased; "that the first year of biological, chemical, and physical science is becoming increasingly popular with students but for some reason within or without their control, these departments fail to hold students for advanced work in them." A careful study of the figures accompanying Grier's report indicates, however, that in no case are the increases or decreases, either in all or in beginning science courses, large, or probably significant. At the same time, it is clear from the same figures that during the period 1912-1922 the total enrollment in these institutions increased from 25 percent to 150 percent. Two facts are evident, therefore: first, that total enrollments

---

* This chapter has been prepared by Victor H. Noll, Specialist in School Organization, Office of Education, Washington, D. C., at the invitation of the Committee because of Mr. Noll's participation in, and familiarity with, the significant studies in science teaching at the University of Minnesota.

[1] Grier, N. M. "A preliminary report on the progress and encouragement of science instruction in American colleges and universities, 1912-1922." *School Science and Mathematics,* 26: 1926, 753-764; 872-881; 931-940.

in these institutions have increased greatly; second, that the percentage of all students enrolled in science courses has been practically constant.

It is not the purpose here to overemphasize the importance of these data or to go into an exhaustive analysis of the causes underlying the results shown, but merely to present them as part of the picture of the development of science teaching in colleges and universities. Unfortunately, no similar data are available for the period of 1922 to the present, but it is very unlikely that any marked change has taken place. It seems more likely that, since the period 1912-1922 was one of great popularization of science and of college and university education, the last decade would show a continuation of what has been shown for the preceding one or, possibly, an even more definite decline.

In order to appreciate the significance of the decline in the popularity of the study of science, it is necessary to go back several hundred years in the history of our higher institutions. By so doing, this failure to continue gaining relatively as well as absolutely may be seen in relation to what has gone before as well as to what is going on at the present. It will become evident that the decline may be considered both as cause and effect—cause of the present greatly increased interest in problems of science teaching, and effect of the super-promotion which science courses received at the hands of some of their perhaps too ardent advocates and the highly standardized and devitalized character which the courses took on.

Instruction in the natural sciences has been offered in American colleges and universities almost since the founding of these institutions. Astronomy and the "Nature of Plants" were offered at Harvard as early as 1690.

> During the eighteenth century Yale, Princeton, King's (afterward Columbia) all came to offer work in this latter subject or in natural history, which might then be used to denote physics, chemistry, geology, and astronomy, as well as botany and zoölogy. As far as physics was concerned, before the Revolution it seems to have been a subordinate branch of mathematical instruction and owing to the limitations of scientific knowledge at the time, to have consisted simply of lectures on mechanics, hydrostatics, pneumatics and optics, with possibly brief discussions on heat and sound and a few experiments in electricity. There was even less biology taught.[2]

---

[2] Graves, Frank P. *A History of Education.* New York: Macmillan, 1914, pp. 346-347.

From the latter part of the eighteenth century until the middle of the nineteenth, instruction in the natural sciences became a very definite portion of the college curriculum. The various sciences were differentiated from each other and separate courses were offered in each. The first professor of chemistry in this country was Dr. James Smith (appointed in 1768) at the College of the Province of New York.[3] Graves also states that separate chairs of chemistry were established at Princeton in 1795, at Columbia in 1800, at Yale in 1802, at Bowdoin in 1805, at South Carolina and at Dickinson in 1811, at Williams in 1812, and thereafter at other places, until it had been recognized by almost all institutions as an important branch of study. This early instruction in chemistry was in the main introduced in connection with the establishing of medical schools and was usually considered a part of medical training. Geology was included in the early professorship of chemistry at Yale. Mineralogy, geology, and botany were introduced at Princeton in 1830.

Although science subjects were coming into prominence during this period, the instruction was almost entirely by lecture and demonstration on the part of the teacher. Very few laboratories were in existence and these were entirely for the use of the instructor. President Charles W. Eliot[4] of Harvard, in an address made in 1906, said:

> When I was a student in the Harvard College (about 1850) there was not a single laboratory open to the students on any subject, either chemistry, physics, or biology. The only trace of such instruction open to students was in the department of botany and that was only for a few weeks with a single teacher, the admirable botanist, Asa Gray, and he had neither apparatus nor assistants, and it was a hopeless job which he undertook for a few weeks in May and June. I was the first student who ever had the chance to work in the laboratory in Harvard College and that was entirely due to the personal friendship of Professor J. P. Cook, who fitted up a laboratory in the basement of University Hall, entirely at his own expense. That was the situation of the colleges in the country—for Harvard was by no means peculiar in this respect—only sixty years ago.

One of the earliest attempts to include laboratory work by the student in the natural sciences was in connection with the founding of Rensselaer Polytechnic Institute in 1825. It was planned that in the

[3] Williams, Rufus P. "The planting of chemistry in America." *School Science and Mathematics,* 2: April, 1902, 75-82.

[4] Eliot, Charles W. "Laboratory teaching." *School Science and Mathematics,* 6: November, 1906, 703-707.

teaching of science in this institution students should be required to lecture and perform demonstration experiments before the class as part of the required work in the course. It was not, however, until the latter part of the nineteenth century and the early part of the twentieth that individual laboratory work on the part of the student in science courses became at all common.

This development came about through a number of causes. Chief among these was the influence of such men as Charles W. Eliot, William J. Youmans, Louis Agassiz, Asa Gray, William B. Rogers, and Amos Eaton. These men, by precept and example both in teaching and writing, did much to popularize natural-science courses and especially the use of the laboratory by the student. Another factor tending to popularize laboratory instruction was the founding of such schools as Rensselaer Polytechnic Institute (1825), Lawrence Scientific School (1847), Sheffield at Yale (1860), and Massachusetts Institute of Technology (1862). Likewise, the Morrill Act in 1862, appropriating lands to promote education in agriculture, mechanic arts, and natural science, which resulted in the founding of many of the present land-grant colleges, was an important impetus to instruction in science. A fourth factor was the introduction of the elective system, which afforded opportunity for the election of courses in science and a release from the iron-clad classical curriculum. Another factor tending to make science courses popular was the increasing importance of science in industry and everyday life, together with the attendant changing concepts of what constitutes a liberal education, as was so ably set forth by Spencer and Huxley. At the opening of the present century we see science courses reaching the height of their popularity. Students were being urged and required to take courses in science for all conceivable reasons, for the narrowly practical, for strictly disciplinarian, for the broadly cultural.

At about this time a reaction set in. Laboratory facilities were becoming more and more inadequate. Many experiments on transfer of training threw the disciplinary outcomes of science courses into serious question. College and university administrators and instructors began to wonder whether they had not gone too far. Consequently, the unqualified recommendation of science courses to every student began to fall off, science courses ceased to gain in popularity, and students turned to other fields. As a part of this reaction and partly, at least, as a result of it, the whole field of science instruction came into question. Aims, curricula, and methods were no longer accepted, and a period of critical study and evaluation of these elements of the science program began. This is the attitude which is now prevalent. Excepting the fundamental subjects taught in the elementary schools, and the fields of the social sciences on the secondary level, probably no part of the school curriculum has in recent years been so often and so critically subjected to the scientific study of education as the aims, methods, and curricula in science instruction. Some twenty experimental studies of the relative value of lecture demonstration and individual laboratory experimentation alone have been published in the last twenty-five years. These are, it is true, practically all on the elementary-school and secondary-school levels, but the tendency is general.

Some of the reasons for this questioning attitude have already been mentioned. Science instructors are asking themselves what is wrong. Also, the natural sciences lend themselves, perhaps, more readily to scientific study of their methods and subject matter than other subjects. In addition there are undoubtedly social and economic factors underlying this decline in popularity and consequent inquiry into procedures. Whatever the causes, the fact is evident. We are directing science against science; we are subjecting science instruction to scientific study. Witness the two volumes of Curtis' *Digest of Investigations in the Teaching of Science;*[5] witness the founding of the National Association for Research in Science Teaching; witness the forming of the Committee on Educational Research and its subcommittee on the teaching of science at the University of Minnesota, through the activities of which three volumes of research studies have been published.

To recapitulate briefly, science instruction began in colleges and universities almost with their founding. From a small number of lecture courses, it developed into a large number of highly specialized branches, which in turn were subdivided into many courses from introductory to the most advanced and technical. Laboratory work on the part of the student was introduced and promoted, and it gained tremendously in a comparatively short time. A peak of popularity was reached and a plateau developed. At the present time scientific study of procedures is being made: aims, content, and methods are being tested and evaluated.

---

[5] Curtis, Francis D. *Digest of Investigations in the Teaching of Science* and *Second Digest of Investigations in the Teaching of Science.* Philadelphia: Blakiston, 1926 and 1931.

AIMS

To make an all-inclusive or general statement of the aims and objectives of college science teaching is very difficult, if not impossible. Institutions of higher learning have grown up more or less independently; they have built their curricula with different objects in view; they have never had the motivating force of a function, such as college preparation, as secondary schools have had, and they consequently have never been approached by standardizing agencies to the extent that secondary schools have been approached. Their function has been, broadly stated, that of preparation for life, since they have been the last stage in the educational scheme. They have developed a multiplicity of curricula and courses as varied as life itself. Since their function has been essentially that of preparation for life, it may be well to consider the aims of college curricula and courses, and more specifically, college science courses from this point of view. At least three broad types of functions are at once evident: first, the cultural or liberal education; second, the teacher training; and third, the highly specialized, or technical, such as engineering and medicine. In the attempt to fulfill these functions, courses of all varieties have been developed, from the most specialized and technical to the most general.

There is very little evidence, however, to show that the courses have been developed with any difference of function or aims in mind. We find, at least in beginning courses in college science, that students of all types and with all possible variety of purposes in mind, are herded together in the same introductory courses. Johnson[6] showed at the University of Minnesota that "there gradually developed two types of courses in elementary botany (1871-1928), one of which apparently had the primary function of a survey course; the other, the additional functions of a prerequisite. These courses finally merged until at present (1928) one course exists, which, as far as the organization of the curriculum indicates, is designed to have the twofold function— survey and preparatory."

The writer,[7] reporting on beginning courses in chemistry, shows that, although there were in 1926 six different sections in beginning general inorganic chemistry at the University of Minnesota, including students

---

[6] Johnson, P. O. *Curricular Problems in Science at the College Level.* Minneapolis: University of Minnesota Press, 1930. p. 21.

[7] Noll, Victor H. *Laboratory Instruction in the Field of Inorganic Chemistry.* Minneapolis: University of Minnesota Press, 1930. p. 15, Table II.

from the Colleges of Science, Literature and Arts, Engineering, Mining, Dentistry, Medicine, Pharmacy, Physical Education, and Agriculture, the six sections took practically the same course. Some differentiation in number of hours of laboratory work was made between those having had high-school chemistry and those not having had it, but all used the same text and all covered practically the same ground. Moreover, pre-dental, pre-medical, pharmacy, and physical-education students were all in the same section, while science, literature and arts, chemistry, and chemical-engineering majors were together in another. Undoubtedly, the University of Minnesota is not unique in these respects. In smaller institutions where staff and laboratory facilities are much more inadequate, the situation is probably worse. Such a situation in one university, taken with the added diversity in procedures which must exist between such beginning courses in one institution and those offered in a totally different one, obviously indicates a lack of organized study of aims and objectives, at least in so far as their effect upon procedures is concerned.

Of course, the problem of providing courses which meet the different aims of all types of students in a college or university is by no means easy of solution; often it is administratively impossible. Certainly no one would advocate different introductory courses in science for every type of future specialization. However, on the broad lines indicated, it does not seem too much to expect that some differentiation be made. It may probably be safely asserted that the course taken for general education and cultural purposes should differ from that taken as preparation for further specialization. Whether the prospective teacher should have yet another type of course in science is a question not to be settled here.

The aims of the survey type of course should probably include: (1) information, (2) development of interest in science, (3) understanding of the relationship of science to environment and everyday life (applications), (4) understanding of the relationship of the particular science studied to other sciences, and (5) culture.

For the preparatory course, the aims just listed should also function, but the primary aim is there one of preparation for further study and specialization in science.

For the teacher-training courses some combination of these aims or, better still, all of those mentioned should probably function in the planning and teaching of the course. For this reason the prospective teacher would do better to take the preparatory course if a choice had to be made. In this case further work in science should be supplemented and coördinated with work in special methods and psychology.

Only brief mention has been made so far in this discussion of the disciplinary, or training, values of college courses in science. These have not been forgotten by science teachers, however, most of whom still cling to their personal beliefs in the matter, all studies of transfer of training notwithstanding.

Hurd[8] lists forty-three functions of laboratory work in science as proffered by thirty-five science instructors at the University of Minnesota. Among others there are listed the following: to develop manipulative skill (7 instructors); to aid memory (4); to give the scientific manner of thought and training in drawing conclusions (3); to give opportunity for developing sense perception and acquisition of concepts (3); to develop powers of observation (3); to teach a student self-confidence (1); to develop an inquiring mind (1); to develop self-control (1).

A similar questionnaire sent to a group of secondary-school science teachers showed similar beliefs, with the additional statement by nineteen of thirty-three teachers that these abilities could not have been developed by any other procedure than laboratory work (twelve thought they could; two were doubtful).

These science teachers seem to exhibit a degree of faith in the disciplinary outcomes of their teaching that psychological research has so far failed to confirm. Perhaps we have not perfected our measuring instruments sufficiently to detect transfer, or possibly we do not teach in the way conducive to producing the amount of transfer potentially present. The situation as it stands at present has been well summarized by Whipple[9] in the following statement: "Further study is much needed, but difficult. In the meantime the educator is not justified in resorting to any special subject of instruction for the purpose primarily of deriving from it indirect training values, but neither is he justified in neglecting to derive from every subject all the training value that it seems to possess."

The aims of college courses in science stated here are intended to be merely suggestive; actually the aims should be determined much

---

[8] Hurd, Archer W. *Problems of Science Teaching at the College Level.* Minneapolis: University of Minnesota Press, 1929. pp. 9-10.
[9] Whipple, Guy M. "The Transfer of Training." *Twenty-Seventh Yearbook* of this Society, 1928. Part II, p. 208.

more definitely by resort to the best available methods. Freeman[10] suggests the following methods: (1) analytic survey of the literature, (2) analytic survey of present authorities (questionnaire to authorities), (3) study of student personnel (conferences with students to determine what they expect of a course in science), (4) study of alumni occupations. To these might be added a study of life activities of persons who have taken science courses as well as an analysis of textbooks. Whatever the methods used in obtaining an agreement upon aims, the important fact is that, so far as the writer is aware, no organized attempt to do this for college science courses has ever been made.

What has been said in the foregoing pages regarding aims of college science courses applies particularly to the beginning, or introductory, type of course. These are the courses which are taken by the largest number of students, most of whom will never become scientists or technical experts but take such courses to learn something *about* science.

The advanced courses may properly be conducted with different aims, which must, at least for the present, be left largely to the judgment of those who teach them. It will probably have to be assumed for some time to come that the training of specialists in science can most safely be left to those who are specialists in the field.

CONTENT

After the aims of college science courses have been determined (and logically this should be done for particular courses as well as for science courses in general), the next step is to build these courses in accordance with the aims. Is the course to be one for those who may never take another course in the subject? Then we should include a content differing from that of a similar course which is preparatory in function. The latter type must logically be a unit in a series of courses, proceeding gradually from the elementary to the highly technical. Again, is the preparatory course for future chemists, for physicists, for engineers, or for physicians? In each case it may be desirable to make some differentiation from the others. Perhaps this is carrying the matter too far. It may be said, however, that in so far as the aims of

---

[10] Freeman, E. M. *Suggested Program of Investigation Having in Mind the Improvement of Instruction in Science at the University of Minnesota.* (Problems of College Education) Minneapolis: University of Minnesota Press, 1928. pp. 426-443.

such courses differ for various groups, to that extent it seems necessary to differentiate the content and methods of these courses. At least for the two specific types of courses mentioned, the survey and the preparatory, a distinct difference in content would certainly seem justifiable. Some evidence that this does not prevail to any considerable extent has already been cited in the studies of Johnson and of Noll.

Another phase of the curricular problem is that of building a proper sequence of courses. This is necessary not only as within the college but also as between the high-school and the beginning college courses. Koos,[11] in his study of overlapping, showed the need for study at this point.

> Although there are some differences between high school and first college courses in chemistry, they are remarkably alike. . . . If a student takes the course in general inorganic chemistry in college after having had the high-school course, which is often done, he is repeating almost all of it. Even in that relatively small proportion of higher institutions where such a student enters upon a course in general inorganic chemistry presumed to be administered for those who offered the high-school unit for admission, there must be a large amount of repetition.

Hurd[12] made an analysis of those portions of high-school and college texts in physics dealing with mechanics and reports that "while the two contrasted texts, *viz.*, college and high-school, bear upon the same general field, the treatment is so different that what is gained from a study of one does not help greatly in a study of the other. . . . The language [of the college text] is not used in high-school physics to any great extent."

There is apparently a difference between the findings of Koos in chemistry and those of Hurd in physics. Further and more extensive analyses of textbooks and syllabi in these and other courses in science taught on both levels need to be made. Likewise, analyses of textbooks and reference materials used in sequences of college courses need to be made to determine the amount of overlapping, the extent to which courses function as prerequisites, the extent to which advanced courses utilize the knowledge gained in prerequisite courses, and the extent to which all these courses function in the life of the student after leaving college.

---

[11] Koos, L. V. *The Junior College.* (Research Publications of the University of Minnesota, Education Series No. 5.) The University of Minnesota Press, 1924, pp. 474-493.
[12] Hurd, Archer W. "High-school physics makes small contribution to college physics." *School and Society,* 31: 1930, 468-470.

One of the first curricular studies to be made in science on the college level was that of Johnson.[13] In this study, which deals with courses in botany, a careful analysis was made of the courses in this subject offered at the University of Minnesota. The topics included and the amount of time devoted to each were determined for each course from the elementary to the most advanced. In his interpretation of the results of these analyses Johnson, speaking of the introductory course in botany, says "when considered as an entity, General Botany, 4, 5, 6, appear to be a well coördinated course; when considered as a course preparing the student for the pursual of the sequent courses analyzed, its limitations appear insurmountable." When the achievement of students in advanced courses who had taken the elementary botany course was compared with that of students who had not, no significant difference was found.

Another phase of this investigation was concerned with the nature and amount of botanical information retained by students who had taken the course in general botany. It was found that the loss in retention of such information at the end of three months was 43.4 percent; at the end of six months, 47.8 percent. The students who had the most information at the completion of the course retained the most at the end of three or six months, both relatively and absolutely. Certain types of botanical information are retained much better than others. These, especially, are those which occur in the content of sequent courses.

There was also a study made of the effect of certain other factors upon achievement in general botany. Whether or not the course was taken as an elective seemed not to affect achievement. It was also found to be indifferent whether or not students had taken biological sciences in high school. Students who had a strong liking for science were somewhat higher in achievement than the others. Men seemed somewhat superior to women in their achievement in the course.

Out of Johnson's study two proposals for reorganization were made, essentially as follows: first, that students who intend to take sequent courses in botany should have an introductory course which would be definitely preparatory in nature and which would prepare them specifically for future specialization; second, a survey course open to all those students who are not planning to specialize in botany should be

---

[13] Johnson, P. O. *Op. cit.*

offered which would be "a lecture, textbook, demonstration, and class recitation course in the hands of the better instructors."

In another curricular investigation, that of Van de Voort,[14] a study was made of courses in science offered in a large number of teacher-training institutions. The results indicate that the situation in teachers colleges and normal schools is not a reassuring one. For example, in ninety institutions surveyed, 612 courses in chemistry are offered under 66 different titles; in physics, 438 courses under 105 titles; and in the biological sciences, 736 courses under 144 titles.

It was also found in this study that "the offerings in biology, physics, and chemistry to a large extent consider subject matter for its own sake or apart from its professional function in the training of teachers." Evidently a distinct type of course in science for prospective teachers of the subject has not yet commonly found a place in such institutions.

The general recommendations growing out of Van de Voort's study are that courses for future science teachers should be developed which "give a wealth of scientific knowledge organized and adopted for teaching purposes." It is further recommended that these should be supplemented by training in educational psychology and methods. A common nomenclature for titles of science courses should be agreed upon. There should be a national organization to serve as a clearing house for completed research in this field, to prevent overlapping of effort, and to stimulate further research.

A third curricular study, that of Billig,[15] had two objectives. The first was to develop a method for selecting and organizing content for a science course for students preparing to teach in elementary schools. The second was to determine the previous training in science that such students have when they enter teacher-training institutions. The first problem was attacked by making an analysis of thirteen college texts in biology which was checked against an analysis of eight outlines of science now in use in various elementary schools. Certain criteria for selection of items were set up, and the items thus selected were organized into an outline which was submitted for criticism to ten research

[14] Van de Voort, Alice M. *The Teaching of Science in Normal Schools and Teachers Colleges.* New York: Columbia University. Teachers College Contributions to Education. No. 287. 1927.

[15] Billig, Florence G. *A Technique for Developing Content for a Professional Course in Science for Teachers in Elementary Schools.* New York: Columbia University. Teachers College Contributions to Education. No. 397. 1930.

students in science. This procedure furnished what was called the "core" science content. A further analysis of seven books written by scientists for the lay reader was made upon which was based an outline of "marginal" science content.

In the second part of Billig's investigation she found that students coming from the high school show wide variation in knowledge of science as measured by the Powers General Science Test; that the highest percentage of students have had general science, (54.92); next highest biology, (53.56); 42.55 percent have had physics, and 41.82 percent have had chemistry. The study is valuable in the present discussion for the techniques of curriculum-building which it suggests and for the picture it gives of the preparation in science that high-school graduates have when they enter higher institutions.

A study by Curtis[16] in general science, although not on the college level, is to be described for its techniques, which included essentially these seven steps:

(1) The selection of contributing sources of data concerning the materials that should be included in a course in general science. These sources included research investigations, outlines, and syllabi, analyses of textbooks, magazines and newspapers, and committee reports. Criteria which were varied according to the type of source were set up for the selection of these sources.

(2) The tabulation of the materials thus selected. This included tabulation of each topic included and its weighting as obtained from the contributing sources.

(3) The determination of the ranks of topics within each contributing source.

(4) The determination of the weights of each contributing source.

(5) The determination of the relative values of the topics in each contributing source.

(6) The determination of the aggregate value of each topic.

(7) The final reduction of this value to a percentage value.

The last five steps are essentially statistical treatment of the two factors, (3) the rank of topics in each source, and (4) a weight assigned to each source as a whole.

Curtis's study resulted in a comprehensive list of topics in general science, each with a final relative value (Step 7) which is the ratio of the value obtained by Steps 3, 4, 5, and 6 to the highest possible value a topic might have if it were ranked highest in all sources.

His study represents a praiseworthy attempt to develop a workable technique for selection of subject matter for courses in general science.

---

[16] Curtis, Francis D. *A Synthesis and Evaluation of Subject-Matter Topics in General Science.* Boston: Ginn, 1929.

When contributing sources as used here are available for college science courses, similar techniques can be used for selection of subject matter in such courses.

Another study suggestive in its technique is that of Menzies.[17] Ten college textbooks in biology were analyzed to determine the percentage of word space devoted to generalizations and their applications. The results show that while in no case less than 78 percent of the word space is devoted to generalizations, the most that is devoted to applications of biological laws to life situations is 9.3 percent.

Probably the most difficult problem of all is to determine what content meets the aims of a course, once they are determined. In this phase of curriculum construction, we are as yet in the 'authority stage.' Studies aiming to discover to what extent a certain type of curriculum functions when actually put to the test have yet to be made. We do not know why a student preparing to enter the medical profession should be required to take as much as eighteen quarter-credits of chemistry, including advanced quantitative analysis and physical chemistry. The only reason we have for requiring medical students to take a large amount of chemistry, often over and above such purely medical courses as physiological and bacteriological chemistry, is that the persons who have been the administrative heads of medical schools and chemistry departments, together with their faculties, have arbitrarily decided that the requirement is desirable. No one, so far as the writer is aware, has ever attempted to determine by an objective and quantitative method just how much and what kinds of chemistry a physician needs in the practice of his profession. The same statement applies to practically all other professions and all other sciences. We can only say that our higher institutions are turning out many physicians, engineers, dentists, and similar professional men who are filling positions and serving humanity faithfully and well. Whether they would perform their services more or less efficiently with different training we do not know.

What is true of chemistry is equally true of other sciences. We need to know not only what kinds of chemistry and how much chemistry a physician needs before we can build that portion of the medical curriculum on a foundation of fact, but also how much physics, botany,

---

[17] Menzies, Jessie A. *An Analysis of the Generalizations and Applications in Ten College Textbooks in Biology.* Chicago: University of Chicago (Unpublished master's thesis), 1927.

zoölogy, bacteriology, geology, or other science his occupation requires. Does a sanitary engineer need bacteriology? Obviously, he does. How much does he need? In many cases as much as the heads of engineering schools think he has room for in an already crowded program; that is often the determining factor. These are not problems upon the immediate solution of which depends the continued existence of colleges and universities, but they are real problems to the administrators and teachers of such institutions who have such decisions to make and who are possessed of an inquiring mind and a disregard for tradition.

METHODS

President Eliot, in 1906, said: "There are then two quite distinct functions which school and college laboratories perform. They tend to raise the observational powers of the average, and they give a chance to men of remarkable capacities to develop these capacities."[18] In making this statement President Eliot imputed to a particular method of instruction certain values which he evidently believed peculiar to that method. Whether or not this statement was based upon more than personal opinion and observation is not known. That it had not been subjected to experimental verification is almost certainly true. It is with the answers to problems such as this that the study of methods of teaching college science is concerned. The study of the effectiveness of the various methods of teaching now employed by science instructors in higher institutions lends itself well to experimental and quantitative measurement and is receiving some attention at the present time.

It has been mentioned that the experimental comparison of individual laboratory work and lecture demonstrations has already been made in some twenty different situations on the elementary-school and secondary-school levels. Similar studies need to be made on the college level. The college science teacher uses a wide variety of methods of instruction; common among them are lecture, recitation, individual laboratory, demonstration of experiments, quiz (oral and written), project, outside reading, and field trips. What is the relative effectiveness of each of these in teaching the same or different types of subject matter? What combinations of methods are most effective? How much of the total time in a course in science should be devoted

---

[18] Eliot, Charles W. *Loc. cit.* (Footnote 4).

to each method? These are questions upon which we need to accumulate objective evidence.

The proportions of the total time in the course which are devoted to each method vary greatly between different subjects and between different courses. These time arrangements have been worked out through the experience and judgment of the instructors in these courses, and we may safely assume in most cases that they have exercised much care and have devoted a large amount of thought to these arrangements. But, does anyone know how much difference an hour more or less of lecture, recitation, individual laboratory, or any other method will make in the final achievement of the student? What evidence has actually been accumulated in favor of individual laboratory work as a teaching method in college science? Much has been said and written about it, both for and against it, but how much of this has been based upon more than mere opinion? Less than fifty years ago school authorities were certain that individual laboratory work in high-school chemistry and physics was the *sine qua non* of courses in these subjects, but to-day the authorities are by no means so certain. We cannot be any more certain of our methods of teaching college science until we have accumulated objective evidence.

One of the first published experimental studies of methods in college science teaching is that by Hurd.[19] He reports several studies carried on at the University of Minnesota. The first deals with the teaching of human anatomy. Instead of having two students work on a cadaver, as was customary, he formed one group in which four students worked on a cadaver. The achievement of these students was compared with that of students in another group who worked in pairs as usual. The groups were equated as carefully as possible and achievement was measured both by written and by performance tests. No significant differences in achievement were found.

Another study by Hurd is in the teaching of human physiology. One group of students took five hours of lecture, two hours of quiz, and seven and one-half hours of laboratory work per week. A second group, matched in ability and previous training with the first, had the same instruction, except that they had five hours of laboratory work and two and one-half hours of outside reading on assigned topics in physiology per week. Each student in the latter group had to prepare a talk on a topic assigned by lot and give this talk before the class.

[19] Hurd, Archer W. *Op. cit.* (Footnote 8).

Significant differences in achievement were found favoring the group having seven and one-half hours of laboratory work.

In another study the achievement of two groups of students in physics was compared in which one group had three hours of lecture, one of quiz, and two of laboratory work per week and the other group had identical instruction but no laboratory work. The results showed the latter group to be lower in achievement, but whether or not this difference was significant was not determined.

Such studies as these indicate rather clearly that our usual methods of teaching science in higher institutions may undergo considerable modification without our being able to detect any large or significant differences in the results.

Another group of studies on the college level is reported by Noll.[20] The primary purpose of these studies was to evaluate individual laboratory work in chemistry as a method of instruction. As a result of a preliminary study of 580 students in six sections in general inorganic chemistry at the University of Minnesota, it was found that reliable differences existed between the achievement of the six sections as measured by an objective test based on material taught in all sections.

A vital problem of this investigation was the construction of reliable and valid measures of achievement. Two such were constructed: one, a test of general information and ability to solve problems and to write formulae and equations; the other, a test of laboratory aptitude and techniques. Both tests had high reliability and validity.

When two equated groups were compared in achievement (both general and laboratory), one group having had five hours of laboratory work per week, the other having had three hours of laboratory work and two hours per week of outside reading on assigned topics in chemistry, the former group showed consistent and, in some instances, almost certainly reliable, superiority. Instruction, except for laboratory and outside reading was identical for the two groups.

A comparison of two equated groups, one having five hours of laboratory work per week, the other having three hours of laboratory work and one hour of oral quiz and recitation per week, showed the latter group to be superior in achievement, although never by a statistically significant amount.

Comparison of two equated groups, one having five hours, the other having only three hours, of laboratory work per week, showed the former group to be consistently superior in achievement.

[20] Noll, Victor H. *Op. cit.* (Footnote 7).

In the last-mentioned study the group having five hours of laboratory work were chemistry majors, while the group having three hours per week had elected chemistry to fulfill science requirements for graduation. This difference was presumed to have some bearing on their interest in the subject and, therefore, perhaps some effect on achievement. When two other groups were compared, supposedly differing in interest, but with identical instruction, the group majoring in chemistry (and the one supposedly more interested in chemistry) showed consistent superiority in achievement.

Comparisons of groups differing only in sex showed no consistent superiority for either sex.

Comparison of two groups, one having had no chemistry in the high school, the other having had chemistry in the high school, showed a very significant superiority for the latter group at the beginning of the college course, but no such superiority after two quarters of very similar instruction in general inorganic chemistry at the University of Minnesota.

In all these experiments the control and experimental groups were matched as carefully as possible on ability and on previous preparation and aptitude in chemistry. Instruction was always identical, except for the amounts of laboratory work or except as otherwise stated.

As a result of these experiments the Division of Inorganic Chemistry at the University of Minnesota has modified its laboratory requirements by reducing the number of hours of individual laboratory work required in certain groups.

One more fact needs to be pointed out in connection with the study of methods in science teaching. No other phase of the problem is quite so important to the administrator. Laboratory teaching is expensive. This fact is almost self-evident, but it also has been shown in the reports by the Educational Finance Inquiry Commission,[21] by Lindsay,[22] and by Noll.[23] Because of the methods used, the supplies and materials needed, the space required, and the time involved, science sub-

---

[21] Elliott, E. C., and Stevens, E. B. *Unit Costs in Higher Education.* (Volume 13 of Reports of Educational Finance Inquiry Commission.) New York: Macmillan, 1925, pp. 77-94.

[22] Lindsay, E. E. "Laboratory costs in state institutions of higher learning." *School and Society,* 20: 1924, 537-542.

[23] Noll, Victor H. *The Effect of Varying Amounts of Laboratory Work Upon Achievement in General Inorganic Chemistry.* Minneapolis: University of Minnesota (Masters Thesis), 1927. Chapter 5.

jects cost more than any others. Consequently, studies which present objective evidence on the relative effectiveness of different methods of teaching science hold possibilities of indicating in what ways time and money can be saved. It is not meant to imply that this alone is sufficient justification for changing methods of instruction in science, but its importance cannot be denied as a reason for experimental investigations.

On the whole the study of methods of teaching college science presents great and interesting possibilities. The field is almost untouched, and college and university administrators are becoming increasingly awake to its promise.

In closing the discussion of the experimental study of the problems of teaching science in higher institutions, a number of general considerations should be mentioned. In the first place, many of the published studies of science teaching on the lower levels may be criticized for lack of the application of statistical techniques. In the majority of instances there is no indication of the application of criteria for the reliability of obtained differences. Much of the value of such studies is lost when the investigator fails to do this. There is some hope of adding to the significance of the results of such studies by repeating them over and over in different situations with the possible accumulation of small differences all, or nearly all, in the same direction. The value of such procedure has been pointed out by Buckingham,[24] although in a slightly different sense. In the evaluation of the results of individual studies, however, statistical criteria of the reliability of obtained differences are absolutely necessary if we are to place any reliance upon their findings. The persons who will conduct the investigations must be trained to do the necessary statistical work. The individual who conducts an experimental study in college science teaching—whether it be a curricular or a methods study—should have training in educational statistics and in educational psychology, so that he may properly interpret the results of his endeavors. Another type of training which he needs quite as much as that just mentioned is in the subject matter of the science in which he conducts his investigation. The latter is necessary if he is to work with and secure the coöperation of the specialists in botany, physics, or other field of science in which the study is being made. He should be able to speak the language of the instructor in science as well as that of the educator.

[24]Buckingham, B. R. "The accumulation of minute advantages." *Jour. of Educ. Research,* 16: September, 1927, 136-138.

Another factor of importance in the study of college science teaching is the development of valid and reliable measuring instruments. These are essential in the evaluation of different methods of teaching, as well as in studies of the curriculum. Too often educational experiments are conducted and the results determined on the basis of measurements whose validity and reliability are unknown quantities.

In constructing measures of the results of science teaching, two lines of endeavor are apparent. The first is that of measuring information. This is by far the simpler of the two. The second is that of measuring the less tangible outcomes of science instruction, those bordering upon the disciplinary, or mental training, type.

A few attempts to measure such outcomes have been made on the secondary-school level. One of the most significant of those published is by Horton[25] in high-school chemistry. In this study Horton constructed some laboratory performance tests in high-school chemistry involving ability to make chemical preparations and manipulations without directions and also a test of ability to set up apparatus for certain experiments. The results of the study indicate that tests which involve laboratory performance can be devised which will bring out differences in laboratory skills as developed by different laboratory methods of teaching. The study presents some interesting techniques for measurement of these less tangible values of instruction in science and is suggestive of what may be done on the college level.

Because of the nature of the subject matter, objective measurement in the natural sciences is relatively easy as compared, for example, with the social sciences. Science teachers have long had certain semi-objective types of questions, such as problems, equations, formulae. On the other hand, the so-called 'intangibles' present what is perhaps as baffling a problem as any in the field of educational measurement. One of the first steps to be taken in attacking the problem is to define the elements to be measured. What is scientific attitude? Power of observation? Ability to generalize? These terms have different meanings in the minds of different instructors. Once the terms have been defined objectively and accurately, we have made a long step toward the construction of measures of these qualities.

---

[25] Horton, Ralph E. *Measurable Outcomes of Individual Laboratory Work in High-School Chemistry.* New York: Columbia University, Bureau of Publications (Teachers College Contributions to Education, No. 303), 1928.

CHAPTER XVIII

PROGRAMS FOR THE EDUCATION OF SCIENCE TEACHERS IN STATE TEACHERS COLLEGES[1]

A program for the education of teachers must be so planned as to meet the needs of teachers preparing for service in the schools. These needs are defined in the program that is set down and developed in the preceding pages of this volume. The teachers of the elementary school, of the junior high school, and of the senior high school should obtain an education that will prepare them for the work of these respective levels. Throughout the foregoing pages the Committee has stressed the liberalizing function of the school. Education should liberate from ignorance. Speaking positively, the liberally educated person should be able to make intelligent adjustments to the stimuli which are associated with rich living. In order that the teacher may effectively contribute to this program of liberal education the teacher must be liberally educated. The program of liberal education must be supplemented with such additional education as will enable the teacher to meet the specialized demands of professional service. In other words, the program of teacher education should be judged from the standpoint of its adequacy for liberal education and from the standpoint of its adequacy for professional education. The *sine qua non* for success in teaching is liberal education. The standards for liberal education of teachers and professional education of teachers are, therefore, in large part synonymous.

In order to define the work of the public school, including the teachers college, we may think of the liberally educated person as one who has explored widely into the fields of human thought and at the same time as one who has a measure of command in some specialized field. Evidence in hand points rather clearly to the fact that in current practice in state teachers colleges an adequate attainment of these standards for the education of teachers is not secured or even closely approached.

---

[1] For the Committee, by S. Ralph Powers. Most of the data in this article have been assembled by him.

SCIENCE COURSES TAKEN IN PUBLIC SCHOOLS BY
FUTURE TEACHERS

For practical purposes the education that should function in teaching may be thought of as beginning in the secondary school. The provision that has been made for training on this level corresponds rather closely to the recommendation of the Commission on the Reorganization of Science.[2] In common practice, general science is a required subject and the three additional subjects are offered as electives. Figures on enrollment published by the Bureau of Education[3] show that the number of students enrolled in biology (in 1928) is considerably in excess of the number in either of the other two elective subjects, and that there is considerable enrollment in botany, zoölogy, human physiology, physiography, and some other subjects.

TABLE I.—DATA FROM RECORDS OF 1586 STUDENTS ENTERING STATE TEACHERS
COLLEGES IN PENNSYLVANIA, SHOWING NUMBER WHO HAD
STUDIED SCIENCE IN EACH GRADE

Subject	Grades						Total
	VII	VIII	IX	X	XI	XII	
General Science	5	0	1163	60	19	10	1257
Biology		1	22	941	98	74	1136
Chemistry				3	345	552	900
Physics				10	402	278	690

The data in Table I, from the records of 1586 students entering state teachers colleges in Pennsylvania, show the number that had studied each of the four most commonly recognized branches. All of these students had studied at least one of these subjects; approximately 80 percent of them had taken a course in general science; nearly 72 percent had taken biology; about 56 percent had studied chemistry; more than 43 percent had studied physics. Some 87 percent of these students had taken two or more sciences in high school; more than half of the two-subject combinations were general science and biology. Some 55 percent had taken three sciences, nearly half with the combination: general science, biology, and chemistry.

The extent and nature of the training in different school systems varies somewhat. In most of the schools from which these students had been graduated each subject is taught five periods each week for

---

[2] See Chapter I for some discussion of the report of this Commission.
[3] Office of Education Bulletin No. 16, 1930, p. 1057.

a period of one year, but there was considerable variation in the provision that was made for laboratory work. Cases in which laboratory work had been included in instruction in general science were rare, and in most cases no provision had been made for this type of instruction in biology. More than 33 percent of the cards of students who had studied chemistry showed that no laboratory work had been included. The corresponding percentage for physics is even slightly larger.

Comparable figures from other states show that Pennsylvania has probably made as liberal an allotment of time for instruction in high-school science as other states have made. In general, then, the students enter the teachers college with a background of two or three years' training in science, but with relatively little direct experience with laboratory work.

Another survey[4] to determine the range of study in high-school science has been made in which data were gathered from fourteen state teachers colleges located in thirteen states. Each of these fourteen colleges offered a course designed to give professional training in science for students preparing to teach in elementary schools. The data were gathered from the students enrolled in these professional courses. The report shows, therefore, the background of training in science of students entering this professional course. Tables show the number of students that had studied each of several sciences in the high school. Other tables report the scores of students in these classes on the Powers General Science Test. The tests were given during the first week of the professional course. These scores give some notion of the extent of the students' acquaintance with science at the time when they begin their professional education. The variability of the background of students entering these fourteen colleges is about the same as it is in the colleges of Pennsylvania.

Data are given concerning 954 students. The modal student, in the distribution showing the number of sciences studied, had been enrolled in two high-school sciences. General science showed the greatest frequency of recurrence; biology was second; physics and chemistry were third and fourth, with frequencies about equal. Other subjects showing considerable recurrence, and arranged in order of frequency, are botany, hygiene, agriculture, human physiology, zoölogy, and geology. Approximately 68 percent of these 954 students

---

[4] Billig, Florence G. *A Technique for Developing Content for a Professional Course in Science for Teachers in Elementary Schools.* Teachers College Contributions to Education, No. 397, Chap. IV.

reported that they had 'taken' three or more sciences in the high school. It should be noted, however, that in many cases the course was of less than one year's duration.

The scores on the test extend over a wide range. Some few students made scores of fewer than ten items correct out of a possible hundred. In only two of the fourteen schools was the mean score up to the standard set by high-school students in ninth-grade general-science classes!

These two studies, the one of five colleges in Pennsylvania and the other of fourteen colleges distributed in thirteen states, show the futility of attempting at present to accomplish an integration of the professional college course in science with the science courses offered in the high school. The variability in science courses taken in the high school by students entering the teachers colleges is very large, and the variability in ability in the field of science, as shown by scores on the Powers General Science Test, is even greater. The prevailing practice is to set no prerequisite for entrance to the professional course in science for the elementary school and few prerequisites for the professional course of other levels.

Provisions that have been made in normal schools and teachers colleges of different states for extending the students' training in science are also characterized by great variability. Practices are by no means standardized. The variation is seen in the range of fields of science that are offered and in an enormous range of courses offered in each of the fields.

Table II is a summary of the titles listed in the bulletins of 196 teacher-training schools for the academic year 1927-1928. The great diversity in course titles is illustrated by the fact that of 689 titles listed there are 414, or 60 percent, that occur only once, and there are but 68 titles, or fewer than 10 percent, that have occurred ten times or more. Many of these courses reflect, in content as well as in name, the idiosyncrasies of the instructor or department head. Such courses doubtless have some value, but all too often they follow by-paths of learning which lead nowhere, in the sense that they do not qualify the student to go on to more advanced work; in a word, they are 'blind-alley' courses.

It is clear, from reference to Table II and to the descriptions of courses in the catalogs, that practices in science teaching are by no means crystallized. The descriptions of courses for both elementary- and secondary-school teachers suggest that the offerings are in many cases given as short-cuts to success and by implication show something

TABLE II.—DISTRIBUTION AND FREQUENCY, BY SUBJECT, OF TITLES OF SCIENCE COURSES OFFERED IN 196 TEACHER-TRAINING SCHOOLS FOR THE YEARS OF 1927-1928

Subject	Number of Courses	Total Number of Titles	Numbers of Titles Appearing			
			Once	Twice	Three Times	Ten Times or More
Nature Study and Elementary Science	179	41	26	8	2	3
General Courses in Science	126	33	23	7	1	2
Biology	1126	243	127	24	12	28
Health, Hygiene, and Sanitation	117	37	30	4	0	1
Chemistry	774	114	70	7	6	7
Physics	525	149	90	16	13	9
Geology and Physiography	109	29	16	4	1	3
Astronomy	39	9	7	0	1	1
Agriculture*	25	7	5	0	1	1
Geography*	102	27	20	2	1	3
Totals	3122	689	414	72	38	68

* Courses in agriculture and geography were included only if they were listed as being given by the Natural Science Department.

of the standards for training for work in science teaching. Witness the following one-term course:

Teachers Course in Physics. Intended for students preparing to be teachers of physics in secondary schools. The student will perform many experiments, so as to acquaint himself with the best laboratory devices, the History of Physics, and the best methods of teaching it. Open to those who have completed one year of college physics or who have had one unit of entrance physics and are employed at the time as teachers of physics in approved high schools.

It is clear that the instructor in charge of this course is attempting in his one-term course to make high-school teachers of physics out of students who have no larger background of training than that which comes from the study of physics in the high school. This illustration is not an isolated case.

It is quite common to find in practice that a single course in "Nature Study" of two or three periods each week for a term constitutes the total preparation of elementary-school teachers for their work in science. This short course is commonly one in which the major work is in the nature of learning the names of trees, flowers, birds, and other living things, making collections of minerals and rocks, and learning the names of constellations.

The movement which has been in progress for the past few years to convert normal schools into teachers colleges has placed these institutions in what may be properly described as a state of transition. It is fair to say that in a great many cases the change has been made without adequately enlarging the staff. In fact, there are not enough properly trained instructors available to fill the positions that have been created by the change. Many of the teachers in charge of the work are not qualified to give instruction in college classes. The result is that teachers with definitely crystallized normal-school traditions and inadequate training are planning and teaching the courses in many of these new institutions. This conclusion is based upon analysis of the printed matter in catalogs of these institutions and is, we believe, well-founded; it describes a typical, and apparently a modal, situation, though we recognize that there are among these institutions some that are well staffed and that are offering work in the training of science teachers that measures up to a high standard of excellence.

Table III shows some of the data to support the foregoing statements. It permits a comparison of the degrees attained by members of science faculties in state teachers colleges and in state universities or recognized colleges of the same state. The last two entries compare data from state normal schools with data from state universities. There were 63 members of the science teaching faculties in the state teachers colleges. Of these, 16, or approximately 25 percent, had attained the doctorate degree. Nine of these men, or approximately 14 percent, were listed among American Men of Science. In the state universities and colleges of the corresponding states there are 211 members of the science teaching faculties. Of these 132, or more than 62 percent, have the doctorate degree, while 93, or 44 percent, are listed in American Men of Science.

A study of teachers colleges selected at random in an effort to define constructive measures would certainly be nearly fruitless. The foregoing observations have already shown that in general the work in these schools is very elementary—certainly not up to any acceptable standard of college work, that it is poorly planned, and that it is quite inadequate for developing any acceptable standards of scholarship in science. Attention is therefore directed to a few selected

Table III.—Comparison of Science Faculties of State Universities and State Teachers Colleges and Normal Schools

Institution	Total Number of Faculty Teaching Science	Number Having Ph.D. Degree	Number Having M.A. or M.S. Degrees	Number Having Only A.B. or B.S. Degrees	Number of Science Faculty Listed in American Men of Science
University of Arizona	29	18	5	6	16
Arizona Teachers Colleges (2)	6	2	1	3	1
University of Colorado	42	20	15	7	13
Teachers Colleges of Colorado (2)	9	5	4	0	3
Ohio State University	35	30	5	0	27
Teachers Colleges of Ohio (2)	7	2	5	0	1
Penn State College	61	38	21	2	17
Teachers Colleges of Pennsylvania (13)	32	5	20	7	3
Rutgers University	44	26	12	6	20
Teachers Colleges of New Jersey (2)	9	4	3	2	1
University of Maryland	28	18	6	4	14
Maryland State Normal Schools (4)	4	0	2	2	0
University of Washington	28	18	6	4	14
Normal Schools of Washington (2)	7	0	7	0	0

institutions. The institutions chosen are, in each case, colleges in which there has been conscious and deliberate effort to analyze and to meet the problems of educating teachers. In this analysis our attention is directed to three different curricula: (1) for training elementary-school teachers, (2) for training junior-high-school teachers, and (3) for training science teachers for the senior high school. Tables are presented which show the percentage distribution of the credits required for graduation in each of these curricula.

Table IV shows the requirements of the curricula for training teachers for elementary schools. These are commonly differentiated into curricula for kindergarten-primary grades and for intermediate

TABLE IV.—TRAINING OF ELEMENTARY-SCHOOL TEACHERS: PERCENTAGE ALLOTMENT
OF TOTAL CREDITS IN FOUR-YEAR COURSES FOR ELEMENTARY-SCHOOL
TEACHERS AT SELECTED TEACHERS COLLEGES

Location of Teachers College	Science Required for All	Added Science for Science Major	Education Courses Required	Other Courses Required	Elective Courses
Bellingham, Wash.	12.4	...	28.5	36.5	22.6
Buffalo, N. Y.	4.0	15.0	31.7	37.3	12.0
East Stroudsburg, Pa.	10.3	...	50.0	38.2	1.5
Greeley, Colo.	8.3	...	38.5	30.2	22.8
Kalamazoo, Mich.	2.1	...	12.5	45.8	39.6
Pittsburg, Kan.	5.0	...	31.7	33.3	30.0
San Francisco, Calif.	9.6	9.6	34.0	17.7	29.0
Terre Haute, Ind.	10.4	6.2	48.9	23.0	11.5

grades. But these differentiated curricula do not differ except in details that are finer than those shown in these tables. There is some
requirement in science in each of the eight schools. In Greeley, the
requirement includes a course, Outlines of Science (in other colleges
called an "orientation course"), with content selected from all the
major divisions of science and organized to accomplish an integration
of these fields. Additional required courses are Biological Elementary
Science (a professional course), and Heredity and Eugenics. A course
similar to Outlines of Science is required in all the curricula of Bellingham and of San Francisco. East Stroudsburg requires educational
biology, nature study, economic biology, and descriptive astronomy. A
large percentage (too large?) of the requirement for graduation is for
work in education, which here is taken to include requirements in soci-
ology and psychology. In one of the schools this total in education is
equal to half the requirements for the degree. Other required courses
include English, history, art, music, etc. In five of the eight institutions there is ample allowance for electives to make it possible for a
student to work fairly intensively into some field. The student who
chooses, for example, to apply his electives in the field of science has
time to acquire a respectable standard of scholarship in this field.
From the point of view of the needs of the field and the satisfaction
of the students, this provision of electives seems very commendable,
and students should be advised to apply their electives in the manner
suggested, namely, to acquire a respectable scholarship in a major
subject. In but three of the eight institutions is there definite recog-

nition of a science major for students in training for teaching in the elementary school.

It is impossible to teach any subject well without an adequate background of subject-matter training. Courses in methods and in other phases of education constitute a necessary part of the equipment of the teacher, but these courses should be considered always as additional to those required to provide a necessary background of subject matter; they should never be permitted as substitutes for subject matter.

TABLE V.—TRAINING OF JUNIOR-HIGH-SCHOOL TEACHERS: PERCENTAGE ALLOTMENT OF TOTAL CREDITS IN FOUR-YEAR COURSES FOR JUNIOR-HIGH-SCHOOL TEACHERS AT SELECTED TEACHERS COLLEGES

Location of Teachers Colleges	Sciences Required for All	Added Science for Science Major	Education Courses Required	Other Courses Required	Elective Courses
Bellingham, Wash.	6.5	16.1	26.3	25.3	25.8
Buffalo, N. Y.	4.0	15.0	35.0	31.7	14.3
East Stroudsburg, Pa.	4.4	13.2	33.1	33.1	16.2
Greeley, Colo.	4.2	14.6	32.3	12.5	36.4
Kalamazoo, Mich.	...	15.6	12.5	29.2	42.7
Pittsburg, Kan.	...	33.3	16.7	7.5	42.5
San Francisco, Calif.	9.6	19.3	25.0	16.1	30.0
Terre Haute, Ind.	7.3	16.6	30.2	29.2	16.7
Worcester, Mass.	4.4	...	25.0	29.4	41.2

Table V shows the percentage of time allotted to various requirements in curricula that are prescribed for junior-high-school teachers. In Greeley, Bellingham, and San Francisco the course corresponding to outlines of science is required as a first-year course in all curricula. The requirement in education is, in nearly every case, less than that made of elementary-school teachers, and the same is true of the requirement of "other courses." Definite provisions are made for a major sequence of courses, and there is more leeway for electives. In these colleges and in others it is common to require two major sequences or a major and minor. The percentage of the students' time that may be applied to the development of these sequences ranges in these nine institutions between 33 and 75 percent of the total requirements for the baccalaureate degree. These percentages are the sum of the three entries: science required for all, added science for science major, and elective courses.

TABLE VI.—TRAINING OF SENIOR-HIGH-SCHOOL TEACHERS: PERCENTAGE ALLOTMENT OF TOTAL CREDITS IN FOUR-YEAR COURSES FOR SENIOR-HIGH-SCHOOL TEACHERS AT SELECTED TEACHERS COLLEGES

Location of Teachers College	Sciences Required for All	Added Science for Science Major	Education Courses Required	Other Courses Required	Elective Courses
Albany, N. Y.	4.8	9.7	12.9	22.6	50.0
Greeley, Colo.	4.2	27.1	19.8	27.1	21.8
Kent, Ohio	16.7	16.7	18.7	25.0	22.9
Montclair, N. J.	4.2	35.4	25.0	20.8	14.6
Pittsburg, Kan.	...	25.0	16.7	7.5	50.8
San Francisco, Calif.	9.6	19.3	4.9	16.2	50.0
San Jose, Calif.	9.2	43.9	18.8	17.9	10.2
Terre Haute, Ind.	6.2	29.2	14.6	10.4	39.6
Worcester, Mass.	4.4	...	25	29.4	41.2

Table VI shows the percentage of the total time allotted to various requirements in curricula that are prescribed for senior-high-school teachers of science. In every case but one (Pittsburg, Kansas) there is a science requirement in all secondary-school curricula. In these curricula there is a further reduction of required "Education." Greeley shows an increased requirement of "other courses," and Terre Haute a decreased requirement, while in some of the schools considered the requirement under this heading is about the same as in their junior-high-school curricula. There is allowance for a science major and considerable allowance for free electives. The allowance for "Science for All," "Science for a Science Major," and "Electives," is, in each case except Worcester, more than 50 percent of the total requirement for a degree. The extent to which this opportunity for specialization that appears on paper is actually realized cannot be determined except by analysis of transcripts of credits offered by students to meet the requirements for graduation.

The criteria already proposed for evaluating the program offered by a student to meet the requirements of a degree are by no means mutually exclusive. These are (1) that the student may be prepared for the responsibilities of teaching in the position he is to fill, and (2) that he shall have attained respectable scholarship in his field.

Satisfaction of the first criterion demands respectable scholarship in a major field, and it demands professional training that will give command of methods of teaching the body of content from his field that is taught in the elementary or secondary schools. The teachers college cannot escape responsibility for giving this specific professional training. Even though professional training may be in evidence in all the courses of the college, there is still a real need for a course, the core of which is the same as the core of the course or courses that the student is preparing to teach. Such a course will give training in content and in specific methods of teaching that content. A practical measure of attainment of respectable scholarship (the second criterion) is obtained through consideration of the qualifications of the student for graduate study in the field of his major and possibly in related fields. Qualifications for graduate study in chemistry can hardly be met in less than three years of study in college, which should include mathematics through the calculus. Three years of work in physics, possibly two and one-half years together with mathematics through the calculus, may be an adequate minimum for this field. At least three years will be required for attainment of this standard in both botany and zoölogy.

One further consideration in connection with the demands for secondary-school teaching which has thus far been recognized only by implication is the fact that teachers, especially during their first years of service, are almost certain to receive assignment for teaching more than one subject. In current practice the combination of subjects is most likely to be general science together with one or more of the special sciences, although it may be a combination of two or more of the special sciences. The combination may be of science subjects with other subjects outside the field of science, but in teacher-training practice no recognition should be made of this possibility, unless possibly recognition be made of mathematics. This consideration emphasizes the need for breadth of training in science. Foregoing considerations have already emphasized the need for thoroughness.

Another convincing argument for breadth of training is emphasized by the fact that biology, physics, and chemistry are so closely related. *Qualifications for success in one major field are greatly strengthened by training in related sciences.*

'ORIENTATION' COURSES

There is increasing recognition in the printed matter issued by these state teachers colleges of a course carrying some such title as 'Science in Civilization,' 'Outline of Science,' or 'Orientation Course in Science.' In some schools the work is given as a unit in physical science and a unit in biological science. In this case the biological unit is designated by some such title as 'Educational Biology,' or 'Biological Foundations of Education.' In other schools the work is offered as a course running for one year with recognition of a division between physical and biological science. Practical considerations relating to the qualifications of instructors for this work will probably demand some recognition of at least these two divisions.

In order to illustrate clearly the type of training advocated by this Committee, there is here included a detailed description of the work in science in the State Normal School at Bellingham, Washington, which is arranged for the education of students preparing for service as teachers in elementary schools. This account includes a rather full statement of the objectives and methods used in the Orientation Course and in the Professional Course, and a briefer statement of the work offered for specialization.

THE SCIENCE PROGRAM IN THE WASHINGTON STATE NORMAL SCHOOL
AT BELLINGHAM, WASHINGTON[5]

During the years 1923 to 1925 the faculty of the Normal School at Bellingham, Washington, undertook a study of its problems of teacher training. The result was a reorganization of the curricula of the school. In this reorganization two significant features guided the thoughts and actions of the faculty. These are described in the present school bulletin as follows:

Teaching may well be considered as a particularly active and useful type of citizenship. In view of such prospective citizenship, there is need of curricula which will develop well-informed, clear-thinking individuals who are self-disciplined, capable of forming judgments on adequate information, and having many-sided life interests. To this general training there must be added that which will fit the student for the particular teaching service in which he will engage. Any course in any curriculum may be interpreted as contributing both to the general cultural development and to the professional training of the student. A course may be planned more particularly for the one of these objectives, but will nevertheless contribute to the attainment of the other.

---

[5] The Committee is indebted for this description to Miss Leona Sundquist, Washington State Normal School, Bellingham, Washington.

It is necessary to keep in mind these two fundamental considerations of the entire teacher-training program since it is around these aspects that the science program has been planned and organized.

In view of the general cultural training of the student, an orientation course, entitled "Science and Civilization," is required of all freshmen. This course is a 10-credit course, meeting five times each week for two quarters. Each class meeting is of 50 minutes' duration. The main objectives of this course were drafted with the assumption that there is an ever-present need for effective adjustment of an individual to a constantly changing condition of life. Effective adjustment is possible only when there is understanding. What are these understandings in science which have contributory values for an individual living at this day and age? There must be an attainment of understanding of those generalizations and principles of science which constantly apply to human experiences in their physical, social, and mental aspects. It is necessary that there should be understanding and intelligent interpretation of natural phenomena which arise in life's experiences. The value of intelligent interpretation of natural phenomena is for its far-reaching influence upon our mental attitudes and behavior. It is in this respect that science provides a valuable contribution to a background for ideas and beliefs.

Since the background which the course prepares is considered of vital importance to the student and the professionalized subject-matter courses which follow, the major considerations incorporated in the work of the course are listed thus:

(1) A study is made of the nature of the known universe as seen by the astronomers of the past and the present, and of how this has led to the concept of universal order and evolution.

(2) The geological development of the earth is studied, and the interpretation of its history as recorded in rock strata and formations.

(3) Consideration is given to those aspects of physical science which have produced changes in our ideas regarding the nature of matter and energy and their transformations. The theories and implications of the newer physics and chemistry are given in this connection in contrast to the past developments in these fields.

(4) A study is made of the inorganic basis of life. This requires an understanding of the physical and chemical nature of protoplasm and its colloidal organization.

(5) Fundamental vital processes are given considerable emphasis. An understanding of these processes is necessary in the interpretation of interdependence of organisms and their relationship to the physical environment. Structures of typical plants and animals are studied insofar as they contribute to an understanding of vital functions.

(6) A survey is made of the outstanding results of organic development in terms of adaptation. This leads inevitably into a study of heredity and variation and a consideration of organic evolution.

(7) Attention is given to the basic developments in the fields of genetics and eugenics.

(8) Throughout the course consideration is given at various points to the possibility of man's control of his physical and biological environment and the importance of a sane and wholesome philosophy of life, in order that man may effectively and satisfactorily utilize the means of science for the attainment of desirable results in living.

This course has been given for seven years as a requirement for all freshmen. Time and experience have strengthened the conviction that it plays a dominant and vital part in the science teaching program. The course gives a fundamental setting and perspective for the presentation of the content materials which are given in succeeding courses.

A professionalized subject-matter course in "Science for the Elementary School" is required of all those who plan to teach in the first six grades of the elementary school.[6] This course continues throughout the year and is a 6-credit course. The class meets twice each week in periods of two hours' duration. Another content course is given in "General Science," which is designed to meet the needs of teachers who plan to teach science in the upper grades and in the junior high schools. These courses present materials which are adapted to the interests, needs, and experiences of the child at each grade level. Selection is made of content which will give the child at the various stages an understanding of the larger generalizations and concepts of science and an intelligent interpretation of natural phenomena that come within his experiences. In this respect there is a definite integration between the Science and Civilization course and the required content or professional courses.

The professionalized subject-matter courses are definitely planned to meet the needs of students as they enter upon their practice teaching in the training school of the institution. It follows, therefore, that the same fundamental plan of science education which characterizes the required science program for the teacher in training has also been adopted in the training school.

Besides these science courses, a course in "General Hygiene" (5 credits) is required of all students. This is designed to give students a knowledge of the body and how to maintain its health. Personal, school, and community hygiene are treated.

The Department of Home Economics offers a course in "Nutrition" (2 credits), which is also required of all students of the school. This course provides an understanding of the problems of nutrition as they are encountered in daily life and in the schools.

That concludes the required aspects of the science program. Upon that background, students who are especially interested in science may elect the more specialized courses in the separate branches of science, as physics, chemistry, botany, and zoölogy.

Having received the elementary diploma, the students are qualified to teach in the public schools of the state. Before the life diploma is granted, each student must present evidence of successful teaching experience and must return to the institution for an additional quarter's work. This additional quarter is usually taken in the summer session. For those especially interested

---

[6] Recommendations for such a course are given in some detail in Chapter XI.

in science and science teaching, advanced field courses have been organized. These take a greater advantage of the ideal location of the school in respect to its physical and biological environment and provide a more extensive experience in field work than has been possible in previous courses. Within a few minutes a class may find itself in the depths of a forest or in open fields or at a seashore where a great variety of animal and plant life is found in abundance. Two lakes, a river, salt- and fresh-water marshes, and peat bogs are found within a radius of a few miles of the school. Advantage is taken of the ideal location near Mt. Baker and surrounding foothills. Studies are made of glaciers, snowfields, moraine formations, extinct volcanic cones, stream erosion, mountain meadows, alpine forests, and areas of lower elevations. Before taking these field courses, students have had the background of the required science courses, and that has added tremendously to the understanding and enjoyment of the many natural phenomena at their disposal.

As a result of these experiences in science teaching, it has been discovered that the success of the professionalized subject-matter courses, field courses, and the more specialized science courses depends to a great extent upon the background and perspective which the students have obtained in the Orientation Course, which has come to be considered a most vital and important part of the science program in teacher training for work in the elementary school.

It should be clear that this Bellingham program is planned for the education of teachers for work in the elementary schools. In this program the professional demands for special training are less than in the program for the education of senior-high-school teachers. In the senior high school the demands for special training are so great that it seems almost unwise to attempt to meet these demands in a four-year program of undergraduate training. Unquestionably the administrators of the state teachers colleges that are attempting to train senior-high-school teachers must assume responsibility for giving to their students a background of training that will enable the student to enter a graduate school and pursue his work in science without embarrassment.

Recommendations for the Education of Science Teachers

Analysis of the needs of the field and of practices in selected institutions has guided the Committee in making its recommendations for the education of teachers. Our plan of courses will function as a foundation for the attainment of the standards that we believe are practical and necessary if the needs for professional service in the field are to be met. Our arrangement recognizes the limitations of a four-year program of training and recognizes the need for breadth and for thoroughness of training. It also recognizes the importance of sequence, and it arrays the suggested offerings so that the work of each year-level is most important for that level for its functional value, and so that each year-level is a background for the work of the succeeding year. There are no blind-alley courses. The work as a whole is arrayed as of three levels.

I. *General or Orientation.* A course required of all elementary-school and secondary-school teachers. The units of this work will be built around those generalizations and principles of science that relate most immediately to the needs and interests of liberally educated people. These will be chosen irrespective of the special field of science to which they may be related (8 or 10 semester-hours of credit).

II. *Beginnings of Specialization.* Introductory courses in each of the special sciences—chemistry, physics, and biology. Courses in botany and zoölogy may be offered instead of biology (18 to 24 semester-hours of credit).

III. *Specialization.*
    A. Chemistry
        Second-year chemistry   (8 hours credit)
        Third-year chemistry   (8 hours credit)
    B. Physics
        Second-year physics   (8 hours credit)
        Third-year physics   (4 hours credit)
    C. Biology
        Second-year biology   (8 hours credit)
        Third-year biology   (8 hours credit)

IV. *Electives*
    A. Geology   (4 hours credit)
    B. Physiography   (4 hours credit)
    C. Astronomy   (4 hours credit)
    D. Bacteriology   (4 hours credit)

The foregoing courses are suggested as a minimum for specialization. They satisfy the criterion of "respectable scholarship," in that the student who has attained this degree of specialization will, assuming reasonably good instruction, have met the requirements for graduate study. This proposal assumes a schedule of four years of 16 hours each week, with 128 credit-hours as the requirement for graduation.

Analysis of practices in the selected institutions shows that more than 60 percent of the time of students preparing for service in junior high schools may be used for preparation within the subject in which they are preparing to teach. More than 50 percent of the students' time may be allowed for a major for students preparing to work in senior high schools. 'Major,' as defined above, requires but 48 hours of credit, or less than 40 percent of the students' time. This program allows, therefore, for some specialization in one, or possibly two, more subjects. In addition to the courses listed, students will take a professional course in the teaching of science for the level in which their major interests lie.

Some consideration needs to be given to the question of what should constitute the content of the second- and third-year-level courses in chemistry, physics, and biology. There has been a tendency to say that all the courses in teachers colleges should be adapted to the special needs of students preparing for service as teachers. There has been a feeling that the traditional liberal-arts courses are not satisfactory. However, it must be recognized that the need for this instruction exists at the present time, and since there are but few courses and texts organized for work on these levels, other than what have been developed for the liberal-arts college, it would seem that the teachers college has no other alternative than to accept in substance the texts prepared for use in the liberal-arts college. After attention has been focused upon the special needs of the teachers college (if there be any that are distinct from those of the liberal-arts college), we may expect that textbooks will be written to meet these needs.

For the present at least, second-year chemistry may be interpreted as qualitative and quantitative analysis or as qualitative analysis and organic chemistry. Third-year chemistry may be interpreted as quantitative analysis and biochemistry. It should be clear, however, that the Committee offers this suggestion of the nature of second-year and third-year chemistry merely as an illustration of what, in its opinion, is an acceptable interpretation.

Second-year and third-year physics may be interpreted as work in mechanics, heat, electricity, and optics. Second-year and third-year biology may be interpreted as work in plant physiology, vertebrate zoölogy, plant and animal ecology, entomology, heredity, and eugenics.

The Committee recognizes that the instructors in many of the state teachers colleges are not prepared to offer a program such as is suggested in the foregoing recommendations. Schools such as these should work immediately toward the elevation of their standards, and, until they have developed some approximation to an acceptable standard, they should not attempt to educate teachers for service in secondary schools.

It is suggested that teachers for the different grade groups—elementary, junior high school, and senior high school—take as a minimum (in semester-hours) the following:[7]

Elementary Teachers of Science
1. Orientation   8 hours
2. Introductory course in one special science   8 hours
3. Professional course in elementary science   4 hours
4. Electives in science   8 hours

Junior-High-School Teachers of Science
1. Orientation   8 hours
2. Introductory courses in three special sciences   24 hours
3. Specialization courses   8 hours
4. Professional course in junior-high-school science   4 hours
5. Electives in science and in mathematics—at least 16 hours

Senior-High-School Teachers of Science
1. Orientation   8 hours
2. Introductory courses in three special sciences   24 hours
3. Specialization courses   16 hours
4. Professional course in major subject   4 hours
5. Electives   8 hours

Reference to the solution that has been made in other countries of the problem of educating teachers may throw some light on our own

---

[7] Compare this recommendation with those made by Curtis, by Palmer, and by Webb:

Curtis, Francis D. "What constitutes a desirable program of studies in science education for teachers of science in secondary schools." *Science Education,* 15: November, 1930, 14-22.

Palmer, E. Laurence. "What constitutes a desirable program of studies in science education for teachers of science in the elementary school." *Science Education,* 15: January, 1931, 101-110.

Webb, Hanor A. "The training of science teachers for secondary schools." *Science Education,* 15: November, 1930, 1-8.

problem.[8] Attention is directed to the plan that has been developed for Hamburg and certain other German states. Both elementary and secondary teachers are trained in Hamburg at the University of Hamburg. Elementary teachers follow a program of three years of training, and secondary teachers take four years. Graduation from a secondary school is required for entrance to the university. The program of training in the elementary and secondary schools extends over a period of fourteen years. In the *Oberrealschule* 47 semester-hours of work in science, most of which are taken after the student is sixteen years of age, are included in the program of studies required for graduation. The modal figure for science taken by the graduates of Pennsylvania high schools who entered teachers colleges is 20 semester-hours (2 high-school units), most of which are taken before the student is sixteen years of age.

"Professional training [in Hamburg] is obtained by at least a three-year period of study at a university, in which is included the practical pedagogical training necessary to entrance into the profession. The training concludes with an examination which covers the theory of education and allied sciences and also an elective subject of academic, artistic, or technical nature."[9] The elective subject occupies about one-third of the student's working time. The student who enters the University from the *Oberrealschule* and chooses an elective from the field of science will, by the time that he is certificated for teaching, have attained the equivalent of more than 80 semester-hours of training in this subject. If the choice of an elective is in another field, the extent of his specialization will approximate the equivalent of about 80 semester-hours. This plan aims at two purposes: first, to give the professional training necessary for success in teaching in the elementary school, and second, to develop "educated men."[10]

---

[8] See, for example, (1) Meier, Lois. *Natural Science Education in German Elementary Schools.* Teachers College Contributions to Education, No. 445, 1930, Chap. XIX, and (2) Kilander, Holger F. *Science Education in the Secondary Schools of Sweden.* Teachers College Contributions to Education, No. 463, 1931, Chap. V.

[9] The Hamburg Teachers Training Law—Section 2. Quoted by Carl Schietzel, "New teacher-training work in Germany." *Teachers College Record,* 32: March, 1931.

[10] Schietzel, *loc. cit.*

Summary

1. Administrators in state teachers colleges may assume that most of the students entering from the high school will have taken courses in general science and biology. A considerable number will have had physics and chemistry, but relatively few will have had laboratory experience in connection with their study of science.

2. The typical offering in science in normal schools and state teachers colleges consists of relatively few courses, uniquely named, with a decided tendency to make each course a unit unto itself, with few or no prerequisites, and with little or no recognition of sequence between courses.

3. In selected teachers colleges sequences are planned for definite curricula and with programs so made that a student may devote somewhat more than 50 percent of his time to study in the field of an elected major.

4. The plan proposed by this Committee recognizes the need for breadth and for thoroughness of training and clearly recognizes the need for sequence. The plan is proposed with the thought that such a program calls for a most economical use of the student's time in training for professional service and with the thought that this program may develop respectable scholarship to the extent that the student who succeeds has the qualifications for graduate study in the field of his major interest.

5. The Committee recognizes that the training of the instructors in many of the state teachers colleges is inadequate for the program outlined above. Such schools should not attempt to educate secondary-school teachers of science until their faculties have been made adequate to the work.

REPORT OF THE REVIEWING COMMITTEE[1]

I

COMMENTS ON THE YEARBOOK FROM THE PSYCHOLOGICAL POINT OF VIEW

FRANK N. FREEMAN
Professor of Educational Psychology
University of Chicago, Chicago, Illinois

The present Yearbook makes an important contribution to the teaching of science and will stand as one of the landmarks in the field, along with earlier committee reports. It is noteworthy for a number of reasons. In the first place, it has undertaken to develop a unified plan for the teaching of science from the beginning of the elementary school to the college. In the second place, it has proposed a thorough reorganization of the objectives and character of science work in the school, and has attempted to apply this reorganization systematically throughout the school. Finally, it has taken cognizance of scientific investigations and of psychological theory and has attempted to make use of fact and theory in working out its plan. All this represents an ambitious undertaking, and the results of the Committee's labors will serve as a center of discussion and of reorganization for some time to come.

The success of the Committee, in the judgment of the reviewer, varied somewhat in the different parts of its undertaking. This is only to be expected. The initiation of a plan for the reorganization of science teaching is in itself a worthy contribution, and if the plan has not been worked out successfully in all its details, this merely means that there is further work to do. The central feature of the plan is illustrated with sufficient detail so that it is possible to evaluate it and to consider whether it is suitable as a principle of reorganization of the teaching of science throughout the school. We may first consider in its

---

[1] The policy of the Board of Directors with respect to the appointment and the province of the Reviewing Committee and the difficulties attending this section of the Yearbook are explained in the Editor's Preface. It should be added here that the three reviewers have had no opportunity to confer with one another, so that their contribution is, in one sense, not that of a committee at all, but the expression of three individual opinions about those features of the Yearbook that have interested them personally.—*Editor.*

broad outline the principle that the Committee has adopted and afterwards consider its detailed application and the psychological interpretation that is given to support it.

The fundamental principle which the Committee has adopted as the basis of its reorganization is that science deals with interpretations and with generalizations rather than with objects or raw facts. The Committee, in fact, proposes a series of broad generalizations, which are to be used as the objectives of instruction in science throughout the entire range of the school. These principles number in all thirty-eight. The following illustrate them:

1. The sun is the chief source of energy for the earth.
2. Through interdependence of species and the struggle for existence a balance tends to be maintained among the many forms of life.
3. The earth's position in relation to the sun and moon is a determining factor of life on earth.
4. All life comes from life and produces its own kind of living organism.

The entire list is given in Chapter IV and the selections from this list are repeated in later chapters. The Committee recognizes that this list is incomplete and in need of refinement, but it may be taken as illustrative of the type of generalizations that may finally be worked out.

The steps to be followed in organizing instruction on the basis of such principles as these consist first in developing a series of subordinate principles and finally in developing a series of learning elements under each of these subordinate principles.

The plan seems to the reviewer to be essentially sound. It provides an opportunity for the child to follow the normal learning procedure, which is to begin with relatively particularized experiences and proceed by gradual steps to those that are more general and abstract. It recognizes the principle that generalization is an essential characteristic of the higher forms of learning and of intellectual activity. It provides a means of arranging a bewildering array of scientific facts into an orderly scheme. This principle will probably, therefore, enjoy wide acceptance and will serve as the fundamental basis of the organization of instruction in science as long as our present conceptions of learning hold.

Whether the organization of the material of science about large generalizations has been worked out in the present report with entire success is another question. In the first place, there is some ambiguity with reference to its application in the lower elementary grades. The general theoretical presentation of the scheme in the earlier chapters seems to imply that the child in the primary grades or in the lower intermediate grades may be expected to grasp some or all of these generalizations. This implication was doubtless not intended by the authors of the Yearbook, but the sharp criticisms which they make of the teaching of science by the advocates of nature study in the elementary school and the vivid colors in which they paint the contrast between the new conception and the old, as well as their enunciation of the general psychological principle that children's intellectual life is substantially the same throughout the entire course of development, suggests strongly the view that the ability of the young child to draw broad generalizations is not very different from that of the adolescent or the adult. The Committee does, to be sure, from time to time, point out that there are some differences between the intellectual power of the child at different ages, but the general tenor of their discussion minimizes this contrast. This, therefore, points to one of the broad contrasts that will be given further consideration in a moment. The question is, namely: What is the difference in the intellectual outlook and the intellectual power of children at different ages, and how does this difference affect instruction in science?

The second problem in the application of this general principle appears in the work of the more specialized sciences, beginning at the senior high school. The fundamental principle works out very nicely in the organization of general science in the junior high school. When we come to the specialized sciences of general biology, physics, and chemistry, however, the application of the principle is not quite so clear. The Committee has justly criticized the general conduct of the work in these sciences for being unduly minute and lacking in principles of organization. This criticism is doubtless justified. Nevertheless, it is recognized that these subjects involve specialization. Just what is the nature of this specialization, and just what difference in treatment is involved from that which has been used in the elementary-school and junior-high-school science? The Committee recognizes that its proposals for the organization of these specialized sciences are incomplete and somewhat tentative, but it may be questioned whether they recognize with sufficient clearness the fundamental problem that is involved in the union of specialization and of the attainment of broad generalizations.

The problem may be put more generally. How may the stages in the development toward the broad generalizations be marked off? The

Committee minimizes differences in stages of development. Accordingly they not only set up broad principles as objectives throughout the entire school, but they also set the more immediate detailed objectives at various points in the course. This involves what appears on the surface at least to be a good deal of repetition. The problem seems to the reviewer to be an important one and to merit detailed illustration. Other illustrations might be found. The examples to be cited are found in the chapter on "The Program of Science in the Elementary School," Chapter X, and in the chapter on "Instruction in Physical Science in the Secondary Schools," Chapter XV. Certain principles which appear in the objectives for both levels in the school are reproduced in parallel columns below:

1. The sun is the chief source of energy for the earth.
2. Distances in space seem incredibly great when compared to distances on earth.
3. Chemical and physical changes are manifestations of energy changes.
4. Sound is caused by waves which are produced by a vibrating substance and which can affect the auditory nerve of the ear.
5. Gravitation is the attractive force which influences or governs the movements of bodies.
6. All matter is probably electrical in structure.
7. Any machine, no matter how complicated, may be analyzed into a few simple types.
8. There are less than one hundred chemical elements.
9. Every substance is one of the following: (a) a chemical element, (b) a chemical compound, (c) a physical mixture.
10. The properties of the different elements depend upon the number and arrangement of the electrons and of the protons contained in their atoms.

1. The sun is the original source of energy for the earth.
2. Space is vast.
3. Chemical and physical changes are manifestations of energy.
4. Sound is caused by waves that are produced by a vibrating body and that can affect the auditory nerves of the ear.
5. Gravitation is the attraction between bodies. It has profound influence upon the movements of astronomical bodies.
6. All matter is probably electrical in structure.
7. Any machine, no matter how complicated, may be analyzed into a few simple types.
8. There are fewer than one hundred elements.
9. Every substance is one of the following: (a) an element, (b) a chemical compound, (c) a mechanical mixture.
10. The properties of the different elements depend upon the number and arrangement of the electrons and protons contained in their atoms.

The principles in the left-hand column are quoted from Chapter XV on "Physical Science in the Secondary Schools" and the parallel principles in the right-hand column are quoted from Chapter X on "Science in the Elementary School."

Doubtless the Committee expects and intends that in all such cases where the same topics are placed at the different levels they will be treated differently. Just what the difference in treatment should be is not clear, however; and the emphasis that the Committee places upon the sameness in objectives throughout the entire school leaves one in serious doubt as to just what kind of differentiation may be made. Unless a clear-cut principle of differentiation can be worked out and can be applied in detail, it appears to the reviewer that there will be serious overlapping, occurring several times in the course of the child's career even before he enters college. This applies in all the divisions of the field.

The general question may be raised, therefore, whether in setting forth its own theory in contrast to the older theory and in elaborating the psychological justification for its own theory, the Committee has not somewhat over-reached itself. This brings us to a consideration of some of the more specifically psychological aspects of the basis of the Committee's position.

We may, of course, distinguish between the Committee's concrete proposals and the justification of these proposals in terms of its psychological theory. On the whole, the Committee has not been so radical in the details of its plan as in some of its pronouncements on psychological principles. Nevertheless, the psychological theory cannot be considered as negligible, and it does undoubtedly influence practice in definite ways, as the foregoing illustrations will indicate. I shall discuss two of the psychological principles which are emphasized by the Committee in addition to the fundamental one of generalization that has already been discussed. I shall attempt to show that the Committee has been more extreme in its statement of psychological principles than it has in its practice and that it is in a measure inconsistent. Its extreme form of statement, however, in discussing the psychological principles has to some extent led it to underemphasize certain factors in the child's mental development.

The two psychological principles that I shall consider in somewhat greater detail are the principle of mental growth, or mental development, and the principle of transfer of training, or generalization in training.

The Committee criticizes severely the theory that the child develops in definite stages and that these successive stages are marked by the appearance of radically new forms of intellectual activity or of thinking. This is the so-called 'saltatory' theory of development, which has commonly been identified with the writings and investigation of G. Stanley Hall. The criticisms of this theory are familiar. Hall was given to exaggeration and his statements taken literally are certainly without scientific justification. All the chief features of intellectual life appear in the early life of the child and his development is not marked by the acquisition of any fundamentally new abilities. When this is said, however, the questions about the mental development of the child are not fully answered. The extreme position which the Committee takes on this psychological principle appears to be motivated by its wholehearted rejection of the principles and practices underlying the so-called 'nature-study movement.' This movement is founded upon the principle, according to the Committee, that the interests and abilities of the young child are totally different from those of the older child, and that this requires a radically different approach.

It is unfortunate, sometimes, that we should have to consider our theories in the light of current practices. This frequently causes us to react from one extreme to the other, and this reaction in turn produces a subsequent reaction in the opposite direction. If we could consider this problem without regard for the nature-study movement and without regard for the extreme view of saltatory development that was enunciated by Hall and his pupils, we would, I believe, arrive at a somewhat more balanced view than has been set forth by the Committee. After all, we should build up our conceptions of the child's growth, not in terms of a saltatory theory or a theory of continuous development or any other such theory, but in terms of our actual observation of the mental processes of children at different ages.

If we base our conceptions of the child's growth upon such observations, we shall have to conclude that there are relatively important differences in the child's reaction to the world about him and in his mode of thinking at different ages. How far these differences are due to changes in the child's own organism, particularly his nervous system, and how far they are due to the accumulation of experience, we may not be able to say. The origin of the differences is immaterial, but their existence has to be taken into account.

Many illustrations might be gleaned from mental tests, since these tests have been standardized to conform to the abilities of children at different ages. The child's reaction to pictures may be cited as one example. In the Binet Scale three successive stages of mental development are distinguished. In the first, the child merely enumerates the objects that he sees in the picture; in the second, he describes the actions which are going on; and in the third, he gives an interpretation of the picture. The second example may be taken from the interpretation of fables. At one level the child is not able to make any interpretation of the fable at all; at the second level he is able to make a particularized interpretation applying to the particular situation described in the fable; at the third level he is able to generalize upon the lessons in the fable.

We need not, of course, conclude that generalizations occur at the same age with all types of material. The child may generalize within narrow limits and with very concrete types of material at a lower age and may be able to reach a broader generalization only at a higher age; but this means that with a particular type of material the child does go through successive stages. The Committee has recognized this fact in part, but because of its general point of view it has minimized these stages and has, therefore, failed to differentiate between the type of work suitable for children of different grades as clearly as it might have done.

The second psychological principle that I shall consider is the principle of transfer of training. The Committee rejects what it calls 'the old theory of transfer of training.' Here, again, its rejection of theory is connected with its rejection of a particular kind of teaching of science. The Committee is justified in criticizing some of the old statements and aims and some of the old practices in science. It has not distinguished, as clearly as it might, however, between the erroneous conception of transfer and the justifiable conception of transfer. In emphasizing only the rejection of the erroneous conception and in failing to set up in its theoretical discussion a statement of a justifiable conception, the Committee has appeared to be involved in another contradiction. This contradiction grows out of the fact that the Committee itself repeatedly emphasizes the importance of the general outcomes of science instruction. It does not by any means, in its detailed organization, in its setting up of objectives, or in a statement of the outcomes of science teaching, adhere to the doctrine of particularized effects of learning. The very central principle of the whole plan involves a most fundamental kind of transfer, namely, generalization. Beyond this the Committee emphasizes over and over again the importance of attitudes, not only those attitudes that are involved in the intellectual pursuit of science and the adherence to the scientific method, but also those still broader attitudes that involve the recognition of the social implications of scientific knowledge and discovery. The Committee believes, in other words, that the child should not only learn to use scientific methods and become familiar with scientific generalization, in itself involving transfer, but that he should also acquire the disposition to utilize scientific knowledge for human welfare rather than for human exploitation or the destruction of human values. All this is very good, but it is very far from the notion that the teaching of science is highly particularized in its outcomes.

It would have been desirable for the Committee in its theoretical discussion of transfer of training not to have emphasized alone the negative side, and not to have left in the mind of the reader only the criticism of the older view, but to have analyzed more in detail the error in the older view and to have set forth the correct view in its place; for, as has been said, the very practices which the Committee itself recommends rest upon a conception of a very broad form of transfer.

Among the difficulties with the old conception of transfer, some may be mentioned. One difficulty was that it undervalued content. It erred, not in its estimate of the importance of form, but rather in its neglect of content. Now content is necessary for the development of form. The two must go hand in hand. Important subject matter is essential to the development of significant modes of procedure. The neglect of this principle frequently led to the absurd conclusion that ability would be transferred to other fields which was never developed in the first place. The reliance on the doctrine of transfer was so implicit that it led to a complete faith in the development of certain mental traits in the study of the original material as well as in their transfer to other fields of thought. The critical examination of transfer should be directed in the first place toward the measurement of the amount of gain in the ability that is the objective of instruction in the field in which the instruction occurs. After this has been done, we can set ourselves to the measurement of the fraction of this gain that is carried over to other fields.

Related to the first error was the erroneous assumption that the desired abilities or attitudes would be developed automatically in the pursuit of a given subject and that the transfer to other fields would also take place automatically. In other words, the faith in the general principle of transfer was extended to cover the particular instances without examining in detail to see whether or not the conditions necessary for transfer were realized. One of these conditions is the recognition of the possibility of transfer and the definite setting of the stage so that it will occur. The Committee has in point of fact provided these conditions to a large extent in its detailed plan. If the reader will direct his attention chiefly to the detailed provisions and will not be misled by the unduly critical theoretical statements, no harm will be done, for in its detailed plan the Committee has presented what amounts to a strong argument in favor of a reasonable conception of transfer of training.

II

COMMENTS ON THE YEARBOOK BY A SCHOOL
ADMINISTRATOR

J. Cayce Morrison
Assistant Commissioner for Elementary Education
New York State Education Department, Albany, New York

There is a saying that each generation rewrites history for itself. It appears that our profession must rewrite science every five or six years. In 1920, we had the Report of the Committee on the Reorganization of Science in Secondary Schools. In 1926 and 1927 the Department of Superintendence gave us the Fourth and Fifth Yearbooks, which stressed science respectively in the elementary and in the junior high school. Now, we have this Thirty-First Yearbook of the National Society devoted to the teaching of science. Judging from the list of unsettled issues revealed in this report, we recommend the appointment of another committee to continue the investigation of those questions which this present Committee modestly admits it cannot answer.

These are a few of the issues which the Committee generously bequeaths to its successor, issues that await the further scientific study of science teaching:

   a. the selection and sequence of courses within the curriculum,
   b. the grade placement of topics,
   c. the determination of the principles of science toward the development of which courses should be directed,
   d. the grade placement of experiences to develop scientific attitudes and to impart skill in scientific thinking,
   e. the best plan or plans of organization of curriculum content,
   f. the influence of the present type of instruction on the relative decrease of enrollment in high-school science classes,
   g. the selection and organization of content to furnish specific training in scientific thinking and in producing scientific attitudes,
   h. the real value of homemade apparatus and of supplementary teaching aids, and
   i. the experimental evaluation of procedures.

The foregoing list is by no means exhaustive, but it is long enough to indicate the distance we have yet to travel before we can speak with scientific authority concerning many of the issues involved in science instruction. One of the most practical elements in the Committee's recommendations is the proposed "national organization to serve as a clearing house for completed research in this field, to prevent over-lapping of effort, and to stimulate further research."

Though tested knowledge in this field is small indeed, the Committee proposes a practical program in harmony with the proved trends of educational practice.

It is a program built in full understanding of the problems of administration and organization in public schools. It embraces a continuous sequence of science instruction from kindergarten to normal school and college. In the elementary school, Grades I to VI, it absorbs the best of the program heretofore known as 'nature study' and the scientific foundations of health instruction. It is equally adaptable to a school organized on the traditional subject basis and to the progressive school stressing the project method or the activity curriculum. For the junior high school it proposes a three-year general-science curriculum gradually revised to capitalize the attainments or experiences of children who have benefited from the elementary-school program. It is equally adaptable to those schools organized on the 8-4 and the 6-6 or the 6-3-3 plan. For the three-year senior high school there is proposed an elective offering of at least four one-year units. "Ideally these should probably be organized as two two-year sequences, one in the field of biology and the other in the field of physical science." Here the Committee leaves the door open to the widest possible range of experimentation, including half-year units of other sciences, *e.g.*, geology, physiography, botany, zoölogy, and astronomy.

From the purely administrative point of view, certain proposals will be well received. The elimination of the double laboratory period and the acceptance of an hour period (55 minutes in the clear) will help in program-building. Placing science at the close of the day in the elementary and junior schools will facilitate the use of museums and excursions. The review of researches as to the relative merits of different methods of instruction suggests economies in the provision of space and equipment for science as well as more efficient results of instruction. The chapter devoted to "Science Rooms and Their Equipment" will prove useful to those who wish to provide adequately for science instruction, yet secure a more economical use of the school plant.

The Committee's review of researches in this field is in itself a substantial contribution to the thinking of teachers, supervisory and administrative officers. There are two chapters summarizing the contribution of educational research to the solution of teaching problems. These include such issues as the vocabularies of science textbooks; the value of extensive supplementary reading; the effect of teacher preparation upon pupil achievement; adjusting instruction to differences in intelligence; studies in pupil progress and classification; the value of various types of visual aids; the influence of directed study; the relative merits of the topical *vs.* the problem method of study and of the topical method *vs.* project-teaching, of the Morrison unit *vs.* the assignment-recitation plan, of residual teaching *vs.* the socialized report, of the individual *vs.* the demonstration method of conducting laboratory exercises, of performing laboratory exercises in pairs or in groups; the merits of study guides and contract teaching, of the new-type examinations as teaching devices, of correlating class and laboratory work. In brief compass the Committee thus reviews a wealth of material to guide teachers and supervisory officers in improving their instructional service in the realm of science.

To those confronted with revising their curricular offerings in science the Yearbook offers substantial assistance. There are chapters on the principles, organization, and content for each of the three school divisions—elementary, junior high, and senior high. The investigations as to content are summarized. One chapter is, in effect, a suggested syllabus for Grades I to VI and another illustrates how the principles involved in such a program are developed. Another chapter proposes principles for selection and organization of content in junior-high-school science. A chapter devoted to the course of study in biology contains a list of principles based upon substantial evidence. Similarly, there is suggested content for physics and for chemistry with typical units of work developed to illustrate the procedure involved.

The chapters devoted to "Science Teaching on the College Level" and "Programs for the Education of Science Teachers" bring into relief the problems involved in correlating the work of the secondary school with the college and in securing adequately prepared teachers of science for the public schools.

The Committee has based its program upon a theory that this is an age of science and that the primary purpose of science instruction in the public school is to lay such a foundation through experience as will enable children to gain a better understanding of the world in which they live and thereby be better able to meet successfully the problems that they will have to meet. To attain this goal the Committee proposes that "the work of successive grade levels—elementary, secondary, and collegiate—will take departure from the earliest offering and be conclusively and intelligently connected with each preceding step." The Committee has recognized the need for gradually revising the content of the intermediate, the junior-high-school, and the senior-high-school grades in harmony with the actual attainments of children as they pass through the periods of instruction in the preceding grades. Likewise, the Committee has pointed out the present lack of coördination in the realm of science between the secondary school and the college, and it has brought a strong indictment against present practices in the preparation of teachers for science instruction in the public schools.

There are questions, of course, that the Committee does not answer. There are implications that raise other questions in the reader's mind. The Committee raises, but does not answer, the question, "What does it mean to say, 'This is an age of science'?" Again, it suggests that "the senior high school offers an opportunity for exploration in the special fields." If it assumes that the whole of life's study is but an exploration, then its position is well taken. In the treatment of the elementary-school program it says, "Introduce children to big ideas and do it early." Such a proposal is purely academic. A committee on science instruction should know that children in this generation are introduced to big ideas whether the school functions or not.

While the Committee points out clearly enough the lack of coördination between the high school and the college, at no place, so far as I can find, does it take the position that the college should help correct the present wasteful practices. Unless the high school can offer courses in physics, chemistry, and biology that give those who pursue these courses an advantage in college over those who do not pursue them, the high schools had better forever abandon their claim to prepare youth for college.

"The Committee unqualifiedly condemns . . . assigning any science course to a teacher who is not adequately prepared in the subject matter of that course"; yet the elementary school must depend for the success of this program upon teachers who fall far short of the ideal preparation proposed by the Committee, and most of the smaller high schools will be obliged to depend upon teachers inadequately prepared as measured by these standards.

In reviewing the evidence as to the relative merits of various types of visual-instruction equipment, the Committee appears to be fearful either of its evidence or of giving offense to certain powerful interests in the field. In the study of methods in science teaching we can scarcely afford to avoid the facts.

Nowhere do I find that the Committee has adequately differentiated between the science to be taught in the elementary school and in the junior high school or between the experiences that should be developed and organized on these two school levels to develop adequately the further generalizations essential to the understanding of principles.

Throughout the yearbook the Committee takes exception to the topical organization of subject matter. Rather, it proposes to develop content around large generalizations or truths that affect people's living together. Concretely applied to the science content for the elementary school, the plan of organization results in a series of facts called 'concepts,' stated in the form of simple declarative sentences. But by the unskilled teacher these simple declarative sentences will be treated on the same factual basis as has the material heretofore organized on the topical basis. Something more is needed for those teachers who, without adequate background, must master the field of science for elementary schools.

It is unfortunate that a report in so significant a field should be submitted without having eliminated from it certain glaring inconsistencies and certain plausible proposals bearing more the earmark of literary fantasy than tested scientific thought. One illustration will suffice. In Chapter XIV there is a discussion of the need for "units to develop desirable scientific attitudes and units to give skill in scientific thinking. . . . these two outcomes are major goals of science teaching quite as important as the knowledge goal." And in various other chapters scientific attitudes and scientific thinking are stated or implied as commonly accepted goals of instruction. Yet in Chapter XV is found this criticism: "Until these problems are attacked by the techniques of modern experimental education, such objectives as the development of training in scientific methods and the building of scientific attitudes will continue to be will-o'-the-wisp catch words to enchant unscientific science teachers. Instead of using these as means to befuddle issues in teachers' gatherings and to decorate the reports of committees, a frank facing of present ignorance and a definite program of attack is needed." Not often does a Committee publish so violent an appraisal of one of its own pet hobbies!

Through its clarification and indorsement of certain fundamental ideas does the Committee make its most practical contribution to the teaching of science.

A "continuous and correlated program of study" from kindergarten to senior high school inclusive, built around the development through organized experiences of certain basic and generalized truths, is a new departure in curriculum-making. Our generation will accomplish something if teachers of science can help us visualize those basic truths that determine the character and set the problems of our present civilization, that influence the thinking, "the mental and social adjustments of the individuals of our society." Science does have a contribution to make to the liberal education of man through helping him to understand "the character of the age in which he lives and something of the conditions that have produced it." In "the simple generalization of childhood" we find the beginning of that process of tested thinking which gradually increases man's power to shape his destiny.

III

GENERAL COMMENTS ON THE YEARBOOK BY A FELLOW-WORKER IN SCIENCE

E. Laurence Palmer
Professor of Rural Education
Cornell University, Ithaca, New York

A commentary limited to two thousand words is necessarily incomplete. This one purports to deal with certain features of this Yearbook that I should have included, some of which are unfortunately omitted, and others that I should have excluded. The commentary is made in a spirit of helpfulness. I believe that the adverse comments could have been omitted had the Committee seen fit earlier to make the report more truly representative. I particularly regret making adverse criticisms, since none is here made of my own activities.

As pointed out in Chapter X, much of the philosophy proposed accords with that of Jackman presented in the *Third Yearbook* of this Society, in 1904. It accords with my views in that it calls for a continuity of program in science from kindergarten through college, in that it recommends substitution of larger integrated units of study for haphazardly selected unrelated activities. I approve the recommendations against catechismic teaching, against the practice of giving physical science unwarranted emphasis in junior-high science, and I favor in general the curricular recommendations of Chapter IX, much of the criticism of the Fourth and Fifth Yearbooks of the National Education Association, and agree as to the desirability of striving for understandings rather than memory of rules. I particularly favor, with minor reservations, the analysis of inductive and of deductive thinking outlined in Chapter XIV and the warning in that chapter, apparently unheeded elsewhere, against the placing of certain content too low in the offerings to the grades. In general I prefer the grade allotments proposed in Chapter XI to those proposed in Chapter XII, partly on the ground that they seem to be more truly integrated and partly because they lend themselves more satisfactorily to the grade grouping necessary in rural schools. Many parts of the report would have been improved had the writers heeded the implication in Chapter VI that it is desirable to express ideas as simply as possible.

Each chapter would have been improved by supporting references, such as those that follow in Chapter XV. It may be noted that not one reference is given in Chapter III. This chapter is unnecessarily verbose, and the topic has been repeatedly handled better, as for example, in the A.A.A.S. Committee report on the Place of Science in Education. In regard to this chapter, the question arises as to whether the reputed deplorable condition of civilization at present is due to the teachings of science or to the failure of their application.

Much of the first section of Chapter II would seem to have been written by someone uninformed as to what is justly called "true nature study" in Chapter X. I am not aware that any of the three "best thoughts" are in accord with the writings of Jackman, Needham, Downing, Comstock, Craig, or myself and regret that the chapter contains no reference as to their source. Much of the criticism of the Fourth Yearbook of the National Education Association, in Chapter II, is justified, but that report was not a product of a professional group identified with nature study. Nature study cannot be "killed" by the burning of so unrepresentative a straw man as that set up in this chapter. Too much good work has been accomplished by leaders in nature study to be offset by any such unfounded charges as this chapter makes against it. In Chapter X my views as to the proper attitude toward differences between nature study and elementary science are repeated. It does not seem as though the first part of Chapter II is consistent with most of Chapters X, XI, and XII. The admirable report of Cunningham on types of questions in general science shows definitely that that subject failed to emphasize generalizations and is entitled to the same criticisms that inspired the attack against nature study in Chapter II.

It seems inconsistent that, while Chapter IV contends that "it is fundamental that things belonging together should be brought together," there is really so little logical arrangement of the master list of generalizations appearing earlier. Furthermore, the disproportionate emphasis on physical science in that list is hardly supported by recommendations found in Chapter IX and elsewhere, even though it is admitted that the list is incomplete. The proposed generalizations might have been grouped under such headings as those pertaining to the study of energy, of time, of place, of character, and so on. I have elaborated this theme in public and in the *Cornell Rural School Leaflet*. I believe that while the Committee has repeatedly dwelt on the desirability of keeping to large generalizations, it has not consistently selected those that are large. With minor reservations, I favor the suggested illustrative development.

In connection with the recommendation for avoidance of specialization in lower grades, it is difficult to justify such divisions as appear in the proposals in Chapter XII and the separation of content pertinent to plants and to animals as recommended in Chapter XI. Neither do I feel that Chapter XI carries out the Committee's recommendation in Chapter XIV of relating units.

It is difficult to agree with the statements in Chapter X that the first thing in planning a course is to decide upon content, that consideration of exotics in the lower grades is entitled to the recognition given them in the Horace Mann outline, that one must first turn to authorities for help on what constitutes the social life of animals. I question whether it is of paramount importance that a lower-grade child should learn to look repeatedly to authorities for proof. I prefer practices, apparently recognized in Chapter XIV, which will look to proof for authority rather than to authority for proof.

In regard to content selection, it is difficult to reconcile the just criticism in Chapter VIII of the influence of colleges on science content in the lower grades with the philosophy of Powers and Billig of looking largely to specialists in different fields of science for content suggestions.

Consideration of procedures in the selection of content refers to the Curtis study on evaluation of topics in general science. It is approved in Chapters IV, VIII, XIII, and XVII without mentioning its rather serious weakness due to the use of unreliable basic studies. If we accept it, we must agree that the study of Mars has a valuation of 72.3, which is higher than most topics in biology and much higher than that given to man, the valuation of which is 49.3. In my judgment, this study of Curtis is below his standard set elsewhere and is taken too seriously. One of the basic studies is Pollock's interest study, the validity of which is denied in Chapter XIII, but supported apparently in Chapters II and VIII.

Other studies reported as authoritative, but the validity of which I cannot accept, are the Dvorak studies, used as though reliable in Chapters IX and XIII, and those based upon the Powers General Science Test and reported in Chapters IX, XVII, and XVIII.

While the Dvorak study is a doctorate dissertation, the resultant test seems practically valueless as an instrument of measurement. It *reports* "thirty levels of increasing difficulty, each level being 0.1 P.E. more difficult than the preceding level." In spite of this, it may be said conservatively that better than 17 percent of the units are unreliable because of the nature of the factual material presented. For example, a multiple-choice unit asks the person examined to indicate that in a flower the petals are colored while the sepals, pistils, stamens, and corolla are not. Obviously any of these parts may be colored and if the petals are colored, the corolla must be. Detailed evaluation of this and other high-school tests in biology and general science appear in a Cornell master's thesis by Diamond.

I believe that better than 9 percent of the units of the widely used and accepted test in general science by Powers are subject to similar criticisms. In my judgment the nature of the errors in these tests invalidates the results obtained from their use and the studies that are based largely upon their validity. This involves the study by Ashbaugh, reported in Chapter IX, as well as others. These studies and tests are there regarded as valid in spite of the fact that their weaknesses has been called to the attention of members of the Committee and in spite of the fact that they have been criticized effectively in print. The Cunningham study, listed supposedly as authoritative at the end of Chapter XV, purports to evaluate existing tests, but fails entirely to consider the nature of the factual material submitted.

The Committee fails to serve science education by not attempting a really careful evaluation of science tests commonly used. It would seem as important for workers in science education as it is for workers in botany, physics, geology, or any other science to be critical of studies offered as authoritative. These criticisms are made in the same spirit I have made criticisms in the field of zoölogy—with the hope that they will lead to real progress. I hope that they will be received in that spirit.

While I believe sincerely in the value of general science and on the whole approve of much of the treatment given it in Chapter XIII, I do not share the optimism expressed in that chapter that its support is justified in part at least because of the increase in the numbers of students it has enjoyed. On the contrary, if we accept Monahan's report, we must recognize that the proportion of high-school students taking science in 1928 was less than that before general science had wide introduction. During the period from 1915 to 1928 the percentage of students taking biological science dropped from 19.2 to 16; of those taking physical science from 21.6 to 14, and of those taking earth science from 15.4 to 2.86. It is a challenging thought to realize, not only that the total percentage of students taking high-school science has dropped, but also that an increased proportion have limited their science training apparently to the earlier years. This is particularly discouraging when it seems that high-school students take, on the average, less than one course in science. This situation in high schools is apparently comparable to that reported by Noll for colleges in Chapter XVII. It was not, however, mentioned.

I question the statement in Chapter XVIII as to what constitutes the common practice in subject combinations of high-school teachers. It is contrary to a number of printed reports. The theme is worthy of greater elaboration.

I feel that much of the material in Chapter XVIII, which was prepared by examination of announcements and by collecting data from a limited number of schools, has inferior value to unmentioned material published in the *Nature Almanac* by the American Nature Association. This *Almanac* material involved personal visitation to institutions, following examination of exhaustive questionnaires received from every state of the Union and from a majority of teacher-training institutions.

I believe that, had the parts of the Yearbook been more succinct and more closely integrated by extending the project over a period comparable to that which produced the *Twenty-Ninth Yearbook,* there would have been ample space to have considered problems which receive no treatment, such as problems of training of teachers in service; of improving teaching at the college level, particularly in beginning years; of teachers' salaries; of rural situations; of state-wide programs; of teaching loads at various levels; of practices observed by administrators in the selection of science teachers; and of special methods, such as those associated with field trips.

In spite of the adverse criticisms I have made of this Yearbook, I believe it contains enough of good to be valuable. I shall gladly supplement these comments by correspondence with any who may be interested.

INFORMATION CONCERNING THE NATIONAL SOCIETY FOR THE STUDY OF EDUCATION

1. PURPOSE. The purpose of the National Society is to promote the investigation and discussion of educational questions. To this end it holds an annual meeting and publishes a series of yearbooks.

2. ELIGIBILITY TO MEMBERSHIP. Any person who is interested in receiving its publications may become a member by sending to the Secretary-Treasurer information concerning name, address, and class of membership desired (see Item 4) and a check for $3.50 or $3.00 (see Item 5).

Membership may not be had by libraries or by institutions.

3. PERIOD OF MEMBERSHIP. Applicants for membership may not date their entrance back of the current calendar year, and all memberships terminate automatically on December 31st, unless the dues for the ensuing year are paid as indicated in Item 6.

4. CLASSES OF MEMBERS. Application may be made for either active or associate membership. Active members pay dues of $2.50 annually, receive a cloth-bound copy of each publication, are entitled to vote, to participate in discussion, and (under certain conditions) to hold office. Associate members pay dues of $2.00 annually, receive a paper-bound copy of each publication, may attend the meetings of the Society, but may not vote, hold office, contribute to the year-books, or participate in discussion. The names of active members only are printed in the yearbooks. There were in 1931 about 1100 active and 1100 associate members.

5. ENTRANCE FEE. New active and new associate members are required the first year to pay, in addition to the dues, an entrance fee of one dollar.

6. PAYMENT OF DUES. Statements of dues are rendered in October or November for the following calendar year. By vote of the Society at the 1919 meeting, "any member so notified whose dues remain unpaid on January 1st, thereby loses his membership and can be reinstated only by paying the entrance fee of one dollar required of new members."

School warrants and vouchers from institutions must be accompanied by definite information concerning the name and address and class of membership of the person for whom membership fee is being paid.

Cancelled checks serve as receipts. Members desiring an additional receipt must enclose a stamped and addressed envelope therefor.

7. DISTRIBUTION OF YEARBOOKS TO MEMBERS. The yearbooks, ready prior to each February meeting, will be mailed from the office of the publishers, only to members whose dues for that year have been paid. Members who desire yearbooks prior to the current year must purchase them directly from the publishers (see Item 8).

8. COMMERCIAL SALES. The distribution of all yearbooks prior to the current year, and also of those of the current year not regularly mailed to members in exchange for their dues, is in the hands of the publishers, not of the Secretary. For such commercial sales, communicate directly with the Public School Publishing Company, Bloomington, Illinois, which will gladly send a price list covering all the publications of this Society and of its predecessor, the National Herbart Society.

9. YEARBOOKS. The yearbooks are issued about one month before the February meeting. They comprise from 700 to 800 pages annually. Unusual effort

has been made to make them, on the one hand, of immediate practical value, and on the other hand, representative of sound scholarship and scientific investigation. Many of them are the fruit of coöperative work by committees of the Society.

10. MEETINGS. The annual meetings, at which the yearbooks are discussed, are held in February at the same time and place as the meeting of the Department of Superintendence of the National Education Association.

Applications for membership will be handled promptly at any time on receipt of name and address, together with check for the appropriate amount ($3.50 for new active membership, $3.00 for new associate membership). Generally speaking, applications entitle the new member to the yearbook slated for discussion during the calendar year the application is made, but those received in December are regarded as pertaining to the next calendar year.

GUY M. WHIPPLE, Secretary-Treasurer.

10 Putnam Street,
Danvers, Mass.

PUBLICATIONS OF THE NATIONAL HERBART SOCIETY

(Now the National Society for the Study of Education)

PUBLICATIONS OF THE NATIONAL SOCIETY FOR THE STUDY OF EDUCATION

Eighteenth Yearbook, 1919, Part I—The Professional Preparation of High-School Teachers. G. N. Cade, S. S. Colvin, Charles Fordyce, H. H. Foster, T. W. Gosling, W. S. Gray, L. V. Koos, A. R. Mead, H. L. Miller, F. C. Whitcomb, and Clifford Woody 1.65

Eighteenth Yearbook, 1919, Part II—Fourth Report of Committee on Economy of Time in Education. F. C. Ayer, F. N. Freeman, W. S. Gray, Ernest Horn, W. S. Monroe, and C. E. Seashore... 1.10

Nineteenth Yearbook, 1920, Part I—New Materials of Instruction. Prepared by the Society's Committee on Materials of Instruction............................ 1.10

Nineteenth Yearbook, 1920, Part II—Classroom Problems in the Education of Gifted Children. T. S. Henry... 1.00

Twentieth Yearbook, 1921, Part I—New Materials of Instruction. Second Report by the Society's Committee.. 1.30

Twentieth Yearbook, 1921, Part II—Report of the Society's Committee on Silent Reading, M. A. Burgess, S. A. Courtis, C. E. Germane, W. S. Gray, H. A. Greene, Regina R. Heller, J. H. Hoover, J. A. O'Brien, J. L. Packer, Daniel Starch, W. W. Theisen, G. A. Yoakum, and representatives of other school systems..... 1.10

Twenty-first Yearbook, 1922, Parts I and II—Intelligence Tests and Their Use. Part I—The Nature, History, and General Principles of Intelligence Testing. E. L. Thorndike, S. S. Colvin, Harold Rugg, G. M. Whipple. Part II—The Administrative Use of Intelligence Tests. H. W. Holmes, W. K. Layton, Helen Davis, Agnes L. Rogers, Rudolph Pintner, M. R. Trabue, W. S. Miller, Bessie L. Gambrill, and others. The two parts are bound together.................... 1.60

Twenty-Second Yearbook, 1923, Part I—English Composition: Its Aims, Methods, and Measurement. Earl Hudelson.. 1.10

Twenty-Second Yearbook, 1923, Part II—The Social Studies in the Elementary and Secondary School. A. S. Barr, J. J. Coss, Henry Harap, R. W. Hatch, H. C. Hill, Ernest Horn, C. H. Judd, L. C. Marshall, F. M. McMurry, Earle Rugg, H. O. Rugg, Emma Schweppe, Mabel Snedaker, and C. W. Washburne.............. 1.50

Twenty-Third Yearbook, 1924, Part I—The Education of Gifted Children. Report of the Society's Committee. Guy M. Whipple, Chairman...................... 1.75

Twenty-Third Yearbook, 1924, Part II—Vocational Guidance and Vocational Education for Industries. A. H. Edgerton and others............................ 1.75

Twenty-Fourth Yearbook, 1925, Part I—Report of the National Committee on Reading. W. S. Gray, Chairman, F. W. Ballou, Rose L. Hardy, Ernest Horn, Frances Jenkins, S. A. Leonard, Estaline Wilson, and Laura Zirbes................... 1.50

Twenty-Fourth Yearbook, 1925, Part II—Adapting the Schools to Individual Differences. Report of the Society's Committee. Carleton W. Washburne, Chairman 1.50

Twenty-Fifth Yearbook, 1926, Part I—The Present Status of Safety Education. Report of the Society's Committee. Guy M. Whipple, Chairman................. 1.75

Twenty-Fifth Yearbook, 1926, Part II—Extra-Curricular Activities. Report of the Society's Committee. Leonard V. Koos, Chairman.......................... 1.50

Twenty-Sixth Yearbook, 1927, Part I—Curriculum Making: Past and Present. Report of the Society's Committee. Harold O. Rugg, Chairman.................... 1.75

Twenty-Sixth Yearbook, 1927, Part II—The Foundations of Curriculum-Making. Prepared by individual members of the Society's Committee. Harold O. Rugg, Chairman 1.50

Twenty-Seventh Yearbook, 1928, Part I—Nature and Nurture: Their Influence Upon Intelligence. Prepared by the Society's Committee. Lewis M. Terman, Chairman 1.75

Twenty-Seventh Yearbook, 1928, Part II—Nature and Nurture: Their Influence Upon Achievement. Prepared by the Society's Committee. Lewis M. Terman, Chairman 1.75

Twenty-Eighth Yearbook, 1929, Parts I and II—Preschool and Parental Education. Part I—Organization and Development. Part II—Research and Method. Prepared by the Society's Committee. Lois H. Meek, Chairman. Bound in one volume. Cloth Edition 5.00
Paper Edition 3.50

370   *A PROGRAM FOR TEACHING SCIENCE*

PUBLIC SCHOOL PUBLISHING COMPANY, BLOOMINGTON, ILLINOIS
Agents—The Baker and Taylor Company   New York